STUDY GUIDE

TO ACCOMPANY
THE NATURE OF LIFE

Deborah M. Brosnan

Oregon State University

Donald J. Reinhardt

Georgia State University

McGRAW-HILL Publishing Company

New York St. Louis San Francisco Auckland Bogatá Caracas
Hamburg Lisbon London Madrid Mexico Milan Montreal New Delhi
Oklahoma City Paris San Juan São Paulo Singapore Sydney Tokyo Toronto

STUDY GUIDE to accompany
THE NATURE OF LIFE

1 2 3 4 5 6 7 8 9 0   8 9 4 3 2 1 0 9

ISBN 0-07-557352-0

Project was supervised by George Calmenson, The Book Company

Illustrators: Martha Blake, Wayne Clark, Cyndie Clark-Huegel,
Cecile Duray-Bito, Paula McKenzie, Linda McVay, Elizabeth
Morales, Victor Royer, Carla Simmons, John Waller, Judy Waller

Cover illustration: Zebra butterflies (*Heliconius charitonius*,
subspecies *tuckeri*) by Larry West/Bruce Coleman.

Contents

To the Student

This Study Guide has been designed with you, the student, in mind. It accompanies your text, *The Nature of Life* by John H. Postlethwait and Janet L. Hopson. Our enthusiasm for that superb biology text generated like enthusiasm for writing a study guide that would enable you, as an introductory biology student, to understand the fascinating natural world of which we are a part.

This Study Guide aims to:

- Help you identify the primary areas covered in each chapter of *The Nature of Life* and assess their relative importance.
- Enable you to recognize the type of material you might find in both multiple choice and essay questions.
- Allow you to test your overall understanding of the subject presented in each chapter of *The Nature of Life*.

Each chapter in the Study Guide follows the corresponding chapter in the text, and we recommend that you use the Guide as a tool for learning and remembering the information covered in your text and lectures. To help you succeed in your biology course, each Study Guide chapter contains:

- **Chapter in Brief**: a quick summary of the material contained in the chapter.
- **Perspective and Review**: A brief overview of the important concepts and facts prese. ted in the chapter, and their relationships to the field of biology.
- **Summaries and Concept Tables**: Summaries parallel the corresponding sections in the text chapter. Use them to review the main points covered in each section. Concept Tables are intended as concise pretest study aids. Each Concept Table highlights the major points of a specific topic and will help you review important facts quickly. Most chapters in the Study Guide include a Concept Figure that presents a review activity based on text art.
- **Thought Provokers and Self-Tests**: to test your knowledge of the material covered in each chapter. Use them to prepare for exams and quizzes.

- **Key Terms**: listed at the end of each chapter, giving text page numbers on which the terms are defined and discussed. Use these key terms as an additional review exercise by simply working through the list, writing out your own definition of each term, and then checking your definitions against those given in the text.

Strategies for Biology and Other College Courses

The following commonsense guidelines can help you succeed not only in your studies of biology, but in all your college courses.

1. **Attend all lectures**. You will learn much by listening carefully during lectures, and by paying attention to visual aids such as overhead transparencies and slides. At the least, you will gain insight into the topics your instructor considers the most important. Your instructor may also lecture on subject areas not covered in the text, or expand on topics the text discusses only briefly.

2. **Take good class notes**. Make your notes as complete as possible, and include material written on chalkboards and in overheads as well as concepts discussed in spoken lecture.

3. **Read your text assignments in advance**. If this is not possible, read assignments soon after the corresponding lecture. Then, study the corresponding chapter in this Study Guide, paying particular attention to the Concept Tables. When you feel ready, take the chapter's Self-Test and, if possible, work through the Thought Provokers. Compare your answers to those in the Answer section at the back of the book. Although your instructor may ask other questions or omit essay questions from exams, each chapter's Thought Provokers and Self-Test will enable you to thoroughly review at least 75–85% of relevant text material. But no matter how much you review, remember: A study guide is only a *supplement* to the text, *not a replacement* for it. Always read your text assignment carefully and thoroughly.

4. **Ask questions**. Whether before, during, or after class, most instructors welcome questions to clarify topics students find unclear. Chances are, your instructor will be happy to accommodate you. And when asking a question, try to frame it clearly and succinctly.

5. **Determine the instructor's testing strategies and prepare accordingly**. Are tests all multiple choice, all essay, or a combination of both? Will exams cover material mainly from the text, from both text and lectures, or primarily from lectures?

6. **Stay current**. Don't let yourself fall behind in either reading or lab assignments. It's hard to play catch-up.

Finally, remember to maintain an appropriate balance between your academic and your nonacademic activities. Studying is important, but you need time for relaxation and recreation. Your creativity and academic performance will be all the better if there is a little fun in your life.

Acknowledgments

We wish to thank Beverly Fraknoi of McGraw-Hill for editing and coordinating this Study Guide. We are grateful for her continual encouragement, thoughtfulness, and insight as the book developed. For Deborah Brosnan, Professor Steven Courtney at the University of Oregon reviewed each chapter and offered numerous valuable suggestions for improvements. He also deserves special thanks for providing essential child care and meals at critical periods. To Joseph and Katherine Reinhardt goes deep appreciation for their love, devotion, and encouragement.

Deborah Brosnan
Donald Reinhardt

The Nature of Life

CHAPTER IN BRIEF

Perspective and Review

Living organisms are amazingly varied, and each one represents a success story—a victory of survival and the reproduction of its kind. There are literally millions of species of plants, animals, microbes, and other organisms—some small, some large, and many in between. All life forms are organized into distinct structures, and each structure, as well as the larger organism, functions in precise ways. **Biology**, the science that studies life, recognizes that all living things share certain characteristics. This chapter provides some insights into those characteristics, and into some of the ways biologists think about and study the living world.

Living things interact with both living and nonliving components of their environment. In the process, they must solve two fundamental problems:

1. In order to remain alive, organisms must take in energy to overcome the tendency toward disorder and to maintain their life processes.

2. Living things must reproduce in order to overcome the death of individuals.

Biologists observe that the following characteristics are common to most life forms.

1. **Order**—specialized structure and arrangement of parts.

2. **Adaptations**—structures and activities that leave an organism better suited to its environment.

3. **Metabolism**—the chemical conversion and use of energy compounds.

4. **Movement**—the ability to change position or shape.

5. **Responsiveness**—the ability to detect and react to environmental changes.

6. **Reproduction**—the capacity of an organism to make more of its kind.

7. **Development**—change from one form to a more specialized form or type.

8. **Genes**—inheritable chemical units that carry the information that governs development and other life functions.

9. **Evolution**—the process through which life forms adjust to environmental variations and which alters a species' traits over time.

Life exhibits both **unity** and **diversity**. Unity is manifest in the genetic code of DNA common to all life forms and the many similarities in the basic structures of cells. Diversity is obvious in the many different types of plants, animals, and other life forms and, as you will see in later chapters, in the broad spectrum of differences that exist at the molecular and chemical levels of life.

Features of Life That Maintain Life Processes

■ **Order** Life forms are highly ordered; each part of an organism contributes to the unified functioning and survival of the whole. Yet, much as an automobile requires regular maintenance and occasional repair, living things and their parts are subject to wear and tear, damage from injuries and accidents, and other events that tend to create <u>disorder</u>. To combat the tendency toward disorder and keep the whole functioning smoothly, organisms must take in energy and materials. These become the resources for growth, maintenance, and other activities necessary to survival.

Throughout this book you will see that living systems are organized in special and predictable ways. Concept Table 1.1 shows the basic organization seen in all life forms. You will study each of these levels in later chapters. Keep in mind that even though organisms may vary significantly, there are many similarities in the chemical and molecular plans upon which life forms are built.

```
Concept Table 1.1  Organization in living systems

                        Organism
                        Organs
                        Tissues
                        Cells
                        Organelles
                        Molecules
                        Atoms
                        Subatomic particles
```

Concept Table 1.2 shows levels of organization in the entire intermix of living and nonliving components on Earth. How do the various levels relate to each other? Organisms that can interbreed are said to be members of the same <u>species</u>, but within species there are often several (or many) <u>populations</u>. A few or many different populations of interacting species in a particular area form a <u>community</u>. The community in turn fits into a particular <u>ecosystem</u>, such as a woodland, a grassland, or an ocean. Notice that an ecosystem contains both living and nonliving components. The <u>biosphere</u> is the sum total of the physical Earth and its lower atmosphere—all of the places where life can exist.

Biologists also organize the diversity of living things into a hierarchy of groups. At the bottom of this **hierarchy of life** is the <u>species</u>, which encompasses structurally similar individuals with the potential to successfully breed with each other. Related and similar species can make up a <u>genus</u>, genera may be grouped into <u>families</u>, families into <u>orders</u>, orders into <u>classes</u>, and classes into <u>phyla</u> or <u>divisions</u> (plants). The many divisions and phyla are ultimately assigned to five **kingdoms**, as shown in Concept Table 1.3.

```
Concept Table 1.2  The Earth and its biological components

              Biosphere
              Ecosystems (living/nonliving components)
              Communities
              Populations
              Organisms
```

■ **Adaptations** Structures, mechanisms, and behaviors that enable organisms to carry out their own special ways of life are **adaptations**. As you study the biology of particular organisms, try to note the special adaptive roles of the various—and sometimes unique—structures and functions different life forms possess.

Concept Table 1.3 Five kingdoms of living organisms

Kingdom	Type/characteristics of organisms
Monera	Prokaryotes—single cells with no true nucleus *Examples:* bacteria and cyanobacteria

Continues

Concept Table 1.3   Five kingdoms of living organisms (continued)

Kingdom	Type/characteristics of organisms
Protista	Simple eukaryotes—have a true nucleus *Example:* protozoa
Fungi	Single-to-many-celled eukaryotes, all of which are decomposers *Examples:* yeasts, molds, mushrooms
Plantae	Photosynthetic eukaryotes *Examples:* eukaryotic algae, mosses, liverworts, conifers, flowering plants
Animalia	All remaining eukaryotic life forms; complex and varied *Examples:* sponges, worms, insects, vertebrates

■ **Metabolism**   Within the cell or cells of an organism, **metabolism** is the organized series of chemical steps that breaks down energy-containing compounds and other materials and rearranges them into products that are the raw materials for cell processes of building and repair.

■ **Movement**   All life forms show some type of movement. This activity may be as simple as the internal flowing of a cell's contents or as complex as a cheetah stalking its prey. In general, plant movements are restricted and slow, while animals and many protists move more quickly.

■ **Responsiveness**   Organisms have the ability to react to environmental cues. Thus, plants grow toward or away from stimuli such as light and gravity. Animal responses may range from the movement of an amoeba toward or away from traces of a particular chemical, to a dog smelling a buried bone, digging for the bone, and finally gnawing upon it for hours.

The foregoing five categories describe characteristics that help organisms maintain life processes and avoid disorganization. The flow of energy and the cycling of materials are all a part of this pattern.

Features of Life That Overcome Death: Reproduction, Development, Genes, and Evolution

■ **Reproduction**   Organisms may reproduce sexually or asexually. In sexual reproduction, two specialized sex cells, one from each parent, unite to produce a new individual. In asexual reproduction, a single cell divides to give rise to two new individuals. Both processes have the same result: The species will continue even after the parent organism(s) dies.

■ **Development**   Organisms that arise through sexual reproduction usually undergo **development**, a sequence of defined changes that generally result in an individual that resembles and has all the important features typical of its species. Genes orchestrate and regulate this process.

■ **Genes**   Genes are discrete segments of DNA, the master molecule of heredity in most life forms. Genes are passed from one generation to another and contain the chemical information necessary to guide the development of each specific physical, chemical, or behavioral trait that each organism will have.

■ **Evolution**   All species of organisms alive today arose by descent from a common ancestor. Gene modifications, or <u>mutations</u>, have been (and continue to be) the raw material of evolution. In the early 19th century, Jean-Baptiste Lamarck suggested that evolution occurred through the <u>inheritance of acquired characteristics</u>. In Lamarck's scenario, the children of a weight lifter could inherit enlarged muscles without ever working out. Later, Charles Darwin and Alfred Wallace noted that members of the same species do in fact inherit variations (based on actual modifications of genes) that can in turn be passed on to subsequent generations. They also noted that populations of a species tend to produce more offspring than there are environmental resources to support, so that individuals must compete with each other for those resources. From these two observations Darwin promulgated the idea of evolution by **natural selection**: Individuals that have useful inherited variations can obtain or use resources more effectively and will be more likely to survive to reproduce (the "survival of the fittest"). In short, in nature individuals with the most advantageous adaptations will become the "preferred" parents of the next generation. Through a century of testing these ideas, biologists have confirmed that natural selection is the major mechanism leading to evolutionary change.

The Scientific Method

Biology is an organized body of knowledge founded on the **scientific method**—a technique for gaining knowledge that involves both inductive and deductive reasoning. Concept Table 1.4 outlines the scientific method.

Concept Table 1.4 The scientific method

1. **Observation.** The senses detect and recognize an event or object, and the observer records this information. The observer can then ask a specific question to clearly define the situation: What kind of creature is this? What is this organelle? What does this structure do? How do birds migrate?

2. **Hypothesis.** The observer suggests an answer to the question that offers a reasonable explanation for the observation. For example, "Birds rely on light and magnetic signals to guide their migration."

3. **Experimentation.** The observer designs and executes tests that can prove or disprove the hypothesis.

4. **Conclusions.** The observer uses the test results to arrive at a final statement that supports or contradicts the hypothesis.

The various conclusions, ideas, and concepts found in science textbooks are the result of many thousands of hypotheses and experiments and many millions of observations.

Thought Provoker

In this and subsequent chapters, Thought Provoker questions will help you organize and integrate the facts and concepts you have studied. Answer them briefly in the space provided or on a separate sheet of paper. Suggested answers appear in the Answers section at the back of the book.

1. Describe two basic requirements of living organisms and explain how particular characteristics of life help organisms meet these requirements.

Self-Test

For each statement or question choose the best response and mark your choice in the space provided. Answers are in the Answer section at the back of the book.

_D_   **1.** Which term encompasses all the others?

        a. population   **b.** community   **c.** organism   **d.** ecosystem   **e.** organ

_A_   **2.** Which structure encompasses all the others?

        a. organ   **b.** cell   **c.** organelle   **d.** tissue   **e.** molecule

_B_   **3.** Which step comes first in the scientific method?

        a. experimentation   **c.** conclusion   **e.** data-gathering
        b. observation   **d.** hypothesis

_B_   **4.** Of the following, the smallest is:

        a. a molecule   **c.** a cell   **e.** a compound
        b. an atom   **d.** an organism

_D_   **5.** Which person is associated with the concept of "inheritance of acquired characteristics"?

        a. Charles Darwin   **c.** Robert Hooke   **e.** Anton van Leeuwenhoek
        b. A. R. Wallace   **d.** Jean-Baptiste Lamarck

_B_   **6.** Genes are best characterized as:

        a. proteins   **c.** sugars   **e.** amino acids
        b. nucleic acids   **d.** lipids

_A_   **7.** The fundamental source of energy for virtually all life on earth is:

        a. sunlight   **c.** oil   **e.** metals
        b. chemicals   **d.** coal

_A_   **8.** Repair processes in cells are necessary to combat:

        a. disorder   **c.** metabolism   **e.** acids
        b. death   **d.** growth

_E_   **9.** Which choice best illustrates the concepts associated with "the survival of the fittest"?

        a. rabbits   **c.** insects   **e.** dinosaurs
        b. turtles   **d.** plants

_B_   **10.** If an organism cannot reproduce or grow, it obviously:

        a. is dead   **c.** cannot repair itself   **e.** is an animal
        b. will have no offspring   **d.** is a plant

Key Terms from the Text Chapter

adaptations *text page 4, 9*   hierarchy of life *6*   order *4, 5*
biology *3*   hypothesis *18*   prediction *18*
development *4, 13*   kingdom *9*   reproduction *4, 12*
diversity *4, 7*   metabolism *10*   responsiveness *10*
evolution *4, 14*   movement *4, 10*   scientific method *18*
genes *13*   natural selection *15*   unity *14*

2

Atoms, Molecules, and Life

Perspective and Review

Chemistry, the subject of this chapter, is a vital part of the study of life. In fact, it is not much of an exaggeration to say that the "nuts and bolts" of life are the chemical interactions between the different kinds of matter that make up organisms. Matter is anything that occupies space and has weight. Your body is matter. Anything you can touch, see, taste, or smell is matter.

  The material world in which organisms live is composed of 92 natural **elements**—the fundamental kinds of matter known to exist on Earth and in the larger universe. Each element has a name and a symbol—for example, silver (Ag), gold (Au), and magnesium (Mg). Of the 92 natural elements, however, only six occur in measurable amounts in living things: carbon (C), hydrogen (H), oxygen (O), nitrogen (N), phosphorus (P), and sulfur (S). These materials and traces of other elements such as iron, potassium, and zinc play vital structural and functional roles in every organism.

Every element is different from every other. The reason for these differences lies in the fine structure of each element, its constituent atoms. An **atom** is the smallest part of an element that still has all the properties of that element. Scientists can explain the varying properties of the different elements by looking at the characteristics—the internal organization—of their atoms.

The Structure of the Atom

Every atom of every element consists of a specific number of subatomic particles: positively charged **protons**, noncharged **neutrons**, and negatively charged **electrons**. Electrons orbit continuously in cloud-like regions, or orbitals, around the atom's central **nucleus**, while the neutrons and protons reside within the nucleus. Because opposite charges attract, under stable conditions the number of electrons (negative charge) in an atom equals the number of protons (positive charge).

Although electrons have very little mass, they have a great deal of energy. They occur in **energy levels** that correspond to defined distances from the atom's nucleus. The number and positions of an atom's outermost electrons largely determine the atom's chemical behavior. Thus, those that are closest to the nucleus are bound more strongly by the positive charge of the nuclear protons, while those farther away from the nucleus are less influenced by the proton charge. And highly reactive atoms, such as carbon atoms, may have an "incomplete" outermost energy level—that is, not all the "available" electron slots are filled. As a result, carbon tends to bond chemically through the sharing of electrons with many different elements. As you will see in this and later chapters, carbon is a component of an enormous number of compounds found in living organisms.

Concept Table 2.1 compares the structural features of atoms of different elements. As the table shows, atoms of each element have a unique number of protons in their nuclei—nitrogen has 7, oxygen 8, and so on. This unique number of protons is the element's **atomic number**. The **atomic mass** of an element is the sum of protons and neutrons in a standard atom. For example, carbon usually has 6 protons and 6 neutrons and has an atomic mass of 12. If an isolated carbon atom is electrically balanced, how many electrons would you expect it to have? You can determine the correct answer by consulting the table. As you do, notice that the number of neutrons in an atom is always equal to or greater than the number of protons. In one of the heavier atoms, such as uranium, the number of neutrons may be considerably greater than the number of protons.

Concept Table 2.1 Selected characteristics of important elements

Element	Symbol	Atomic number	Atomic mass	Protons	Number of: Neutrons	Electrons
Hydrogen	H	1	1	1	0	1
Carbon	C	6	12	6	6	6
Nitrogen	N	7	14	7	7	7
Oxygen	O	8	16	8	8	8
Phosphorus	P	15	31	15	16	15
Sulfur	S	16	32	16	16	16
Sodium	Na	11	23	11	12	11
Chlorine	Cl	17	35	17	18	17

Isotopes and Ions

Atoms of the same element that have different atomic masses are called **isotopes**. For instance, the isotopes of carbon known as carbon-12 and carbon-14 differ from each other only in the number of neutrons each has in the nucleus. With the exception of their atomic masses, the two carbon isotopes have the same properties. Isotopes like $_{14}C$ are radioactive; the nucleus is unstable and emits energy as it loses the extra neutrons and changes to a more stable form.

An **ion** is another exception to the usual atomic structure. In this kind of atom electrical events increase or reduce the number of orbiting electrons, so the atom has a slight positive or negative charge. In chemical reactions, ions behave differently than do standard atoms of the same element.

Compounds of Atoms, Molecules, and Atomic Bonds

When an atom of one element combines chemically with an atom of another element, the result is a compound. Thus, a **compound** is matter consisting of two or more chemically united elements. A molecule is two or more atoms of the same or different elements joined by chemical bonds. When biologists study molecules and compounds, they are frequently interested in the type of chemical bond that joins the different atoms. Concept Table 2.2 describes the three main types of chemical bonds.

Concept Table 2.2   Chemical bonds and their properties

Bond type	Characteristics/Examples
Covalent	**The linked atoms share electrons.** These extremely strong bonds are typical of organic (carbon-containing) compounds. They are also found in inorganic compound molecules such as water (H_2O), oxygen (O_2), and nitrogen gas. **Covalent bonds** can be **polar** or **nonpolar**, depending on whether the distribution of charge is symmetrical. In diagrams of covalently bound atoms, a single line indicates the sharing of one electron pair, a double line the sharing of two pairs of electrons, and a triple line the sharing of three electron pairs.
Ionic	**A bond formed when one atom gives up an electron and another atom adds the free electron to its outermost orbital.** Here, electrons are not shared; instead, one or more electrons are transferred from one atom to another. As the name of this bond suggests, the atoms involved are ions— each has taken on a positive or negative charge as the result of donating or acquiring one or more electrons. **Ionic bonds** are typically seen in inorganic compounds such as table salt (sodium chloride, NaCl) and inorganic acids and bases.
Hydrogen	**The attraction of the hydrogen nucleus, with its strong positive charge, for electronegative atoms.** The **hydrogen bond** is a relatively weak bond by itself, but many H-bonds acting together may create overall strong bonding. Examples are water-to-water H-bonding and the nitrogen-base bonding in DNA.

Concept Table 2.3 Some important inorganic compounds found in living organisms

Chemical formula	Name
HOH (H_2O)	water
NaCl	sodium chloride (table salt)
KCl	potassium salt (table salt substitute)
KNO_3	potassium nitrate
HCl	hydrogen chloride/hydrochloric acid
$CaCO_3$	calcium carbonate
$CaSO_4$	calcium sulfate
$CuCl_2$	copper chloride
$FeSO_4$	iron sulfate
$NaHCO_3$	sodium bicarbonate (baking soda)

Water: A Key Chemical Compound

The "driest" organism on Earth is roughly 50% water, while some living things are 99% water. It is not surprising, then, that water has properties that are extremely important to living systems.

Water is a bipolar molecule and is an excellent solvent. Any substance that can form a homogeneous mixture with molecules of another substance is a **solvent**. By contrast, a **solute** is the substance that dissolves in a solvent. Water, the "universal solvent," can dissolve many different kinds of compounds, in part because of its relatively weak hydrogen bonds, and also because its polarity (having regions of positive and negative charge) enables it to react with polar compounds and ionic molecules.

Compounds that dissolve readily in water are termed **hydrophilic**, or "water-loving." Those that are **hydrophobic**, or "water-hating," do not easily dissolve in water and include **lipids**, such as fats, oils, and waxes.

Water is a molecule with high specific heat, high heat of vaporization, and high heat of fusion. Numerous properties of water are related to temperature. The specific heat of water is the amount of heat needed to raise the temperature of one gram of water by 1°C. The fact that this value is high means that water changes temperature rather slowly—an essential attribute if the internal and external environments of organisms are to remain relatively stable. Approximately 580 calories are required to evaporate one gram of water—this is water's heat of vaporization. Consequently, water can—in fact, must—absorb a great deal of heat before it becomes gaseous, a property that explains why organisms have evolved water-based cooling systems, such as sweating.

Finally, the rapid breaking and forming of hydrogen bonds in liquid water creates high heat of fusion, so water resists the change to the solid state (ice)—a crucial feature for life forms that depend on water in its liquid form.

Important mechanical properties include the following.

Water molecules show **cohesion**, the tendency to stick to other water molecules.

Water molecules show **adhesion**, the tendency to stick to other types of molecules.

Water molecules show **capillarity**, the tendency to move upward in a narrow space against the pull of gravity.

Water molecules exhibit **surface tension**, the tendency of molecules at the surface of liquid water to cohere to each other but not to the molecules of air above them.

Solid water (ice) tends to float in liquid water. This property, due to the fact that solid water is less dense than the liquid, prevents lakes from freezing solid in winter and thus enables aquatic organisms to survive.

Water, Ionization, pH, Acids, Bases, and Buffers

Because water is held together by covalent bonds, it is an extremely stable compound. It has only a slight tendency to ionize—that is, to dissociate into positive and negative ions. In pure water, there are about one H^+ and one OH^- for every 10 million water molecules. In living systems, however, even this small rate of ionization is important, because it can affect the pH of the cellular environment.

A simplified way to think of pH is as a measure of the acidity or alkalinity of a substance. Actually, the **pH scale** of 1–14 reflects the concentration of hydrogen ions (H^+) in a solution. Any substance that gives off hydrogen ions when dissolved in water—and thereby increases the H^+ concentration of the solution—is an **acid**. On the pH scale, acids have values between 0 and <7. A **base** is a substance that accepts hydrogen ions, or donates hydroxyl ions (OH^-), when dissociated in water; bases have pH scale values between >7 and 14. Basic solutions are also said to be **alkaline**. As your text notes, by the definitions just given, water is (weakly) both an acid and a base. Its pH is the neutral value of 7.

Chemical compounds that help control or regulate pH, preventing potentially harmful fluctuations, are called **buffers**. Buffers are neither acid nor base, but are compounds such as $NaHCO_3$ (sodium bicarbonate) that, because of their chemical makeup, may either donate or accept hydrogen ions.

Organic Chemistry: The Chemistry of Carbon Compounds

Carbon atoms have a striking feature: The outermost energy level is only half full. Instead of a possible 8 electrons, only 4 are present. To make up this electron deficit, carbon atoms easily participate in covalent bonding—the electron sharing described in Concept Table 2.2. Covalent bonds are extremely stable; other biologically important elements that bond in this way include oxygen, hydrogen, nitrogen, and phosphorus.

Because of its structure, carbon can form compounds with other atoms more readily than any other known element. The study of compounds containing carbon—and there are millions of them—is called organic chemistry. Concept Table 2.4 lists the most important organic molecules of living systems, the four main classes of biological molecules: carbohydrates, lipids, proteins, and nucleic acids.

Concept Table 2.4   Important organic compounds (biochemicals) of living organisms

Compound	Constituent elements	Functions/Examples
Carbohydrates	C, H, O	Energy source, component of cell structure Glucose, sucrose, cellulose
Lipids	C, H, O	Energy sources, components of cell structures Fats, oils, cholesterol
Proteins	C, H, O, N, S	Catalysts, energy sources, components of cell structures Enzymes, collagen, hemoglobin
Nucleic acids	C, H, O, N, P	Informational molecules DNA and RNA

■ **Monomers and Polymers** The four classes of biological molecules are all **polymers**, or long chains; in fact, most large molecules in organic chemistry are polymers. These long chains consist of linked **monomers**, which fall into four families: saccharides (sugars), fatty acids, amino acids, and nucleotides. As you study macromolecules, note the basic monomer and the type of bonding that takes place to form the larger structure.

During polymer synthesis water is often removed as the monomers join together. This kind of reaction is known as a **condensation** reaction (or dehydration synthesis). Conversely, when these large molecules are broken down, water is frequently added in what is called a **hydrolysis** reaction.

■ **Functional chemical groups**   As you study biological molecules you will notice that each includes at least one functional group of atoms. A functional group is extremely important, because it gives the larger molecule a specific chemical behavior. Functional groups you should learn to recognize include hydroxyl (OH), carbonyl (C=O), carboxyl (COOH), amino (NH_2), and methyl (CH_3) groups.

■ **Carbohydrates**   These vital compounds are composed of carbon, hydrogen, and oxygen, and play major biological roles as energy sources and components of cell structures. One of the simplest is **glucose**, the "universal fuel" that is the basic energy source for virtually all living organisms. Among the various **carbohydrates** are the pentose, or five-carbon, sugars ribose and deoxyribose found in, respectively, the nucleic acids RNA and DNA. Six-carbon hexose sugars include glucose and its relative fructose and galactose. Each of these sugars has the same types and numbers of atoms, but arranged differently in each case. The hexose sugars are thus isomers—compounds with the same atomic formula ($C_6H_{12}O_6$) but having different properties.

Glucose and its isomers are all **monosaccharides**, or "single sugars." These can be linked into two-unit sugars called disaccharides, such as sucrose (table sugar), or into oligosaccharides ("few sugars") or **polysaccharides** ("many sugars"). The polysaccharides **starch** and **glycogen** serve as primary food reserves in plants and animals, respectively. **Cellulose** (wood fiber) and chitin are tough structural polysaccharides.

■ **Lipids**   Lipids—the fats, oils, waxes, phospholipids, and steroids—also consist of molecules made up of carbon, hydrogen, and oxygen. As you learned earlier, all lipids are hydrophobic, and play important roles as energy sources, as structural molecules, and as specialized molecules such as vitamins and hormones. **Fats** and oils are generally termed **triglycerides**, because they are composed of three fatty acids joined to each of the three carbons of glycerol. Because of the high-energy bonds they contain (C—C and C—H), fats and oils are common energy storage compounds in animals and plants.

Waxes are nontriglyceride lipids that are solid at room temperature and that serve mainly as protective coverings on plant and animal structures. **Phospholipids** resemble fats and oils, except that they have a phosphate group substituted for one of the fatty acids. This structure creates a water-soluble region on an otherwise hydrophobic molecule—a feature that, as you will see in Chapter 3, is of major importance in cell membrane structure. The final lipid group, **steroids**, are soluble in oil or lipid membranes. This characteristic enables steroids to serve as key regulatory molecules such as hormones that must be able to pass into and out of cells easily.

■ **Proteins**   Proteins, the key structural and functional molecules of organisms, are polymers built of amino acid monomers by way of condensation reactions. The bonds between amino acids are peptide bonds; two joined amino acids are thus a dipeptide, while long chains of the subunits are called **polypeptides**. The elements in proteins are typically carbon, hydrogen, oxygen, nitrogen, and sulfur. The catalytic proteins called **enzymes** facilitate virtually all of the processes that go on in living cells.

The unique and varied properties of proteins are directly related by their four basic structural levels:

1. **Primary structure**: the order, number, and arrangement of the individual amino acids that make up the polypeptide.

2. **Secondary structure**: the α-**helix** shape that results from hydrogen bond formation followed by twisting of the molecule. Another type of secondary structure, the β-**pleated sheet** configuration, hydrogen bonds link polypeptide chains that are lying side by side, and the linked chains then crinkle into an accordion-like sheet.

3. **Tertiary structure**: a three-dimensional shape in many proteins due to the cross-linking of the protein by covalent disulfide bonds and some ionic bonds.

4. **Quaternary structure**: a structure that results from the union of two or more polypeptides.

■ **Nucleic acids** The group of **nucleic acids** includes DNA (deoxyribonucleic acid) and RNA (ribonucleic acid), the molecules that serve as the chemical "code of life" and bear genetic information from one generation to the next. Both types of molecules are built of **nucleotides**, each of which is composed of a nitrogen-containing base, a five-carbon sugar (ribose or deoxyribose), and a phosphate group. In cells, the sequences of nucleotides in DNA and RNA code for and direct the assembly of the specific sequences of amino acids that make up different proteins. (As you will learn later, particular DNA sequences on chromosomes make up "genes.")

Another important group of molecules based on modified nucleotides are the adenosine di- and triphosphates, including a vital energy-transfer molecule, ATP (discussed in detail in Chapters 4 and 5).

Thought Provokers

1. In a short paragraph, explain why pH is important in biological systems.

2. If a doctor told you that a disease had stopped all enzyme activity in your body, would you be (a) only a little worried, (b) prepared for an operation, or (c) dead? Explain.

Self-Test

For each statement or question choose the best response and mark your choice in the space provided. For some items you will select your response from a *Key*.

Questions 1–10: Using the *Key*, indicate the constituent elements of each compound.

a. C H
b. C H O
c. C H O N

d. C H O N P
e. C H O N S

ab. O H
ac. N H
ad. C O

_____ **1.** water

_____ **2.** lipids

_____ **3.** glucose

_____ **4.** cellulose

_____ **5.** protein

_____ **6.** DNA

_____ **7.** carbon dioxide

_____ **8.** enzymes

_____ **9.** starch

_____ **10.** fats

_____ **11.** Which is an isomer of glucose?

    a. starch   **d.** maltose

    b. cellulose   **e.** fructose

    c. amylose

_____ **12.** Isotopes of the same element differ in what way(s)? Choose *all* the correct answers.

    a. Chemical reactivity and compounds formed

    b. Atomic weight

    c. Atomic number

    d. Type(s) of bonds formed

    e. Neutron number

_____ **13.** pH is a measure of the concentration of:

    a. hydroxyl ions   **c.** protons   **e.** All of these

    b. electrons   **d.** neutrons

Questions 14–18. Select the pH value from the *Key* that best matches each numbered description.

    a. 0–1   **c.** 6   **e.** 8–9

    b. 2–5   **d.** 7   **ab.** 10–12

_____ **14.** pH value closest to that of human body fluids

_____ **15.** the most alkaline pH value

_____ **16.** pH of fluid in the stomach

_____ **17.** pH of $NaHCO_3$

_____ **18.** most acid pH value

Key for questions 19–30

    a. 0   **ab.** 7   **bd.** 18   **abc.** 101–200

    b. 1   **ac.** 8   **be.** 21   **bcd.** 201–500

    c. 2   **ad.** 12   **cd.** 23   **cde.** 501+

    d. 4   **ae.** 14   **de.** 25–100

    e. 6   **bc.** 16

_____ **19.** Molecular weight of water

_____ **20.** Atomic weight of carbon

_____ **21.** Atomic weight of a proton

_____ **22.** Atomic weight of a neutron

_____ **23.** Atomic weight of hydrogen

_____ **24.** Atomic weight of a molecule of hydrogen gas

_____ **25.** Atomic number of carbon

_____ **26.** Number of electrons in the innermost orbit of most atoms

_____ 27. Atomic weight of an electron

_____ 28. Weight of glucose

_____ 29. Weight of a typical DNA molecule

_____ 30. Number of electrons that carbon can share

Questions 31–35. Using the *Key*, indicate the type of bond in each compound.

a. ionic   **b.** hydrogen   **c.** covalent

_____ 31. a single water molecule

_____ 32. NaCl

_____ 33. glucose

_____ 34. potassium hydroxide

_____ 35. two bonded water molecules

Key for questions 36–40

a. proteins   **c.** RNA   **e.** lipids/fats
b. polysaccharides   **d.** DNA

_____ 36. the largest molecules in living systems

_____ 37. the major storage molecule of living systems

_____ 38. composed of glycerol and long chain acids

_____ 39. a molecule that has messenger, transfer, and ribosomal types

_____ 40. molecules that are catalysts in living systems

Key for questions 41–45

a. element   **d.** molecule   **ab.** compound
b. atom   **e.** isotope   **ac.** isomer
c. ion

_____ 41. the smallest part of an element with the properties of that element

_____ 42. the smallest unit of a compound that is still that compound

_____ 43. a charged atom

_____ 44. There are 92 of these in nature.

_____ 45. Chemical bonds are needed to form this.

Key Terms from the Text Chapter

acid *text page 41*
adhesion *38*
alkaline *41*
α helix *52*
amino acid *42*
atom *29*
atomic mass *29*
atomic number *29*
base *41*
β-pleated sheet *52*
buffer *41*
capillarity *38*
carbohydrate *42*
cellulose *45*
cohesion *37*
compound *28*
condensation *42*
covalent bond *33*
electron *29*
element *28*

energy level *31*
enzyme *50*
fat *49*
fatty acid *42*
glucose *45*
glycogen *45*
hydrogen bond *34*
hydrolysis *42*
hydrophilic *40*
hydrophobic *40*
ion *31*
ionic bond *34*
isotope *30*
lipid *42*
monomer *42*
monosaccharide *45*
neutron *29*
nucleic acid *42*
nucleotide *42*
nucleus *29*

pH scale *41*
phospholipid *49*
polymer *42*
polypeptide *52*
polysaccharide *45*
primary structure *52*
protein *42*
proton *29*
quarternary structure *54*
radioactive *30*
random coil *54*
secondary structure *52*
solute *40*
solvent *40*
starch *45*
steroid *49*
surface tension *38*
tertiary structure *54*
triglyceride *48*

Concept Figure: Chemical Reactions That Create or Break Polymer Compounds

(a)

(b)

Exercise

1. What kind of chemical reaction is taking place in (a)? _____

   in (b)? _____

2. Explain how the chemical reaction (a) links monomer subunits into polymers, and identify the compound that is always a by-product of this kind of reaction.

_____

_____

3. Why would a chemist studying biological molecules be interested in knowing the chemical characteristics of monomer subunits that make up a particular polymer? Give an example.

_____

_____

3

Cells: The Basic Units of Life

Perspective and Review

Understanding the cell and its functions is vital to the study of life. All living organisms, from the simplest to the most complex, are composed of one or more cells. Bacteria, *Euglena*, and *Amoeba* are all examples of unicellular life forms. An adult human is composed of billions of cells, including some 200 different cell types. Yet, as Concept Table 3.1 shows, all cells share certain common characteristics and have similar basic functions.

Concept Table 3.1 Common characteristics and basic functions of cells

All cells:

1. *Possess a cellular membrane, a lipid bilayer known as the plasmalemma.*
   The **fluid mosaic model** portrays the plasmalemma and the proteins that are embedded in it (text Figure 3.13b). Some proteins float in the membrane, some span the entire membrane, and some are on only one face of the membrane. The outer and inner surfaces of the cell membrane tend to be hydrophilic (water-loving) and the lipid, nonprotein portions of the membrane tend to be hydrophobic (water-hating).

   The plasmalemma is critical to life because the proteins embedded in it help regulate the flow of materials into and out of the cell. Water passes through freely via the process of osmosis. Passage of other molecules depends on properties of the membrane that make it selectively permeable.

2. *Have a nucleus, or a nucleoid region, that contains DNA.*
   Cellular DNA contains encoded information that directs the manufacture of all necessary cell proteins.

3. *Produce three types of RNA: messenger, ribosomal, and transfer (soluble).*
   All three RNA types are needed for protein synthesis.

4. *Manufacture structural and functional proteins.*
   Structural proteins serve as building materials, provide cytoplasmic support, and play a role in movement. Enzymes (catalytic proteins) function in the synthesis and breakdown of compounds.

5. *Obtain energy from metabolism of chemical bonds or through photosynthesis.*
   Metabolism of chemical bonds or photosynthesis provides cells with the energy they need for growth and survival. Both processes depend on the presence of enzymes, which catalyze basic reactions.

6. *Reproduce, including all essential cell components.*
   In order to continue life, life forms must reproduce. Reproduction is thus an essential feature of all living organisms.

The information contained in a cell's DNA drives cell functions. DNA specifies the types of protein a cell makes. Typically, cells with less DNA carry less information, and thus make fewer, and fewer kinds, of proteins. The simplest cells, bacteria, have a single, non-membrane-bound **chromosome** (the *nucleoid*) that contains enough information to make about 1,000–2,000 different proteins. In contrast, human cells have 23 pairs of chromosomes (46 altogether) and can make about 50,000–100,000 different kinds of proteins.

The parts of a cell are by themselves not alive. Life depends on the interaction, cooperation, and integration of the activities of all parts of the cell. Modern understanding of the cell emerged from the explorations of early researchers, who used light microscopy in their work. Robert Hooke is credited with recognizing the first cells—the empty, dead cells of cork. Anton van Leeuwenhoek observed living cells. His tiny microscopes magnified objects about 300–500×, and he was the first to describe motile microscopic creatures ("animalcules"). The German botanist Schleiden and the zoologist Schwann concluded after careful study that plants, animals, and indeed all living creatures were composed of cells. <u>Virchow</u> formulated the statement that cells arise only from other living cells. All these findings have withstood decades of investigation and scrutiny. The findings of Schleiden, Schwann, and Virchow are basic principles in biology.

Prokaryotes and Eukaryotes

Some cells are strikingly simple, others are highly complex. The simplest cells are **prokaryotic cells** such as bacteria (text Figure 3.1). Prokaryotes have a cell membrane (plasmalemma), a non-membrane-bound nucleus or nucleoid, three types of RNA, proteins, the ability to reproduce, and photosynthesize or obtain energy contained in chemical bonds. The prokaryote kingdom <u>Monera</u> comprises bacteria and blue-green algae. Many of these organisms possess an outer **cell wall** or <u>envelope</u> that protects the plasmalemma.

Eukaryotic cells differ from prokaryotic ones in distinct ways, including having a membrane-bound nucleus. Organisms in the four remaining kingdoms of life—<u>Protista, Plantae, Animalia</u>, and <u>Mycota</u>—all are eukaryotes. Life forms in these four kingdoms, but most especially plants and animals, show complex cell cooperation and cell specialization. Concept Table 3.2 indicates the significant features of eukaryotes.

Concept Table 3.2   Significant features of eukaryotic cells

All eukaryotic cells:

1. *Have a membrane-bound nucleus.*
2. *Have nuclear DNA organized as a distinct chromosome or chromosomes.*
   A eukaryote **chromosome** typically divides with the assistance of specific proteins known as mitotic spindle proteins. The division process is usually termed <u>mitosis</u> and is distinguished from simple binary fission (seen in bacteria). A portion of the nucleus termed the **nucleolus** is a region enriched with ribosomal-type RNA.
3. *Have a nuclear membrane with pores that permit RNA produced in the nucleus to pass to the cytoplasm.*
4. *Have a distinct cytoplasm between the cell membrane and the nuclear membrane.*
5. *Have various types of <u>organelles</u> in the cytoplasm, each with a specific function:*
   a. **Endoplasmic reticulum.** Membraneous channels that increase internal cell surface area and provide sites for enzyme and ribosome activities.
   b. **Mitochondria.** Organelles that contain their own DNA and RNA, can reproduce by binary fission, and contain respiratory cell enzymes. Mitochondrial functions require oxygen. Mitochondria are composed of a double-membrane system. The inner membrane is infolded and irregular, forming <u>cristae</u> in which enzymes are embedded.
   c. **Ribosomes.** Composed of proteins and RNA. Messenger RNA (mRNA) adheres to ribosomes and, together with enzymes and transfer RNA (tRNA), functions in protein synthesis. Ribosomes are also found in prokaryotes, but are larger in eukaryotes.
   d. **Golgi body** or **apparatus.** A specialized and modified membraneous structure that enfolds or packages substances produced in the cytoplasm—such as enzymes and hormones—for transport outside the cell. Vesicles produced by the Golgi body migrate and fuse with the cell membrane to repair or expand it.
   e. **Chloroplasts.** Chlorophyll-containing organelles found in photosynthetic organisms. During photosynthesis, chlorophyll traps light energy, carbon dioxide is used, and oxygen is released. Each chloroplast is a double-membrane system. Enzymes and pigments are embedded in its thylakoid disks, which are stacked like dimes and form structures called grana.

Continues

Concept Table 3.2   Significant features of eukaryotic cells (continued)

f. **Centrioles.** Found in all eukaryotes except higher plants. Involved in spindle formation and processes that distribute chromosomes.

g. **Basal bodies.** Specialized structures at the base of **cilia** and **flagella**.

h. **Microtubules.** Fibers 20–25 nanometers in diameter, composed of globular tubulin. Microtubules make up the spindle, elements of cilia and flagella, and are responsible in part for amoeboid movement. They are important components of the **cytoskeleton**.

i. **Microfilaments.** Cytoskeletal filaments 3–5 nm in diameter and composed of actin protein that serve as "stress" fibers. Push-pull movements of the cell are related to microfilaments.

j. **Intermediate fibers.** Cytoskeletal proteins, including keratin and others, that help stabilize and anchor the cell. Roughly 10 nm in diameter, intermediate fibers differ from microfilaments and microtubules in that they are not capable of dynamic assembly and disassembly.

k. **Vacuoles.** Single-membrane structures that in plant cells store ions and other materials and decrease the internal volume of the cell. In animals, contractile vacuoles function to maintain osmotic balance.

l. **Lysosomes.** Single-membrane vesicles containing various types of enzymes that digest materials taken into the vesicle, as well as certain substances outside the cell. Lysosome enzymes can digest the cell itself if lysosomes break down.

m. **Microbodies.** Membraneous vesicles that contain one or more enzymes with specialized functions.

n. **Leucoplasts.** Membrane-bound vesicles in plant cells that store starch or oils.

o. **Chromoplasts.** Membrane-bound, pigment-containing vesicles in plant cells.

p. **Cell wall.** In plants and certain other organisms, a protective, strengthening covering over the plasmalemma. Typically composed of cellulose in plants, the initial, or primary, wall may be pushed outward as new secondary wall material is laid down and toughened with lignin.

q. **Flagella** and **cilia.** Protein extensions of the cell that permit or facilitate movement, such as the swimming of human sperm cells and the sweeping motion of cilia in the respiratory tract and oviduct. Mitochondria provide the energy to power cilia and flagella.

Cells within a single organism may vary significantly—that is, they may be specialized. For example, some cells, such as the sieve and tracheid cells of plants, are specialized for materials transport. Other cells, such as epidermal cells, serve as protection. Mucus cells produce slime to lubricate and protect other cells from dehydration. Connective tissue cells produce collagen protein to provide tissue elasticity.

Cells may also vary in their surface area and volume. In a typical sphere, volume varies as the cube of the sphere's radius and area varies as the square of the radius. This means that any growing cell increases its volume much more quickly than its area. For such a cell, acquiring nutrients and eliminating wastes are problems. The dilemma can be resolved if the cell divides, or by infolding and invagination of the cell surface or internal areas. As you study cells and organisms, keep in mind that every time you encounter infolding in a structure, the structure has increased its surface area dramatically.

Thought Provokers

1. What parts and molecules would have to be present in the simplest entity that could still be called a cell? To research your answer, you may want to consider the discussion of prokaryotic cell structure in Chapter 16.

2. Much of a cell's internal character depends on various types of membranes. Name the membrane systems and membraneous organelles that might be found in a composite plant-animal cell, and explain what general advantage an extensive membrane system confers.

3. Eukaryotes and prokaryotes differ distinctly. Characterize these differences at the nuclear level and describe ways in which these two basic cell types are alike.

Self-Test

For each statement or question choose the best response and mark your choice in the space provided. For some items you will select your response from a *Key*.

Key for questions 1–15

a. prokaryotes only   **c.** both eukaryotes and prokaryotes
b. eukaryotes only   **d.** none of these

_____ **1.** What bacteria are.

_____ **2.** What human cells are.

_____ **3.** Amoebae, protozoa, and fungi

_____ **4.** The first cells were probably of this type.

_____ **5.** Chloroplasts are found in these.

_____ **6.** These contain ribosomes.

_____ **7.** These have flagella.

_____ **8.** Cells that undergo classical mitosis and meiosis

_____ **9.** Cyanobacteria

_____ **10.** Viruses are generally placed in this group.

_____ **11.** These possess enzymes.

_____ **12.** These have endoplasmic reticulum.

_____ **13.** These have structures with cristae.

_____ **14.** These commonly have cell membranes.

_____ **15.** These have nuclear pores.

Key for questions 16–36

a. nucleus   ab. ribosome   bc. Golgi body
b. nucleolus   ac. endoplasmic reticulum   bd. lysosomes
c. cell membrane ad. flagellum   be. centrioles
d. mitochondrion ae. spindle   cd. cell wall
e. chloroplast

_____ **16.** Major diffusion barrier of all cells

_____ **17.** Paired structures involved in chromosome movement

_____ **18.** Location of the chromosomes

_____ **19.** Secretory cells always show this specialized structure.

_____ **20.** Some biologists say this originated as an endosymbiotic alga.

_____ **21.** Organelle specialized for movement

_____ **22.** Structure to which mRNA adheres

_____ **23.** Internal cytoplasmic channel system of the cell

_____ **24.** Involved in the packaging of products for export

_____ **25.** Chromosomes attach to this structure during cell division.

_____ **26.** The "powerhouse" of the cell

_____ **27.** The location of the nucleolus

_____ **28.** What makes the rough endoplasmic reticulum appear rough

_____ **29.** Enzyme-containing vacuoles of white blood cells are this.

_____ **30.** Endosymbiotic bacteria might well be this.

_____ **31.** Where most RNA is made

_____ **32.** Plasmodesmata pass through these structures.

_____ **33.** Site of ribosomal RNA manufacture

_____ **34.** This accounts for the rigidity of plant cells.

_____ **35.** Structures that have grana and thylakoid membranes

_____ **36.** Autolysis of dead cells may in part be attributed to these.

_____ **37.** Desmosomes play a role in cell:

    a. motility   **c.** metabolism
    b. reproduction   **d.** structure

_____ **38.** A cell increases in diameter from two to eight micrometers. As a result, this cell's volume has increased:

    a. 2×   **c.** 8×   **e.** 64×
    b. 4×   **d.** 16×

_____ **39.** Cells that grow in size without dividing show what changes?

    a. A significant increase in area versus volume

    b. A significant decrease in area versus volume

    c. The same ratio of area:volume regardless of size

    d. The changes cannot be determined

_____ **40.** Mature red blood cells do not have a nucleus. On the basis of this information we may conclude that these cells:

    a. are prokaryotic

    b. are eukaryotic

    c. do not metabolize or carry out life functions

    d. can survive without a nucleus

    e. are scientific mysteries

Key Terms from the Text Chapter

cell theory   *text page 60*

cell wall   *61, 81*

central vacuole   *80*

chloroplast   *79*

chromosome   *73*

cilium   *80*

contractile vacuole   *80*

cytoplasm   *62*

cytoskeleton   *62*

desmosome   *84*

electron microscope (EM)   *68*

endocytosis   *71*

endoplasmic reticulum   *75*

eukaryotic cell   *61*

exocytosis   *71*

extracellular matrix   *81*

flagellum   *80*

fluid mosaic model   *71*

gap junction   *85*

Golgi body   *75*

intermediate filament   *73*

light microscope   *68*

lipid bilayer   *71*

lysosome   *76*

microfilament   *73*

microtubule   *73*

mitochondrion   *78*

nuclear envelope   *73*

nucleoid   *61*

nucleolus   *73*

nucleus   *72*

photosynthesis   *79*

plasma membrane   *70*

plasmodesma   *85*

prokaryotic cell   *61*

ribosome   *73*

semipermeable   *71*

surface-to-volume ratio   *66*

tight junction   *84*

vesicle   *76*

Concept Figure: Membrane Systems

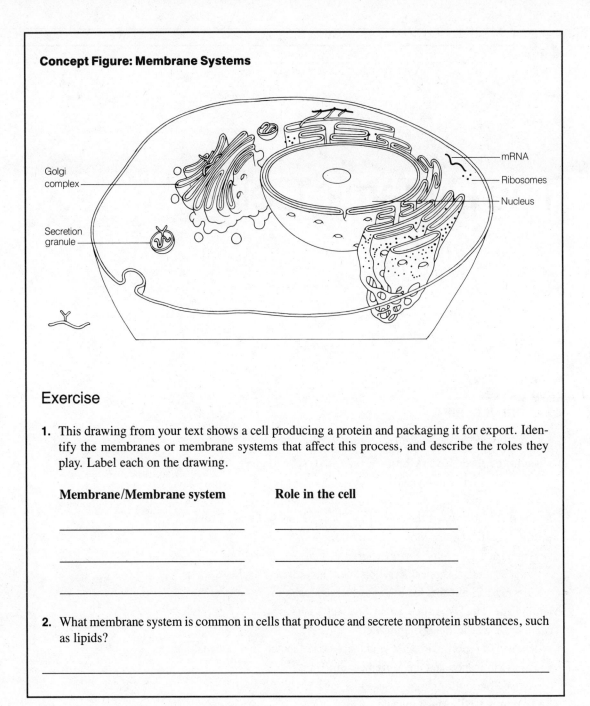

Golgi complex

Secretion granule

mRNA

Ribosomes

Nucleus

Exercise

1. This drawing from your text shows a cell producing a protein and packaging it for export. Identify the membranes or membrane systems that affect this process, and describe the roles they play. Label each on the drawing.

Membrane/Membrane system	Role in the cell
_____	_____
_____	_____
_____	_____

2. What membrane system is common in cells that produce and secrete nonprotein substances, such as lipids?

_____

4

The Dynamic Cell

Perspective and Review

Just as Chapter 3 focused on basic cell structure, this chapter introduces the fundamental chemical tasks cells carry out, and the universal laws of energy that govern such functions.

Laws of Energy

There are two <u>laws of thermodynamics</u>: (1) Energy can be neither created nor destroyed, but can be converted from one form to another; and (2) all things, including natural systems, tend toward disorder.

Energy is the ability to do work. The message of the first law is that there is no such thing as "new" energy: All energy, including the chemical energy that powers life processes, must come from other, existing energy. (Said another way, the universe contains all the energy it will ever have.) Energy exists in several forms, and an important statement of the first law is that energy can be converted from one form to another.

The types of energy include: electrical energy (electrons), light (photons), thermal energy, or heat (molecular/atomic motion), chemical energy (chemical bonds). **Kinetic energy** is energy in motion. Heat is an example of kinetic energy related to the motion of molecules or atoms. **Potential energy** is energy of position; examples include the energy in chemical bonds or represented in a boulder or rock that sits high on a hill.

All of the energy used by Earth's life forms comes from the sun. As you will learn in Chapter 6, plants can convert sunlight into chemical energy, which in turn can be used to perform cellular work and be converted to **heat** energy. These facts support the first law of thermodynamics.

The second law of thermodynamics states simply that any organized natural system tends toward **entropy**—that is, it tends to become disorganized as time passes. Living cells do not readily show an increase in entropy because they constantly take up energy for repair and synthesis, such as the building of proteins. Thus the cell maintains life by acquiring and expending energy.

Concept Table 4.1 shows some of the essential features of energy relationships.

Concept Table 4.1   Energy: The ability to do work

Energy class	Basic energy state
Heat	kinetic
Light	kinetic
Chemical	potential
Gravity/magnetism	potential

Energy Flow and Chemical Reactions

Many different chemical reactions occur in typical cells. These are divided into two basic types: **exergonic**, or energy-producing reactions, and **endergonic**, or energy-using reactions. You can see them compared in Concept Table 4.2.

Concept Table 4.2   Exergonic and endergonic chemical reactions

Reaction	Bond energy	Type of reactions
Endergonic	*Reactants:* lower *Products:* higher	Energy-requiring, such as synthesis, polymerization
Exergonic	*Reactants:* higher *Products:* lower	Energy-producing; catalysis

Cells carry out both exergonic and endergonic reactions. Frequently, energy-requiring reactions are linked to energy-yielding ones. **ATP**, adenosine triphosphate, is an important energy-linking compound that can provide energy for endergonic reactions. Wherever and whenever energy is needed, ATP molecules resulting from energy-yielding reactions are available for endergonic reactions. Chemical reactions occur everywhere in the cell. Together with energy flows in the cell, they are termed metabolism. A **metabolic pathway** is a series of reactions in which the products of one reaction become the reactants of the next.

Cellular chemical reactions are directed by protein **catalysts**, called **enzymes**. Each enzyme molecule has an **active site** that binds with reactants, or **substrate(s)**, in an enzyme-substrate complex. When the binding occurs the substrates—now close together and correctly oriented—can react and form a definite **product**. By bending the shape of the substrate molecules, the enzyme lowers the energy needed for a reaction to occur—that is, the reaction's **activation energy**.

Factors such as pH, temperature, substrate and enzyme concentration, and amount of product all can influence the rate of chemical reactions. Chemical reactions that are in equilibrium have exactly equal forward and backward rates of reaction.

Solutions and Transport

Cells are predominantly water, and as you learned in Chapter 3 the plasma membrane regulates molecular traffic into and out of the cell. When considering a cell, biologists are interested in how materials exit and enter the cell, and in which factors influence these passages. Concept Table 4.3 summarizes the significant concepts related to cell traffic.

Concept Table 4.3 Transport activities of the cell

Transport Type	Definition/example
Active	Energy expenditure required. Protein carrier; ATP utilized. Potassium-sodium pump.
Passive	Protein carrier; no ATP needed.
Osmosis	Diffusion of water across a **semipermeable membrane**.

Special osmotic conditions related to cells:

isotonic	Solute concentration (and water flow) balanced between cell interior and external environment
hypertonic	Solutes at higher concentration than in **intracellular fluid**.
hypotonic	Lower solute concentration than in intracellular fluid

Thought Provokers

1. Indicate the various ways materials get into and out of cells.

2. Explain the laws of thermodynamics and indicate whether living cells behave according to these laws.

3. Define osmosis. Then, using proper terminology and descriptions, explain balanced and unbalanced conditions related to osmosis.

4. Explain why enzymes are important for living organisms. Use all proper terminology as you indicate what enzymes do and how they function.

Self-Test

For each statement or question choose the best response and mark your choice in the space provided. For some items you will select your answer from a *Key*.

Key for questions 1–2

a. ADP   **c.** DNA   **e.** amino acids
b. ATP   **d.** RNA

_____ **1.** An important biochemical that links and drives many metabolic pathways.

_____ **2.** A biochemical involved in the contraction of muscle fibrils and protein assembly.

Key for questions 3–7 (type of energy represented or used)

a. potential   **b.** kinetic

_____ **3.** Chemical bond

_____ **4.** Heat

_____ **5.** Energy related to position

_____ **6.** Muscle contraction

_____ **7.** The flow of cytoplasm

8. Which of the following is not true of red blood cells?
   a. have no cell membrane
   b. lack a nucleus
   c. die after three or four months
   d. contain hemoglobin
   e. are disk-shaped

9. "Active site" is a term most closely associated with:
   a. an enzyme substrate
   b. an end product
   c. any compound
   d. an enzyme
   e. gas molecules

Key for questions 10–14: Given the biochemical reaction X + X + X → X—X—X, where X is a biochemical, indicate the probable nature of the reaction.
a. True   b. False

10. The reaction probably is endothermic.

11. Entropy is higher on the right side than on the left side.

12. The reaction is an example of anabolism (biosynthesis).

13. ATP may be required for the reaction.

14. X should be considered the product of the reaction.

15. The degree of entropy in an animal one hour after death is greater than the entropy in the same animal when it was alive.
    a. True
    b. False
    c. Impossible to tell without laboratory examination

Key for questions 16–20
a. True   b. False.

Enzymes:

16. raise the activation energy of the reaction.

17. break all bonds in the substrate.

18. are changed after the reaction.

19. form a complex with the substrate.

20. orient and change the shape of the substrate.

Key to questions 21–26
a. isotonic   b. hypotonic   c. hypertonic

21. The condition of blood plasma relative to fluid inside red blood cells

22. Condition of cell relative to its solution if it tends to lose more water than it gains

23. Condition of sea water relative to intracellular fluid

_____ **24.** The tonicity of distilled water compared to solutions of water

_____ **25.** Conditions of jams, jellies, and pickling solutions relative to human body fluids

_____ **26.** Condition of a solution relative to a red blood cell that expands and bursts when placed in the solution

Key to questions 27–30

a. papain   **c.** carbonic anhydrase
b. spectrin   **d.** pepsin

_____ **27.** Enzyme that breaks down proteins at an acid pH.

_____ **28.** Enzyme used to digest proteins on contact lenses.

_____ **29.** Protein that releases water and CO_2 from the substrate.

_____ **30.** Contractile protein associated with red blood cells.

Key to questions 31–33

a. True   **b.** False.

_____ **31.** A gradient occurs during diffusion.

_____ **32.** Osmosis can occur in the absence of water.

_____ **33.** The typical cell has a fully permeable membrane.

Key Terms in the Text Chapter

activation energy *text page 98*
active site *101*
active transport *104*
ATP *95*
bulk flow *107*
carrier-facilitated diffusion *105*
catalyst *99*
chemical reaction *92*
coenzyme *102*
diffusion *104*
endergonic *93*

energy *90*
entropy *91*
enzyme *99*
equilibrium point *96*
exergonic *93*
extracellular fluid *103*
first law of thermodynamics *90*
gradient *104*
heat *91*
intracellular fluid *103*
kinetic energy *90*

metabolic pathway *94*
osmosis *105*
passive transport *104*
potential energy *90*
product *92*
productive collision *98*
reactant *92*
second law of thermodynamics *90*
semipermeable membrane *104*
substrate *101*

Concept Figure: Reaction Chains in Living Things

Exercise

1. What term do biologists use to describe the reaction chain depicted in the drawing?

_____

2. Name and describe the characteristics of the two basic categories of chemical reactions depicted:

Reaction   **Description**

1. _____   _____

                                                    _____

2. _____   _____

                                                    _____

3. Add labels to the drawing to indicate the places where each type of reaction is taking place.

How Living Things Harvest Energy from Nutrient Molecules: Glycolysis, Fermentation, and Respiration

Perspective and Review

A major attribute of living cells is the ability to change various biochemicals from one form to another. In effect, cells fashion the molecules and compounds they need to maintain their structures and functions. Living cells also extract, capture, and transfer the chemical energy that powers all life processes. As you learned in Chapter 4, cells use enzymes to accomplish these varied tasks, which include both building-up and breaking-down functions. This chapter explores the enzyme-catalyzed processes and pathways through which cells extract energy.

The Transfer of Energy from Nutrient Molecules

Metabolism is the sum of all of a cell's biochemical activities. It includes building-up processes (anabolism) that are endergonic and thus require energy input, and breaking-down processes (catabolism) that are usually exergonic and thus yield energy. **Glycolysis**, **fermentation**, and **aerobic respiration** are all catabolic pathways. Glycolysis, the breakdown of sugar, is the basic pathway from which fermentation and aerobic respiration proceed.

ATP, the "Powerful Tail"

ATP, adenosine triphosphate, is the energy-storage molecule that links biochemical pathways and provides energy for cell processes. Each ATP molecule consists of adenine, the sugar ribose, and a "tail" of three phosphate groups. The molecule is unique in that it can transfer the terminal phosphate group and its associated bond energy to another compound—via the process of **phosphorylation**. As a result, the recipient biochemical can participate in otherwise energetically unfavorable reactions. ATP can be regenerated from ADP (adenosine diphosphate) by the uptake of a phosphate group. As described in this chapter and Chapter 6, ATP regeneration takes place in chloroplasts during photosynthesis and in **mitochondria** during the **Krebs cycle** and electron transport processes.

Oxidation-Reduction Reactions

Energy transfer in cells involves a flow of electrons that takes place via **oxidation-reduction reactions**. In biological systems oxidation is the removal of electrons, in the form of hydrogen atoms; it is always paired with reduction, the addition of electrons (hydrogens). Hence, when oxidation-reduction reactions occur there is always a donor molecule and an acceptor molecule. Special energy carriers transfer the electrons. Two of these are NADH and $FADH_2$.

Glycolysis, Fermentation, and Aerobic Respiration

Glycolysis, the splitting of sugar, can occur in the presence or absence of oxygen. The nine reaction steps take place in the cell cytoplasm and are enzyme-driven. Each split of a six-carbon glucose molecule yields two three-carbon pyruvate molecules and two ATP.

In **anaerobic** conditions the pyruvate from glycolysis can be further processed via fermentation. In alcoholic fermentation, pyruvate is catabolized into ethyl alcohol and CO_2, a sequence that does not yield ATP but does oxidize NADH to NAD^+, which can then be reused in the pathway as an electron carrier. In lactic acid fermentation (also anaerobic), cells convert pyruvate to lactic acid. Once again, no ATP results, but NADH is oxidized to NAD^+, whch returns to the glycolysis cycle.

In **aerobic** organisms, pyruvate from glycolysis is further processed in the **Krebs cycle**—a series of steps that take place in the mitochondrial matrix and convert the pyruvate to the compound acetyl-CoA and a molecule of carbon dioxide; remaining carbons are released in the waste product CO_2. Two ATPs form, and a large amount of released energy is stored in NADH and $FADH_2$. The cycle serves as a metabolic clearinghouse, in which breakdown products of fats and lipids (taken in as nutrients) enter aerobic respiration, and from which raw materials can be diverted for synthesis of biological molecules.

Concept Table 5.1 summarizes the similarities and differences of glycolysis and the Krebs cycle.

Concept Table 5.1 Glycolysis and the Krebs cycle compared

	Glycolysis	Krebs Cycle
Oxygen required?	No	Yes
CO_2 produced?	Yes, during fermentation	Yes
Energy input	2 ATP	Acetyl Co-A
Energy yield	4 ATP (net gain of 2)	2 ATP
Metabolic end product	Pyruvate	Oxaloacetic acid
Other products derived from pathway	Ethanol, acetic acid	Citric acid, some amino acids

Most of the ATP produced by aerobic respiration is generated in the **electron transport chain**, which receives the high-energy carriers NADH and $FADH_2$ from the Krebs cycle. Electrons (hydrogen ions) are stripped from these compounds, and as they pass down a series of specialized proteins in the inner mitochondrial membrane, they release energy. This energy drives the phosphorylation of ADP to ATP; during this phase as many as 32 ATPs can form. Thus the final energy yield of the glycolysis–Krebs cycle–electron transport chain aerobic pathway is 36 ATP. The final electron acceptor in the chain is oxygen, which joins with hydrogen ions to form water. Concept Table 5.2 summarizes the main events of the electron transport chain, and its associated phenomenon of **chemiosmotic coupling**.

Concept Table 5.2 The electron transport chain

Site	Inner mitochondrial membrane
Main events	1. Transport of electrons down a chain of embedded proteins
	2. Oxidation-reduction reactions that release energy to phosphorylate ADP to ATP
Steps	NADH and $FADH_2$ oxidized, losing electrons and protons
	Electrons pass down a chain of embedded proteins, giving up energy to power-pumping of hydrogen ions (protons) from inner to outer mitochondrial compartment
	Protons flow down **hydrogen ion (proton)** <u>**concentration gradient**</u> into inner compartment through channel proteins
	Ion flow provides energy for phosphorylation of ADP to ATP, the process of **chemiosmotic coupling**. Oxygen acts as final electron receptor.

Control of Metabolism

Metabolic control mechanisms exist that enable a cell to adjust its catabolic and anabolic activities in a changing environment, and to do so in a way that conserves energy. One such mechanism is **feedback inhibition** of **allosteric enzymes**, those having both a catalytic site and a regulatory site. When the end product of a metabolic pathway builds up in the cell, a molecule of the end product can bind to the regulatory site and temporarily shut down enzyme functioning. Only when end product levels fall does the pathway resume.

Thought Provokers

1. Explain why organisms that rely on glycolysis as their sole means of extracting energy will be successful in environments that would be lethal to organisms that metabolize via the Krebs cycle.

2. Describe the advantages of the Krebs cycle and electron transport chain as a means of metabolism.

Self-Test

For each statement or question choose the best response and mark your choice in the space provided. For some items you will select your response from a *Key*.

Questions 1–15: Match each of the following statements with the appropriate metabolic strategy in the *Key*.

a. glycolysis only   **c.** both glycolysis and Krebs cycle
b. Krebs cycle   **d.** neither glycolysis nor Krebs cycle

_____ **1.** Generates the most energy (select A or B).

_____ **2.** Requires oxygen

_____ **3.** Generates NADH

_____ **4.** Generates oxaloacetate

_____ **5.** Associated with mitochondrial activity

_____ **6.** Produces ATP

_____ **7.** Is disrupted by cyanide

_____ **8.** Produces large amounts of CO_2

_____ **9.** Yields pyruvate as its end product

_____ **10.** Involves the enzymes kinase and aldolase

_____ **11.** Biochemical reaction(s) found in body cells

_____ **12.** Involves molecules containing six carbons

_____ **13.** Involves molecules containing three carbons

_____ **14.** Takes place in the cytoplasm

_____ **15.** The most ancient biochemical pathway

Questions 16–18: Using the *Key,* indicate the specific activity of the molecules listed.

a. hydrogen carrier only   **c.** carries both hydrogen and electrons

b. electron carrier only   **d.** carries neither hydrogen nor electrons

_____ **16.** NAD

_____ **17.** FAD

_____ **18.** NADP

Key for questions 19–21

a. citrate   **b.** acetyl CoA   **c.** oxaloacetate

_____ **19.** The 6-carbon compound that is cleaved early in the Krebs cycle in a process that also reduces NAD^+ to NADH and yields CO_2

_____ **20.** A high-energy two-carbon compound that can be shunted out of the Krebs cycle pathway to serve as a raw material in biosynthetic pathways

_____ **21.** A four-carbon compound that is the end product of the Krebs cycle

Key for questions 22–30

a. True   **b.** False

_____ **22.** Fermentation is an anaerobic process.

_____ **23.** Fermentation can produce ethanol.

_____ **24.** Anaerobic activity in muscle produces acetic acid.

_____ **25.** Glycolysis is an anabolic process.

_____ **26.** In ATP there is more energy in the last phosphate bond than there is in the first phosphate bond.

_____ **27.** Niacin and riboflavin are vitamins important in the biosynthesis of cofactors.

_____ **28.** Oxidation is the gain of electrons or the loss of hydrogen.

_____ **29.** Yeasts are economically most important because of their oxidative activities.

_____ **30.** In the chemiosmotic coupling model, a hydrogen ion concentration gradient is key to generating energy in mitochondria.

Key Terms from the Text Chapter

aerobic *text page 112*
aerobic respiration *112*
allosteric enzyme *130*
anaerobic *112*
autotroph *117*
catabolic *114*
chemiosmotic coupling *127*

electron transport chain *123*
feedback inhibition *130*
fermentation *119*
glycolysis *119*
heterotroph *117*
hydrogen ion (proton) gradient *127*

Krebs cycle *123*
mitochondrion *124*
oxidation-reduction reaction *116*
phosphorylation *115*

Concept Figure: The Electron Transport Chain

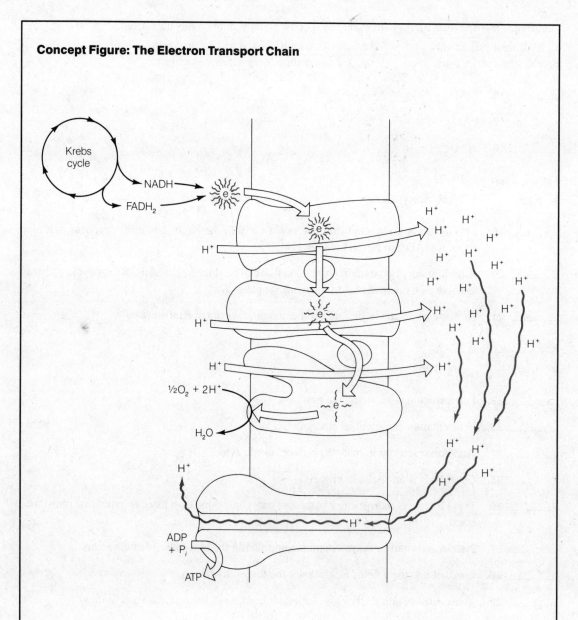

Exercise

1. Add the following labels to this diagram of the electron transport chain. Use arrows as necessary.

inner compartment

outer compartment

inner membrane

site of glucose entry

point at which respiration becomes aerobic

point of energy harvest

proton flow that releases energy

electrons released to electron transport chain

hydrogen ions provide energy to
    phosphorylate ADP to ATP

6

Photosynthesis: Trapping Sunlight to Build Nutrients

Perspective and Review

Photosynthesis is the most extensive biochemical process on Earth. Each year, photosynthesizing plants transform over 200 billion tons of atmospheric carbon dioxide into organic matter. This remarkable process, powered by sunlight, can only occur in organisms that contain the pigment chlorophyll, a unique molecule that absorbs both red and blue light. The light energy trapped in chlorophyll is then made to do the work of splitting water molecules and protons, which in turn liberates electrons and oxygen. Then, through unique electron-transfer mechanisms, plant cells generate the cellular fuel, ATP.

Reactions that are directly related to the light-trapping event are termed the light-dependent reactions of photosynthesis. In addition to ATP, they make available the compound NADPH, which participates in light-independent "dark" reactions. In this second phase of photosynthesis, plant cells use the products of the light reactions to fix carbon dioxide and convert this fixed carbon into useful biochemicals such as glucose, starch, and various three-, four-, and five-carbon sugars. In fact, fixed carbon dioxide eventually finds its way into lipids, proteins, and nucleic acids.

Green plants are thus true <u>autotrophs</u>, or "self-feeders." <u>Heterotrophs</u> are organisms that must take in preformed organic carbon; they cannot use carbon dioxide as their sole source of carbon.

Photosynthesis: An Overview

In a biochemical sense, mitochondria and chloroplasts are exact opposites. In a <u>mitochondrion</u>, glucose that has been converted to acetyl coenzyme A is further broken down to yield carbon dioxide, water, and energy. In the **chloroplast**, light energy powers the manufacture of glucose, using carbon dioxide and water as raw materials. Said another way, in **photosynthesis** light energy is converted into the chemical-bond energy stored in glucose molecules. This chemical energy may later be extracted (via enzyme action) as ATP during glycolysis and the Krebs cycle. As you study this chapter, then, keep in mind the two-sided metabolic coin: building molecules up and breaking them down. On the one hand is photosynthesis, an endergonic, energy-requiring, molecule-building reaction. On the other, glycolysis and the Krebs cycle are exergonic, energy-yielding, molecule-disassembly reactions (see Chapters 4 and 5). See Concept Table 6.1.

Concept Table 6.1   Comparing photosynthesis and glucose metabolism

Process	Significant Features
Photosynthesis	Chlorophyll traps light energy. H^+, electrons, ATP, and NADPH produced. Carbon dioxide is fixed and converted to glucose and other biochemicals needed by the plant. Photosynthesis reaction is: $$6CO_2 + 6H_2O \rightarrow \text{glucose} + 6O_2$$
Glucose metabolism	Glycolysis and Krebs cycle combine to progressively extract useful energy from the glucose molecule. The reaction is: $$\text{glucose} + 6O_2 \rightarrow 6CO_2 + 6H_2O$$

The **chloroplast** is a unique organelle. Concept Table 6.2 summarizes its features.

Concept Table 6.2   Features of chloroplasts

Structure	*Dual membrane systems:* inner and outer membranes. Inner membranes organized into **thylakoid <u>disks</u>**, layered one on another to form <u>grana</u>. <u>Stroma</u> is the nonmembraneous solution inside the chloroplast. The chloroplast also contains DNA, RNA, ribosomes, and enzymes.
Biochemistry	*Pigments:* **chlorophylls** and **carotenoids** and certain enzyme systems are located on the thylakoid disks. Splitting of water, production of H^+, electrons, free oxygen, NADPH, and ATP occur inside the thylakoids. Calvin cycle, light-

Continues

---

independent reactions occur outside the thylakoid, in the stroma. Glucose can exit the chloroplast and travel to the cytoplasm, where it is used for synthetic activities (starch or cellulose manufacture) or catabolic energy needs (glycolysis and Krebs cycle).

Colored Pigments in Living Cells Trap Light

Light is part of the electromagnetic spectrum, and behaves as both a wave and a particle. The light that can be detected with the eye is visible light, found between 380 nm and 750 nm. All electromagnetic radiation has attributes of wavelength and frequency. Concept Table 6.3 gives some important divisions of the **electromagnetic spectrum**, and some basic features of each component.

Concept Table 6.3 Important components of the electromagnetic spectrum

Component	Features
Radio waves	Longest electromagnetic waves, with the least energy
Microwaves	Second longest waves; used for cooking and transmission of signals
Infrared	Heat waves; produced by the sun and special lamps
Visible light	Detected by and affecting many forms of life; vital in photosynthesis
Ultraviolet	Short wavelengths that induce tanning; may damage nucleic acids and proteins
X-rays	Short wavelength, high-speed electrons; penetrate and damage soft tissues; used for medical diagnosis of certain conditions
Gamma radiation	Very short, penetrating, dangerous wavelengths produced by neutron bombs and some radioactive materials

■ **Light, Chlorophyll, and Other Pigments** The perceived "color" of an object derives from the light wavelength(s) it reflects to the retina of the eye. Objects that appear white reflect most of the light wavelengths striking them, while black objects absorb most of the wavelengths. Green leaves reflect green while absorbing blue and red light. Pigments are the colored molecules that absorb radiation; the pigment **chlorophyll *a*** is found in all autotrophs, while higher plants and green algae also have **chlorophyll *b***. **Carotenoids** are orange-yellow-red pigments that absorb mainly green, blue, and violet light. They are accessory pigments in green plants.

Pigment complexes: Energy Capture in the Reaction Center

In a chloroplast the chlorophylls and carotenoids are grouped like antennae around a central chlorophyll *a*. Photons (packets of light energy) that strike the antennae activate electrons, which are passed among the chlorophylls and carotenoids to a **reaction center** containing chlorophyll *a*. There are two reaction centers, called P700 and P680, respectively. Each has a different kind of chlorophyll *a*, and each has different acceptor molecules (see Concept Table 6.4). Reaction center P700 absorbs wavelengths around 700 nm, while reaction center P680 absorbs wavelengths around 680 nm.

Each reaction center chlorophyll lies at the center of its own photosystem, where the actual conversion of light energy to chemical energy occurs. Reaction center P700 is in **photosystem I**, and P680 is in **photosystem II**. Each photosystem is a grouping in the thylakoid membrane of the chlorophyll, its particular set of pigments, and both an electron acceptor and an electron donor. The two photosystems play significantly different roles in photosynthesis, as you can see in Concept Table 6.4.

Concept Table 6.4 Components and functions of photosystems

System	Components/Function
P680 or PS-II	Chlorophyll *a*, which absorbs light at 680 nm. An electron pair is boosted from the reaction center and accepted by an electron acceptor. At the same time, water is split, generating H^+, electrons to replace those lost from P680, and oxygen. The boosted electrons move down an electron transport chain, giving up energy that is captured in ATP.
P700 or PS-I	Another chlorophyll *a*, which absorbs light at 700 nm. The P700 reaction center is the final acceptor for electrons moving down the P680 electron transport chain. These electrons are rebooted by incoming **photons**, accepted by another electron acceptor, and passed down a second electron transport chain, where they generate NADPH from $NADP^+$, using a hydrogen liberated by the splitting of water.

The Light-Dependent Reactions of Photosynthesis

If you study the two photosystems shown in text Figure 6.1, you can see that the electrons normally flow through a zig-zag conduit as long as water is being split. Sometimes, however, the P680 system shuts down. Then, no oxygen is generated and no H^+ or electrons are produced. When this happens, the more primitive P700 system can recycle the same electrons. This recycling of electrons through P700 is called **cyclic photophosphorylation**. It generates ATP but no NADPH, and only a single ATP results rather than the typical two ATP molecules produced in the zig-zag patterns of both systems.

The Light-Independent Reactions of Photosynthesis

The **light-dependent reactions** of photosynthesis harvest ATP and generate NADPH. These molecules in turn drive a second set of reactions that build organic molecules from CO_2 and require no light to proceed. Concept Table 6.5 summarizes the important features of these **light-independent reactions**, which are known as the **Calvin-Benson cycle**.

Concept Table 6.5 Elements of the Calvin-Benson cycle of photosynthesis

Molecule type	Function/role
Carbon dioxide	Will be fixed and reduced by the Calvin-Benson cycle to make glucose
Ribulose biphosphate	A five-carbon sugar to which CO_2 attaches
RBP carboxylase	An enzyme that attaches CO_2 to RBP
Unstable 6-C	The intermediate molecule produced in the preceding reactions
Phosphoglyceric acid	Oxidized breakdown product of unstable 6-C; NADPH reduces this compound to phosphoglyceraldehyde
Phosphoglyceraldehyde	Some is used to make glucose by reverse of glycolysis; rest is converted to RBP

It is important to remember that a plant can generate glucose and RBP as well as starches, lipids, proteins, and nucleic acids. Plants are true autotrophs—they can use carbon dioxide as their sole source of carbon and, typically, do not require organic carbon as a food source for their growth.

Photorespiration and C_4 Plants

In all plants, photosynthesis slows if the level of CO_2 available to cells falls below a certain point. This can happen when the environment is hot and dry and leaf stomata, normally open to take in CO_2, remain closed to prevent excessive water loss. The result is **photorespiration**, in which RBP carboxylase reacts with and binds oxygen. However, **C_4 plants**, such as corn and crabgrass, have evolved an adaptation that circumvents photorespiration. They contain the enzyme carboxylase (phosphoenolpyruvate, or PEP, carboxylase) that joins CO_2 with PEP to form oxaloacetate. In this form, the plant stores CO_2 for later use. When the CO_2 is needed, the oxaloacetate is converted to malate; decarboxylation then occurs, yielding CO_2 plus pyruvate. The photosynthetic **bundle-sheath cells** of C_4 plants are the only cells that carry out C_4 fixation, and only these cells in C_4 plants carry out the Calvin cycle. In contrast, the mesophyll cell chloroplasts of **C_3 plants** perform the Calvin cycle.

The Global Carbon Cycle

Photosynthesis and respiration take place on Earth on a massive scale. In the global **carbon cycle** there is a natural exchange of oxygen released by autotrophs such as photosynthetic plants and green algae, with the carbon dioxide released by heterotrophic organisms and, also, by the burning of wood and fossil fuels such as coal, oil, and natural gas. In recent decades fossil fuel burning, an unnatural intervention in the Earth's ecosystem directly related to human activities, has caused the buildup of excess CO_2 in Earth's atmosphere. As a result, heat is becoming trapped in the lower atmosphere, creating a phenomenon called the **greenhouse effect**. Another potentially frightening situation related to the carbon cycle is **nuclear winter**, a scenario associated with massive fires that would follow a nuclear war. Researchers predict that such fires would pollute the air with massive amounts of CO_2, dust, and debris, which would in turn shield the Earth from sunlight, slow or stop photosynthesis, and cause global temperatures to fall dramatically. The result would be massive death of both plant and animal life.

Thought Provokers

1. You have two neighbors, one a biology student and the other a baker. In the middle of August each asks you the same question: "Why do I have so much crabgrass in August?" In 200 words or less, show how you might explain the presence of crab grass, based on your knowledge of C_3 and C_4 plants, to each neighbor.

2. You are asked to write a summary of photosynthesis for a dictionary and encyclopedia of biology. The editor will pay you 50 cents a word for a clear, succinct, and accurate article of no more than 350 words. Do that assignment!

3. Briefly discuss two different events that might provoke massive and dangerous shifts in Earth's ecological balance and the global rate of photosynthesis.

Self-Test

For each statement or question choose the best response and mark your choice in the space provided. For some items you will select your response from a *Key*.

_____ 1. Chlorophyll is classified as what type of molecule?

    a. a heme   **c.** a protein   **e.** a nucleotide
    b. a nucleic acid   **d.** a carbohydrate

_____ 2. The molecule involved in fixing an atmospheric gas is:

    a. ribose   **c.** ribulose biphosphate   **e.** heptose biphosphate
    b. ribose biphosphate   **d.** hexose biphosphate

Key for Questions 3–11 (on the electromagnetic spectrum)

a. ultraviolet   **ab.** orange-yellow   **bc.** gamma rays
b. infrared   **ac.** black   **bd.** radio waves
c. red   **ad.** white
d. green   **ae.** X-rays
e. blue

_____ 3. Longest wavelength listed

_____ 4. Main heating radiation of the sun

_____ 5. Actual color of most carotenoids/xanthophylls

_____ 6. Visible wavelength typically reflected by higher plants

_____ 7. <u>Two</u> types of radiation that most stimulate photosynthesis

_____ 8. Color that an object absorbing most of the light striking it appears

_____ 9. Type of light, passed through a prism, that produces a spectrum

_____ 10. Color of 4,000 Angstroms, or 400 nm

_____ 11. Mutagenic and harmful solar radiation that directly damages proteins and nucleic acids

Questions 12–15: Using the *Key*, indicate in the blanks the letter of the number that will give a balanced and correct formula for photosynthesis.

a. 1   **b.** 3   **c.** 4   **d.** 6   **e.** 12

12. _____ H_2O + **13.** _____ CO_2 → **14.** _____ glucose + **15.** _____ O_2

Questions 16–17: Using the *Key*, indicate the appropriate enzyme involved in or needed for the process described.

a. aldolase   **c.** kinase   **e.** decarboxylase
b. hydrolase   **d.** carboxylase

_____ **16.** carbon fixation by C_4 plants.

_____ **17.** carbon fixation by plants using the Calvin cycle.

_____ **18.** Which statement is correct with regard to $NADP^+$? $NADP^+$ can carry:

    a. electrons only
    b. hydrogen only
    c. both electrons and protons
    d. neither electrons nor hydrogen

_____ **19.** Which one of the following is not a C_4 plant?

    a. corn   **d.** soybeans
    b. crabgrass   **e.** Kentucky and fescue grasses
    c. cacti

_____ **20.** During photosynthesis, which molecules become reduced? Indicate all molecules.

    a. water   **c.** $NADP^+$
    b. carbon dioxide   **d.** ATP

Key for questions 21–38

a. True   **b.** False

_____ **21.** In typical green plants there are two photosystems.

_____ **22.** Each different photosystem can absorb a different wavelength of light.

_____ **23.** During photosynthesis water is split.

_____ **24.** During photosynthesis carbon dioxide is split.

_____ **25.** Oxygen released by plants comes from carbon dioxide.

_____ **26.** The electrons used in photosynthesis come from CO_2.

_____ **27.** Plants can generate ATP from sunlight.

_____ **28.** At night, plants perform oxidative respiration.

_____ **29.** The Z scheme refers to the pathway of electrons during the light reactions of photosynthesis.

_____ **30.** In photosynthesis, light energy is converted to chemical energy as electrons flow down proton gradients.

_____ **31.** The Calvin cycle is predominantly a five-carbon pathway.

_____ **32.** In plants, for every oxidation event there is a corresponding reduction.

_____ **33.** Plants that can best survive drought are termed Calvin-cycle plants.

_____ **34.** Chlorophyll molecules are found in the chloroplasts and they are typically embedded in membranes.

_____ **35.** Chloroplasts and mitochondria are both double-membrane organelles.

_____ **36.** ATP synthetase is involved in the manufacture of ATP.

_____ **37.** The thylakoid membrane contains chlorophyll, carotenoids, and enzymes.

_____ **38.** Grana are composed of thylakoids.

Key for questions 39–43

a. 1   **d.** 4   **ab.** 6
b. 2   **e.** 5   **ac.** 12
c. 3

_____ **39.** Oxaloacetate has how many carbons?

_____ **40.** The number of electrons released per molecule in the splitting reaction

_____ **41.** The number of turns of the Calvin cycle required to generate a molecule of glucose

_____ **42.** The number of different photosystems in green plants

_____ **43.** The number of carbons in a molecule of glucose

Key Terms in the Text Chapter

antenna complex
 text page 140
bundle-sheath cell *148*
C_3 plant *148*
C_4 plant *148*
Calvin-Benson cycle *144*
carbon cycle *148*
carotenoid pigment *140*
chlorophyll *140*
chloroplast *137*

cyclic photophosphorylation
 143
electromagnetic spectrum
 138
greenhouse effect *149*
light-dependent reaction *141*
light-independent reaction
 144
noncyclic
 photophosphorylation *143*

nuclear winter *149*
photon *138*
photorespiration *148*
photosynthesis *134*
photosystem I *141*
photosystem II *141*
reaction center *140*
thylakoid *137*

Concept Figure: The Light and Dark Reactions of Photosynthesis

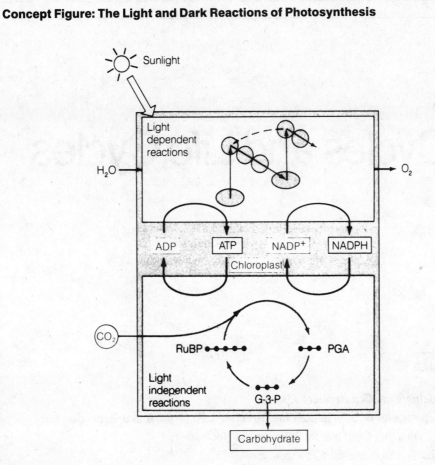

Exercise

1. Where in a chloroplast do the light reactions take place? _____

2. Which compounds store energy captured during the light reactions? _____

_____

3. What role do these compounds play in the light-independent reactions of photosynthesis?

_____

7

Cell Cycles and Life Cycles

Perspective and Review

Reproduction, the production of new organisms similar or identical to the parent or parents, is a diagnostic feature of living organisms. For reproduction to occur, **cell division**, the splitting of one cell into two, must take place. Biologists use the term **cell cycle** to describe the events that occur between one cell division and the next, while **life cycle** describes the events between the initiation and the death of an individual. For prokaryotes the cell cycle and life cycle are the same: A new generation begins when a cell divides in two. Multicellular organisms start life as a single cell, which undergoes many mitotic divisions to give rise to a new individual.

Chromosomes contain the genetic information that directs all cell activities, including when and how many times the cell will divide. Because this genetic information must be passed on to each new generation, before cell division the chromosomes replicate so a copy will be available to each daughter cell.

Eukaryotic organisms reproduce either asexually, by mitotic cell division, or sexually via the fusion of male and female gametes formed by meiosis.

Chromosomes: Repositories of Information for Directing Cell Growth and Reproduction

The nucleus of a eukaryotic cell stores the genetic information that guides cell functions. Thus the nucleus directs activities such as growth, metabolism, and repairs to cell structure, as well as the cell cycle. The genetic information in the nucleus is stored on **chromosomes**, strands of DNA (Chapter 2) carrying chemically coded instructions that direct cell activities. All organisms possess chromosomes, although chromosome number and size vary from species to species. Prokaryotes have a single circular chromosome. Eukaryotic cells have at least two linear chromosomes in the nucleus, each wound tightly around a protein molecule. Human cells have 46 chromosomes in each nucleus, so tightly coiled that if their DNA were unraveled it would be roughly 6 feet long!

The Cell Cycle

Recall that prokaryotes have a single circular chromosome and no nuclear membrane. When a prokaryote reproduces, it simply elongates and splits in two—the process of <u>binary fission</u>. While the bacterial cell is elongating, the single chromosome replicates. As the cell divides, the two circular chromosomes move to opposite ends of the cell, so when division is complete each daughter has one chromosome. The eukaryotic cell cycle is more complex. Eukaryotic cells are generally large and have at least two chromosomes enclosed within a nuclear membrane. The cell cycle is divided into four phases: three growth phases and one cell division phase. Concept Table 7.1 outlines the four phases in the eukaryotic cycle.

Concept Table 7.1   The eukaryotic cell cycle

Phase	Cell activities
G_1 (gap 1)	Cell carries on its normal metabolism. Proteins and new organelles are made.
S (synthesis)	Cell replicates its DNA.

Continues

Concept Table 7.1	The eukaryotic cell cycle (continued)
Phase	**Cell activities**
G₂ (gap 2)	Manufacture of proteins necessary for cell division.
M	Cell division occurs. This phase consists of **mitosis** and **cytokinesis**.

Mitosis and Cytokinesis

As a cell enters M phase, the chromosomes, which are invisible during interphase, become visible as discrete thick strands in the nucleus. By this time they have already doubled (during S phase), and each consists of two identical strands, or **chromatids**. The two chromatids of each chromosome are joined at a single point, the **centromere**. Concept Table 7.2 describes the main features of mitosis. Figure 7.13 in your text illustrates the progression of cell division in an actual cell.

Concept Table 7.2	The main phases of mitosis
Phase	**Significant Features**
Prophase	Chromosomes condense, nucleolus disappears, and **mitotic spindle** forms.
Prometaphase	Nuclear membrane disappears and chromosomes attach to the spindle.
Metaphase	Chromosomes line up along the central axis of the cell.
Anaphase	Centromeres divide. The spindle pulls the chromatids apart, toward opposite ends of the cell.
Telophase	Chromatids (now called chromosomes), are at opposite poles of the cell. Nuclear membrane reforms and spindle dissolves.

Shortly after mitosis the cytoplasm divides, by **cytokinesis**, giving rise to two cells, each half the size of the original cell but with a full complement of DNA. Cytokinesis differs between plant and animal cells because plant cells must form rigid cell walls, while animal cells form only the plasma membrane. Concept Table 7.3. outlines cytokinesis in plant and animal cells.

Concept Table 7.3 Main features of cytokinesis in plant and animal cells	
Plant cells	**Animal cells**
Divide from the inside out. Vesicles filled with cell wall precursors pinch off from the Golgi bodies and collect at the center of the cell. These fuse, forming a cell plate or partition that divides the cell in two.	Divide from the inside out. During anaphase a constriction or dent forms around the cell surface. Actin-containing filaments known as the contractile ring contract, deepening the furrow and eventually squeezing the cell in two.

Regulating the Cell Cycle

It is vitally important that cells "know" when to divide and when to stop dividing. Cell division is controlled by two mechanisms: cell-to-cell contact, and growth factors. Cells will continue to divide until they come into contact with other cells, at which time they stop and remain permanently in G_1 phase. The exact mechanism of this contact inhibition is unknown. Proteins called growth factors stimulate growth and division of certain cell types. Genetic information in the nucleus ultimately controls the timing, speed, and number of cell divisions a cell undergoes.

Cancer results when cells do not respond to contact inhibition and fail to stop dividing. Scientists believe that some cancers are related to changes in the cell's DNA: A cancerous cell might continuously produce growth factors, thus perpetually stimulating itself to divide.

Life Cycles: One Generation to the Next in Multicellular Organisms

Unlike single-celled prokaryotes, eukaryotic organisms have a more complex life cycle and reproduce either asexually or sexually. Concept Table 7.4 compares these two reproductive strategies.

Concept Table 7.4   Asexual and sexual reproduction

Asexual	Sexual
Sometimes called *vegetative reproduction*. Seen in many plants; also in some animals, such as corals and sea anemones, which reproduce by *budding*.	Seen in animals and some plants.
Process: Genetically identical offspring arise from a few body cells of a parent. These cells multiply mitotically, giving rise to a new individual that eventually takes up an independent life.	*Process:* **Gametes** (sperm or egg) are formed by **meiosis**. Sperm and egg fuse (**fertilization**), resulting in a **zygote** that divides mitotically to produce a new individual.
Other: Other forms of asexual reproduction include regeneration, such as the regrowing of a lost arm by a starfish.	

Sexual reproduction involves the fusion of an egg and sperm cell to form a new individual. As a result of **meiosis**, egg and sperm cells receive only half the normal amount of DNA, that is, half the number of chromosomes. When an egg and sperm fuse the new cell formed, the **zygote**, has the normal chromosome number. A cell having the full number of chromosomes is termed **diploid**; one with half the number, such as a gamete, is **haploid**.

Meiosis: A Reshuffling and Reduction of Chromosomes

A diploid cell that divides meiotically yields four new haploid cells. Concept Table 7.5 describes the main phases of meiosis; many of them resemble those of mitosis.

Concept Table 7.5 The phases of meiosis

Phase	Significant Features
Meiosis I	A 4n parent cell divides to form two diploid (2n) cells.
Interphase I	DNA replication occurs, chromosomes condense, the nucleolus disperses.
Prophase I	Nuclear envelope disappears, **homologous chromosomes** pair and are attached at the chiasmata, the spindle forms and attaches to the centromere.
Metaphase I	Paired chromosomes line up at the center of the cell.
Anaphase I	Homologues separate, one of each of the pair moving to opposite ends of the cell.
Telophase I	Nuclear envelope reforms.
Cytokinesis	Cytoplasmic division occurs, resulting in two haploid cells. This marks the end of Meiosis I.
Meiosis II	The two diploid (2n) daughter cells from meiosis divide, creating a total of four haploid (n) cells.
Interphase II	*No DNA replication occurs.* Both cells enter Meiosis II with half the normal chromosome number.
Prophase II	Similar to Prophase I except no pairing of homologous chromosomes.
Metaphase II	The chromosomes line up along the central axis of each cell.
Anaphase II	The two chromatids of each chromosome move to opposite ends of the cell.
Telophase II	Same as in Meiosis I.
Cytokinesis	Same as in Meiosis I.

During meiosis a reshuffling of the chromosomes occurs. This **genetic recombination** leads to new chromosome arrangements, and happens in two ways. In **independent assortment**, chromosomes from each parent are randomly distributed to gametes. Thus, daughter cells receive both maternal and paternal chromosomes and have a new genetic make-up, that is, different from that of either parent. In **crossing over**, there is an exchange of chromosome parts between paired homologous chromosomes. As a result each chromosome carries some genetic material from its homologue, as well as a combination of the original maternal and paternal chromosomes. Independent assortment and crossing over ensure that offspring produced by sexual reproduction are not genetically identical to either parent, but possess genetic information from both in a unique genetic makeup.

Meiosis, Mitosis, Sexual Reproduction, and Evolution

Mitosis and meiosis permit two different types of reproduction—**asexual reproduction** and **sexual reproduction**, each conferring its own particular advantage. For example, in a constant environment, asexual reproduction is favored because it preserves gene combinations that are well suited to the status quo. In a changable environment, by contrast, sexual reproduction allows for new gene combinations that can give rise to new individuals with traits suitable for new conditions.

Thought Provokers

1. Indicate the critical differences between mitosis and meiosis. Also, indicate any similarities in the two processes.

2. Indicate how meiosis, rather than mitosis, could be a major contributory factor to the evolution and development of new varieties and types of organisms.

Self-Test

For each statement or question choose the best response and mark your choice in the space provided. For some items you will select your response from a *Key*.

Key for questions 1–6

a. anaphase   c. prophase   e. interphase
b. metaphase   d. telophase

_____ 1. The disappearance of the nucleolus occurs prior to, or during this phase.

_____ 2. The splitting of the centromeres marks the beginning of this phase.

_____ 3. Cytokinesis occurs following this phase.

_____ 4. DNA synthesis occurs during this phase.

_____ 5. Chromosomes are lined up at the midpoint of the spindle during this phase.

_____ 6. The DNA threads first become visible at this phase.

Key for questions 7–20

a. mitosis only   c. both mitosis and meiosis
b. meiosis only   d. neither mitosis nor meiosis

_____ 7. Cancer cells characteristically show

_____ 8. Gametes are produced by

_____ 9. The most common process in our bodies is

_____ 10. Prior to division the cell contains 4N amounts of DNA.

_____ 11. Known as reduction division

_____ 12. In organisms with an alteration of generations we would expect to see

_____ 13. Genetic diversity in organisms is caused by

_____ 14. Chiasmata frequently are seen in

_____ 15. A spindle is required for

_____ 16. Chromatids may be seen during

_____ 17. Anaphase may be seen during

_____ 18. Occurs during interphase

_____ 19. Radiation sickness is related to defects of

_____ 20. Down's syndrome is clearly related to an error of

Key for questions 21–23

a. microtubules   **b.** microfilaments

_____ 21. The spindle is composed of

_____ 22. The furrowing of cells is related to

_____ 23. Actin is a protein associated with

Key for questions 24–30, on cell phases

a. S   **c.** G_1 **e.** cytokinesis
b. G_2 **d.** M

_____ 24. A cell plate would be most obvious during

_____ 25. DNA polymerase would be functional and active during

_____ 26. This phase apparently critically controls the entire cell cycle and cells may be arrested in this phase for short to very long periods of time.

_____ 27. Spindle proteins are most evident during

_____ 28. Activity of the Golgi, with migration of vesicles to the center of the cells of plants is related to

_____ 29. The chromosomes are actually doubled during

_____ 30. Mark all letters that identify interphase.

_____ 31. In Hammerling's experiments with *Acetabularia*, which of the following statements are correct? <u>Note:</u> More than one letter may be correct.

   a. The organism was an alga.
   b. The cap, stalk, or foot could be transplanted to another *Acetabularia*.
   c. The experiments were not reproducible.
   d. The stalk contained the factor that controlled morphology.
   e. Some parts of different species of *Acetabularia* could be transplanted.

Key Terms from the Text Chapter

anaphase   *text page 164*

asexual reproduction   *167*

cancer   *166*

cell cycle   *154*

cell division   *154*

centromere   *161*

chromatid   *161*

chromosome   *157*

crossing over   *176*

cytokinesis   *160*

diploid   *170*

Down syndrome   *174*

fertilization   *169*

gamete   *169*

genetic recombination   *171*

germ line   *169*

haploid   *170*

homologous chromosomes   *171*

independent assortment   *174*

interphase   *159*

life cycle   *154*

meiosis   *170*

metaphase   *164*

mitosis   *160*

mitotic spindle   *164*

prometaphase   *164*

prophase   *164*

sexual reproduction   *169*

somatic line   *169*

telophase   *164*

zygote   *169*

Exercise

| **1. Cell cycle** | **2. Life cycle** |

1. Make a schematic drawing of a eukaryotic cell cycle. Show all four phases, and explain the events of each phase in the space provided below.

M phase: _____

G$_1$ phase: _____

S phase: _____

G$_2$ phase: _____

2. Make a schematic drawing of the life cycle of a multicellular organism. Be sure to show where in the cycle mitosis and meiosis take place.

In a sentence, explain the basic functional differences between the two cycles.

_____

_____

_____

8

Mendelian Genetics

CHAPTER IN BRIEF

Perspective and Review

The study of **heredity**, how physical, biochemical, and behavioral traits are passed from generation to generation, was pioneered in the 1800s by Gregor Mendel. Mendel's results, together with subsequent work in the 1930s, led to the discovery that the transmission of traits from parent to child is controlled by **genes**, discrete regions on chromosomes. All diploid organisms have two copies of each gene, one on each member of every chromosome pair. Genes may come in different forms, or **alleles**; for example, the gene for human eye color has two alleles, blue and brown. During meiosis the chromosomes segregate out so that each gamete receives one of the two alleles. At fertilization the zygote receives one set of alleles from the mother and one from the father. Genes interact with each other and the environment to affect the **phenotype**.

The knowledge of heredity gained from Mendel's work and the work of subsequent geneticists has had many practical applications for humans, particularly in the areas of crop breeding and human genetic diseases. Many of the principles covered in this chapter are applied in genetic counseling today.

Genetics in the Abbey: How Genes Were Discovered and Analyzed

Prior to the 1850s, scientists believed that a mating between two individuals resulted in their genetic material's being blended in the next generation, in the same way that mixing or blending red and white paint gives pink. Mendel quietly challenged this belief in his particulate theory of inheritance, proposing that units of inheritance were discrete particles that remained the same from generation to generation. To test his ideas Mendel devised a series of critical experiments using garden pea plants. Concept Table 8.1 outlines the predictions of Mendel's theory, and his experiments to test those predictions.

Concept Table 8.1   Mendel's particulate theory of inheritance

Predictions:
If genetic material remains unaltered through generations, then a mating between two hybrids should produce offspring showing the original parental traits.

Experimental test using long- and short-stemmed peas:

First step. Mendel demonstrates that parental, or P, generation breeds pure.

Second step. Mendel performs a monohybrid cross, a mating between two individuals that differ only in one trait. Plants from the resulting seeds are the **first filial**, or F_1, **generation**.

Result:
All F_1 plants have long stems.

Third step. Mendel mates F_1 plants with other F_1s; the resulting seeds form the F_2 generation.

Result:
F_2 generation consists of long- and short-stemmed plants in the ratio of 3:1.

Conclusion:
The genetic material of the parents remained intact through generations, though the short-stem trait was hidden in the F_1.

Mendel worked before the discovery of DNA, genes, or chromosomes. To relate his findings to our present knowledge of genetics, and to better understand the mechanisms of inheritance, review Concept Table 8.2.

Concept Table 8.2   Mendel and modern genetics

Genes	Mendel showed that genetic factors remain intact through generations. Such factors, now called **genes**, control specific traits of an individual. They are located on chromosomes, as discrete regions of the DNA molecule.
Alleles	Genes can come in alternative forms, such as those coding long or short stems; each form is called an **allele**. Diploid organisms have two copies of each chromosome and therefore two alleles of each gene.
Homozygous	If the two alleles of a gene are the same, then the individual is **homozygous** for the trait.
Heterozygous	If the two alleles of a gene are different, then the individual is **heterozygous** for the trait.
Dominant and **Recessive**	A homozygous plant carrying one allele for long stem and one for short stem is long-stemmed. The long-stemmed allele is dominant over the short-stemmed, recessive one. The **dominant** form is manifest in either the homozygous or heterozygous condition, whereas the **recessive** form is expressed only in the homozygous.
Genotype	A **genotype** describes the genetic makeup of an individual.
Phenotype	**Phenotype** defines an individual's physical appearance—the expression of its genes.

Mendel's results led to his first law, or **segregation principle**, which in modern terms is expressed as follows: Sexually reproducing diploid organisms have two alleles for each gene. These two alleles segregate during meiosis to form gametes containing only one allele of each gene. Segregation results from the movement of chromosomes during meiosis.

Genetics in the Abbey Continued: Different Genes Are Inherited Independently

Mendel also considered the simultaneous inheritance of two traits. Concept Table 8.3 outlines this study and how it led to Mendel's second law, the Principle of Independent Assortment.

Concept Table 8.3   Mendel's second law: The Principle of Independent Assortment (Continued)

Mendel's Question:
If white-flowered, short-stemmed plants are crossed with long-stemmed, purple-flowered plants, are all offspring parental types, or do some show purple flowers and short stems, or white flowers and long stems (recombinant types)?

Experiment:
Dihybrid cross (mating between individuals differing in only two traits). Long-stemmed, purple-flowered plants were crossed with short-stemmed, white-flowered plants.

Continues

Concept Table 8.3 Mendel's second law: The Principle of Independent Assortment (continued)

Results:

9 long purple, 3 long white, 3 short purple, 1 short white. This outcome can only result if genes segregate independent of other genes during meiosis.

Conclusion:

Mendel's **principle of independent assortment**: Different genes segregate into gametes independent of each other.

Geneticists Locate Genes on Chromosomes

In the early 1900s, advances in cell studies and the rediscovery of Mendel's work provided insights on a range of genetic phenomena. Studies focused on the fruit fly, which has four pairs of chromosomes—one pair of **sex chromosomes** and three pairs of **autosomes** (non-sex chromosomes). Researchers relied on information provided by mutations, permanent, heritable changes in genes. Looking at mutated **sex-linked** genes, such as the one coding for eye color, that are carried on the **X** or **Y** sex **chromosome**, Thomas Hunt Morgan showed that eye color in fruit flies was determined by the X chromosome—the first strong evidence that chromosomes carry genes. This finding was soon confirmed in studies of nondisjunction, the failure of chromosomes to segregate out properly during meiosis. Scientists working with fruit flies gradually discovered so many mutations that it became clear that each chromosome must contain many different genes.

Modern studies also revealed important exceptions to Mendel's Principle of Independent Assortment. One is **linkage**—that genes on the same chromosome tend to be inherited together. Such genes form a **linkage group**. Crossing over during meiosis (Chapter 7) can result in new combinations of linked genes. Crossing over enabled geneticists to locate the position of genes on a chromosome, the process of gene mapping. Recombination frequencies, how often crossovers occur between specific gene loci, are the tools enabling researchers to identify the relative distances between various genes, and where they lie along a chromosome. This technique has led to two major conclusions: Genes are arranged in a fixed linear sequence on chromosomes, and every gene has a set position, or **locus**.

Gene Interactions: Exceptions Obscure Mendelian Principles

As the study of genetics advanced, scientists discovered more exceptions to Mendel's laws, and it became obvious that genes often interact with each other and the environment. Concept Table 8.4 describes some of these interactions.

The Punnett square (see Concept Table 8.5) makes it possible to predict the genotype frequencies of offspring resulting from a mating between two known genotypes.

The **testcross** is a powerful tool for determining an unknown genotype. By mating an individual of unknown genotype to a homozygous recessive, it is possible to determine the unknown genotype by using the predictions of the Punnett square.

Concept Table 8.4   Exceptions to Mendel's laws—Gene interactions

Interactions Between Alleles

Incomplete dominance	None of the alleles of a gene is completely dominant. *Example:* A cross between a red and a white snapdragon results in a plant that has pink flowers, because it takes two red alleles to make enough pigment for a red flower.
Codominance	No single allele is dominant, and an individual having two different alleles will express both. *Example:* People with both A and B blood type alleles have AB type blood, since both markers are produced.
Many alleles of one gene (*multiple allelic series*)	Some genes have so many alleles that a single individual cannot have all forms. *Example:* Human blood genes have three alleles, A, B, and O.

Interactions Between Genes

Epistasis (*masking*)	Certain genes can mask the effect of other unrelated genes. *Example:* Extension genes can affect the expression of color genes.
Polygenic inheritance	Certain traits are controlled by a group of interacting genes. *Examples:* height and weight.

Multiple Effects of Individual Genes

Pleiotropy	The reverse of polygenic inheritance. A single gene affects two or more apparently unrelated traits. *Example:* The gene responsible for albinism also causes crosseyes.

Environmental Effects on Gene Expression

Environment	Gene expression can be affected by the environment. *Example:* In a poor nutritional environment, a child carrying tall genes will not attain full height—that is, the genes will not be fully expressed.

Concept Table 8.5   How to construct a Punnett square

Aim:
To construct a Punnett square for a mating between a purple flower and a white flower. Purple is dominant over white. The female flower is a purple heterozygote and the male is a white homozygote.

Method:

1. Represent the genotype of each parent plant. Geneticists use letters to denote alleles: Uppercase denotes dominant and lowercase denotes recessive.
   Female: **Pp**, one dominant purple allele and one recessive white allele
   Male: **pp**, two recessive white alleles

Continues

Concept Table 8.5   How to construct a Punnett square (continued)

2. At meiosis the female will produce an ovum with either a **P** allele or a **p** allele; the male can only produce **p** allele pollen. Represent this by putting the female gametes along the side and male gametes along the top of the square:

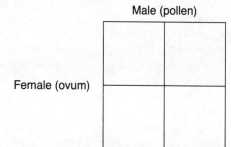

Male (pollen)

Female (ovum)

3. Now, fill in the genotypes of the offspring that will result from the different fertilization combinations.

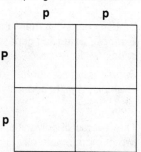

4. Add up your results; your square should yield two **Pp** and two **pp**. This equals a 50:50 ratio of two genotypes.

Conclusion:
You can predict on the basis of your Punnett square that half the offspring will be heterozygotes, with purple flowers (**Pp**), and the other half will be homozygotes and white-flowered (**pp**).

Thought Provokers

1. Define the following terms and use them in an integrated and meaningful paragraph of 150–250 words: locus, gene, allele, diploid, haploid, mutation, dominant, recessive, chromosome, linkage group, F_2 generation.

2. Describe Gregor Mendel's contributions to our understanding of the basic mechanisms of heredity. Then explain at least three different and important concepts of heredity that became known after Mendel's time.

Self-Test

For each statement or question choose the best response and mark your choice in the space provided. For some items you will select your response from a *Key*.

Key for questions 1–10

a. dominant	**ab.** genotype	**bc.** F$_1$ generation
b. recessive	**ac.** phenotype	**bd.** F$_2$ generation
c. mutation	**ad.** monohybrid cross	
d. allele	**ae.** dihybrid cross	
e. gene		

_____ 1. A specific, discrete portion of the DNA molecule in a chromosome

_____ 2. An alternate form of a gene

_____ 3. The expressed traits of an organism

_____ 4. A permanent, inheritable change in a gene

_____ 5. A mating that involves two different genes and their alleles

_____ 6. A character seen only in the homozygous recessive condition

_____ 7. What is responsible for an organism's phenotype

_____ 8. The offspring of the mating of two different lines

_____ 9. Offspring resulting from a cross of the offspring in Question 8

_____ 10. Tall, round-seeded plants mated with short, wrinkle-seeded plants is an example of this.

Key for questions 11–20

a. True   **b.** False

_____ 11. Mendel's discoveries were widely and immediately accepted by the scientific community.

_____ 12. It is possible for some genes to move from one chromosome to another.

_____ 13. Mendel observed with his microscope the chromosomes of pea plants.

_____ 14. Pea plants normally are self-sterile.

_____ 15. The unusual tiger described in text Chapter 8 was white with blue eyes that tended to cross. Two of the tigers were mated to produce F$_1$ offspring with similar characteristics.

_____ 16. An organism can be homozygous for one trait and heterozygous for a different trait.

_____ 17. A haploid organism is neither homozygous nor heterozygous.

_____ 18. Mendel performed only monohybrid crosses.

_____ 19. Pea plants have either male or female sexual structures.

_____ 20. A Punnett square is useful for a probability analysis of the traits that would be present in the offspring resulting from a genetic cross.

Questions 21–30: Using the *Key*, indicate the appropriate genetic concept that best fits the numbered statement or idea.

a. pleiotropy
b. polygenic inheritance
c. epistasis
d. sex-linked inheritance
e. a monohybrid cross

ab. a dihybrid cross
ac. incomplete dominance
ad. codominance

_____ **21.** Genetic basis for dark and mulatto skin color in humans

_____ **22.** A situation in which one gene has multiple effects on phenotype.

_____ **23.** The classical situation in which the F_1 yields a single phenotype and the F_2 yields four different phenotypes.

_____ **24.** That a cross between a red-flowered plant and a white-flowered plant yields pink-flowered F_1 offspring can be best explained as an example of this.

_____ **25.** The mating in Question 24 can be described as this.

_____ **26.** In this circumstance a particular gene controls the expression of another gene (not an allele of the controlling gene).

_____ **27.** **TTrr × ttRR** is an example of this.

_____ **28.** Eye color in fruit flies is specifically used to demonstrate this special feature of heredity.

_____ **29.** Blood group inheritance in humans is a clear example of this.

_____ **30.** In terms of genetics, the height of humans and higher animals is a result of this.

_____ **31.** The most useful organism for a testcross would be:

    a. a heterozygote
    b. homozygous recessive
    c. homozygous dominant

    d. mutant
    e. epistatic

_____ **32.** To determine the position of genes on a chromosome a scientist relies on the phenomenon known as:

    a. nondisjunction
    b. epistasis
    c. pleiotropy

    d. crossing over
    e. mitosis

_____ **33.** A 1:2:1 ratio of offspring is possible with:

    a. genotypes only
    b. phenotypes only

    c. both phenotypes and genotypes
    d. neither phenotypes nor genotypes

Questions 34–40: Two items are compared and contrasted to a concept word. If item A is greater, more frequent, or more likely than B, mark A in the space provided; if item B is greater, more frequent, or likely, mark B; if both items are the same, mark C.

_____ **34.** Heterozygosity   **a.** pure line   **b.** hybrid line

_____ **35.** Flip of coin 100 times   **a.** heads   **b.** tails

_____ **36.** Homozygosity   **a.** TTRR   **b.** ttrr

_____ **37.** F_2 phenotypes from   **a.** dihybrid cross   **b.** monohybrid cross

_____ **38.** Dark color coat of Labrador dog   **a. BBee**   **b. Bbee**

_____ **39.** Colorblindness   **a.** females   **b.** males

_____ **40.** Crossing over   **a.** mitosis   **b.** meiosis

Special Practice in Genetics

The following problems will help you master the basic principles of Mendelian genetics. Work out your answers on a separate sheet of paper. Solutions are in the Answer Key at the end of the book.

1. Mendel crossed a true-breeding pea plant having pinched pods with a true-breeding pea plant having inflated pods. All of the F_1 plants had inflated pods. The F_1 plants were self-pollinated, and 1,000 F_2 plants were produced.
    a. Which trait is dominant?
    b. About how many different plants would you expect of each phenotype in the F_2?

2. A pure-breeding dwarf corn plant with red ears is mated to a pure-breeding tall corn plant with yellow cars. The F_1 generation is self-pollinated, and in the F_2 there are 9 tall red plants, 31 dwarf red plants, 92 dwarf yellow plants, and 28 tall yellow plants. Which of the traits are dominant?

3. Chickens have sex chromosomes called W and Z. The table given here shows what phenotypic sex corresponds to each sex chromosome constitution.

WW male	WWW male	WWWW male	W male	WZZ female
WZ female	WWZ female	WWWZ female	Z dies before you can tell	

How do chromosomes determine sexual phenotype in chickens?

4. Assume that attached earlobes is recessive to free earlobes in humans, and that this earlobe gene is on an autosome. If a heterozygous man marries a homozygous recessive woman, what is the probability they will have a child with attached earlobes?

5. The MN blood group in humans is inherited in a fashion similar to ABO, but it is due to a different gene. The MN blood group has two alleles, called M and N. The two alleles of this autosomal gene are expressed codominantly. A man of blood type M marries a woman of blood type N. What is the probability they will have a child with blood type N?

6. Certain dominant alleles are so important for normal development that the mutant recessive alleles, called lethal alleles, lead to the death of the organism when homozygous (**ll**). In many cases, the heterozygote (**Ll**) is perfectly normal. Consider the mating of two such heterozygotes (**Ll** × **Ll**). Among their surviving progeny, what fraction will be heterozygous **Ll**?

7. In corn, two independent genes control kernel color. One gene is called <u>color</u>, with alleles **C**, colored, and **c**, white; the other allele is called <u>pigment</u>, with the alleles **P**, colored, and **p**, white. If either of the gene pairs is in the homozygous recessive state, then the kernels will be white. However, if at least one dominant allele of <u>each</u> locus is present, then pigment can form in the kernel. Two corn plants with the following genotypes were crossed: female **Cc Pp** × male **Cc Pp**.
    a. What is the phenotype of the parental plants?
    b. How many different genotypes of gametes will the female parent form?
    c. What will be the ratios of colored to white in the offspring?

8. Fruit fly females have two X chromosomes, but males have one X and one Y. The gene for cut wings is on the X chromosome. The dominant allele **C** causes normal wings, but the recessive allele **c** causes cut wings. A heterozygous female with phenotypically normal wings mates to a normal male. What fraction of the sons will have cut wings?

9. A yellow female mouse with short ears is mated to a white male mouse with long ears. The phenotypes of the offspring are given in the table.

	yellow short	yellow long	white short	white long
Females	35	32	37	34
Males	36	33	34	35

Are the coat color and ear length traits controlled by the same gene?

10. A man with blood type A marries a woman with blood type B, and their three children have blood types A, A, and B. What are the genotypes of the parents?

11. In humans, the Rh blood group can be simply represented as having two alleles, **R** and **r**. Genotypes **RR** and **Rr** cause Rh$^+$ blood type, and genotype **rr** causes Rh$^-$ blood type. A woman with blood type AB Rh$^-$ marries a man with blood type O Rh$^+$ and their first child has blood type B Rh$^-$. What are the genotypes of the parents? What is the probability that the next child has blood type B Rh$^+$?

12. The kinked gene in *Drosophila* affects the size of bristles on the fly's back, and displays incomplete dominance. A fly that has short bristles and is homozygous for the kinked mutation mates to a fly with long bristles that is homozygous normal for the kinked gene. All of their offspring have bristles of intermediate size. If the offspring mate with each other, what will be the ratios of phenotypes in the F$_2$?

Key Terms from the Text Chapter

allele   *text page 186*
autosome   *192*
codominance   *198*
dominant   *184*
epistasis   *200*
first filial (F$_1$) generation   *184*
gene   *180*
genotype   *187*
heredity   *180*
heterozygous   *187*
homozygous   *187*

incomplete dominance   *198*
linkage group   *195*
locus   *196*
parental type   *189*
phenotype   *187*
pleiotropy   *201*
polygenic inheritance   *200*
principle of independent
   assortment   *190*
quantitative trait   *200*
recessive   *184*

recombinant type   *189*
segregation principle   *187*
sex chromosome   *192*
sex-linked   *193*
testcross   *189*
wild-type   *192*
X chromosome   *192*
X-linked   *193*
Y chromosome   *192*

Concept Figure: Chromosome Rearrangements

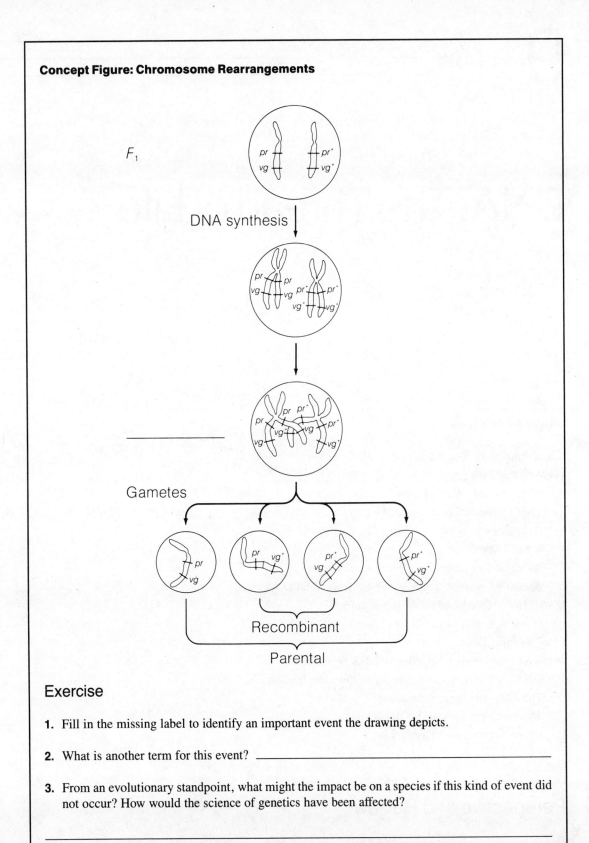

F_1

DNA synthesis

_____

Gametes

Recombinant

Parental

Exercise

1. Fill in the missing label to identify an important event the drawing depicts.

2. What is another term for this event? _____

3. From an evolutionary standpoint, what might the impact be on a species if this kind of event did not occur? How would the science of genetics have been affected?

_____

_____

9

DNA: The Thread of Life

Perspective and Review

Genes are discrete regions of a DNA molecule. Each gene specifies the order of amino acids in a polypeptide chain. Watson and Crick's discovery of the structure of the DNA molecule enabled geneticists to learn exactly how a gene works. The DNA molecule consists of two chains joined in a twisted, ladderlike double helix. Each chain contains a specified order of nucleotide bases that bond in a fixed pattern to

68

bases on the other chain. This structure allows the molecule to replicate itself with tremendous accuracy, and also permits individual genes to specify the amino acid sequence in a polypeptide chain.

DNA transmits its genetic message in the chemical language of the **genetic code**. A particular set of three nucleotide bases (a triplet) codes for a particular amino acid. A gene may therefore be viewed as a specific triplet series that codes for a particular polypeptide chain.

What Genes Do

How genes actually function was first made clear in studies of alkaptonuria, an inherited disease of human infants. Alkaptonuretic babies cannot metabolize tyrosine; normally this amino acid is broken down by two enzymes. The condition, which is caused by a mutant defective gene, results in severe physical disability. After studying the disease, the physician Archibald Garrod reasoned that alkaptonuria is caused by a defective gene that does not produce the correct enzyme; hence, genes must function by allowing particular enzyme reactions to occur.

Subsequently, Beadle and Tatum reasoned that because each step in a biochemical pathway is determined by a gene, and each step requires a specific enzyme, a gene must therefore cause a specific enzyme to be made. This became known as the one-gene–one-enzyme hypothesis. This hypothesis was revised when geneticists found that the only difference between individuals with a normal and mutant gene for sickle cell anemia is the substitution of a single amino acid in the protein hemoglobin. This demonstrated that a gene specifies the amino acid sequence of a polypeptide chain—that is, one gene–one protein.

What Are Genes?

Initially, geneticists believed that genes were made of protein. This idea was challenged in the 1940s, when a group of geneticists found they could transfer an inherited trait into bacteria by inserting DNA. Proof that genes are made of DNA came from **bacteriophages**, bacteria-attacking viruses composed of DNA surrounded by a protein coat. When a phage infects a bacterium, only its DNA enters the cell; this DNA carries the information to produce new phages.

DNA: The Twisted Ladder of Inheritance

The unique structure of the DNA molecule determines the mechanisms by which genes function. Concept Table 9.1 describes this structure and DNA's chemical composition. The molecule resembles a ladder: sugar phosphate groups form the backbone or sides of the ladder, and the nucleotide bases form the rungs. The two chains do not run in the same direction, due to polarity of the sugar group, so the top of the ladder consists of the 5′ carbon end of one chain and the 3′ carbon of the other. The two linked chains twist to form a **double helix**. Organisms differ in the relative amounts of the different bases in their DNA, but DNA structure is the same in all organisms, from plants to earthworms to humans. Figure 9.10 in your text presents a number of different views of DNA structure. Study this figure and learn how the molecule is put together.

Concept Table 9.1   DNA structure and composition

DNA is a linear molecule composed of two nucleotide chains running in opposite directions.

Composition:

1. A sugar

2. A phosphate group

3. Four nitrogen bases: two purines, adenine (A) and guanine (G), and two pyrimidines, cytosine (C) and thymine (T)

Bonding Patterns:

Nucleotide bonding.   Weak hydrogen bonds join adenine of one chain to thymine of the other; similarly, cytosine bonds to guanine.

Sugar-phosphate bonding.   The sugar binds to the phosphate group by stronger covalent bonding, creating an alternating sugar-phosphate backbone for the linked nucleotide chain.

DNA is packed into the cell in either a circular or a linear form; bacterial, viral, and mitochondrial DNA appears as a circle, while most higher organisms have linear DNA molecules packaged in long chromosomes. In order to fit all the DNA inside a cell, and to prevent it from becoming tangled, DNA is wound around proteins called histones, just as sewing thread is wound around a spool. A histone wrapped in two loops of DNA is called a **nucleosome**. Nucleosomes, in turn, are coiled and wrapped in other proteins to form chromatin.

Mysteries of Heredity Unveiled in DNA Structure

The great variety of ways in which bases can be ordered provides the key to DNA's storage capacity. The molecule's shape, with base pairing, allows it to replicate itself with great accuracy, because the existing DNA provides the pattern, or **template**, for its own replication.

The Three Stages of Replication

Concept Table 9.2 outlines the three stages of replication. Since only one of the molecule's two strands or chains is inherited intact, with the other being newly formed, DNA replication is termed semiconservative.

Concept Table 9.2   Stages of DNA replication

1. Unwinding	Enzymes break down the weak hydrogen bonds that join the bases from each strand.
2. Complementary base pairing	The unpaired bases then form bonds with free nucleotides that are drifting close by in the cell. Adenine always bonds with thymine and cytosine with guanine, so that the nucleotide order of the new strand is dictated by that of the old one.

Continues

Concept Table 9.2   Stages of DNA replication (continued)

3. Joining, or polymerization	When **complementary base pairing** is completed, the bases are joined by covalent bonds, a process catalyzed by the enzyme polymerase. The result is two new chains, each identical to the original.

The Amazing Accuracy of Replication

Biologists have estimated that an error in DNA replication occurs once in every 10^9 bases. Such accuracy is essential if DNA is to function in storing and transmitting genetic information, for even the smallest mistake can be costly to the organism. To improve the fidelity of replication, DNA polymerase also corrects mistakes that arise, removing incorrect bases and replacing them with new, correct ones.

Thought Provokers

1. In a brief essay, argue for or against the proposition that, on a faraway planet, life exists for which a protein, rather than DNA, is the master molecule.

2. Describe how a researcher can trace the steps in a biochemical pathway.

Self-Test

For each statement or question choose the best response and mark your choice in the space provided. For some items you will select your response from a *Key*.

_____ 1. The DNA molecule is a _____ helix.
   a. single   c. triple   e. quintuple
   b. double   d. quadruple

_____ 2. DNA replication is:
   a. dispersive   c. conservative   e. none of foregoing
   b. semiconservative   d. all of foregoing

_____ 3. DNA contains how many different kinds of bases, or nucleotides?
   a. 1   b. 2   c. 3   d. 4   e. 5

_____ **4.** How many bases do DNA and RNA share?

   a. 1   **b.** 2   **c.** 3   **d.** 4   **e.** 5

Key for questions 5–10

a. True   **b.** False

Plasmids:

_____ **5.** are larger than the bacterial nucleoid.

_____ **6.** are molecules with a double helix structure.

_____ **7.** are composed of RNA.

_____ **8.** code for specific proteins.

_____ **9.** can be transferred from one bacterium to another.

_____ **10.** frequently enhance an organism's susceptibility/sensitivity to antibiotics.

Key for questions 11–20

a. True   **b.** False

In DNA:

_____ **11.** Bases are bonded to other bases by covalent bonds.

_____ **12.** The molecular "backbone" contains ribose and phosphate.

_____ **13.** The two chains have opposite polarity.

_____ **14.** DNA polymerase is required for synthesis of more DNA.

_____ **15.** The base A regularly pairs with U.

_____ **16.** The base G regularly pairs with C.

_____ **17.** A DNA base sequence may read AGGGCCTTCCGAA.

_____ **18.** Groups of bases make up genes.

_____ **19.** The bases are attached directly to the phosphates.

_____ **20.** The molecule is chemically an acid.

Questions 21–28: Use the *Key* to indicate the individuals responsible for the research or discovery described.

a. Beadle and Tatum   **c.** Watson and Crick   **e.** Franklin and Wilkins
b. Hershey and Chase   **d.** Meselson and Stahl

_____ **21.** X-rays that provided clues to the structure of DNA

_____ **22.** Elucidation of the true structure of DNA

_____ **23.** The finding that viruses infect by injecting their DNA into host cells

_____ **24.** Working with *Neurospora*, proposed the "one-gene–one-enzyme" theory (now modified to the one-gene–one-polypeptide theory)

_____ **25.** Used P32 and S35 to prove their hypothesis

_____ **26.** Required both minimal and complete culture media for their studies

_____ **27.** Used N14 and N15 isotopes to study bacterial replication

_____ **28.** Constructed molecular models to prove their hypothesis

Special Practice: DNA

The following problems will help you master the features and characteristics of DNA. Solutions are in the Answer Key at the end of the book.

1. In the mold *Neurospora*, compound C is essential for growth; in normal molds it is synthesized only by the pathway and enzymes shown here:

$$\text{A} \xrightarrow{\text{enzyme 1}} \text{B} \xrightarrow{\text{enzyme 2}} \text{C}$$

Researchers made a mutation in the gene that encodes enzyme 2, and found that the mutant mold will not grow on a very simple medium that lacks B and C, but it will grow on a complex medium made by adding substances B and C to the simple medium.

	Simple medium	**Simple medium plus B and C**
Growth of the mutant	No growth	Normal growth
Growth of normal mold	Normal growth	Normal growth

  a. Predict the growth of the mutant on medium lacking substance C and substance A but containing substance B.
  b. Predict the growth of the mutant on medium lacking substance B, but containing substance A and C.
  c. Predict the growth of the mutant on medium lacking substance B and C, but containing substance A.

2. Genetic experiments by George Beadle with the mold *Neurospora* provided evidence for the following metabolic pathway:

$$\begin{array}{cccc} \text{gene 1} & \text{gene 2} & \text{gene 3} \\ \downarrow & \downarrow & \downarrow \\ \text{enzyme 1} & \text{enzyme 2} & \text{enzyme 3} \end{array}$$
$$\text{A} \xrightarrow{} \text{B} \xrightarrow{} \text{C} \xrightarrow{} \text{D}$$

Mutations in any of the three genes prevent growth of the mold on normal food. But if compound D is added to the food, all three mutants can grow. Now consider a mutation in gene 2. On what compound(s) will this mutation grow?

3. In your DNA, 20.5% of the nucleotides contain the base C. What percentage contains the base A?

4. In the salt-loving bacterium *Halobacterium solinarium*, 33.5% of the bases are the base G. Does this bacterium have more or less T than you do? (Human data are in Problem 3.)

5. Assume a DNA molecule containing "light" nitrogen replicates once in the presence of bases containing "heavy" nitrogen atoms. Which of the following would best describe the two daughter DNA molecules?
  a. One daughter molecule would have two heavy strands, and the other daughter would have two light strands.
  b. Both daughter molecules would consist of two strands, each strand a mixture of light and heavy.
  c. One daughter molecule would have one light and one heavy strand, and the other daughter would have two strands, each a mixture of light and heavy.

d. Each daughter molecule would have one light strand and one heavy strand.

e. Depends on the type of organism investigated.

6. The base order of one strand of a DNA molecule is: 5'-C-A-T-T-A-G-3'. What is the most likely sequence of the other strand?

   a. 5'-G-T-A-A-T-C-3'

   b. 3'-G-U-A-A-U-C-5'

   c. 5'-C-A-T-T-A-G-3'

   d. 3'-G-T-A-A-T-C-5'

   e. Cannot be determined from the data given.

7. Drawn below is one strand of a portion of a DNA molecule from aardvarks but one of the bases has been replaced by the letter X. From what you know about the order of bases in DNA, what is the most likely base in the position marked X?

   5'-T-T-A-A-A-X-C-G-3'

8. Bacteria grown for many generations in "light" nitrogen are switched to "heavy" nitrogen and cultured for one generation. The cells are then cultured for one more generation in "light" nitrogen, and their DNA is extracted and analyzed.

   a. What fraction of the DNA molecules will have two "light" strands?

   b. What fraction of the DNA molecules will have two "heavy" strands?

   c. What fraction of the DNA molecules will have one "light" and one "heavy" strand?

9. AIDS patients can be helped by the nucleotide analogue AZT. This compound resembles the nucleotide T, except that it has no free 3' OH. What happens to the replication of DNA (including AIDS-causing virus DNA) in a person taking AZT?

Key Terms from the Text Chapter

bacteriophage   *text page 209*

complementary base pairing
   217, 219

double helix   *205*

genetic code   *221*

mutation   *221*

nucleosome   *216*

plasmid   *204*

template   *217*

transformation   *209*

Concept Figure: Semiconservative Replication

Exercise

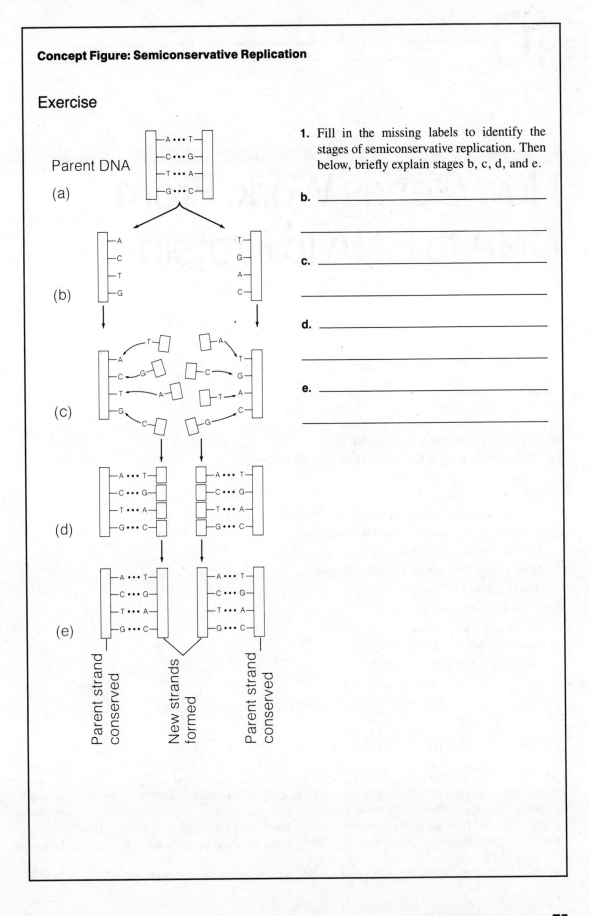

1. Fill in the missing labels to identify the stages of semiconservative replication. Then below, briefly explain stages b, c, d, and e.

b. _____

_____

c. _____

_____

d. _____

_____

e. _____

_____

How Genes Work: From DNA to RNA to Protein

CHAPTER IN BRIEF

Perspective and Review

Genes contain the genetic information necessary for the cell and individual to function. How does this information, contained in a DNA molecule, get translated into a usable form? The answer is **protein synthesis**: information flows from DNA to RNA to proteins. Proteins, often as enzymes, in turn ultimately control all body activities. Geneticists divide the flow of information from DNA into two basic steps, gene transcription and gene translation. Three types of RNA are the main molecules involved in protein synthesis.

Errors called mutations can occur in the DNA base sequence. These mutations can affect protein synthesis at any stage, and can occur in single bases as well as whole chromosomes. In general, mutations are harmful to the organism.

Cells need to control or regulate gene activity—the type and amount of protein made. **Gene regulation** can occur at many levels, from the transcriptional stage to after the protein has been translated. Researchers have learned that gene activity in prokaryotes changes in response to environmental conditions. The more complex eukaryotic system of gene regulation is not so well understood. Directed by genes, eukaryotic cells become specialized for different functions early on in development—a process known as cell differentiation—and retain their function throughout life. Prokaryotic and eukaryotic organisms also differ in gene structure and the organization of genes in the genome.

The Path of Information Flow from DNA to RNA to Protein

In order to make a protein, a gene must transmit its information to the cell. Information flows from DNA (the gene) to RNA to protein in a two-step process that involves:

1. **Transcription**—DNA is copied into RNA.
2. **Translation**—RNA is translated into a sequence of amino acids (a polypeptide chain) in the cell.

Transcription

Transcription occurs in the nucleus of the cell. RNA, the molecule synthesized from DNA in transcription, differs from its parent molecule in four major features:

1. In RNA the base uracil replaces thymine of DNA.
2. The sugar in RNA is a ribose sugar.
3. RNA is a single strand, whereas DNA is double-stranded.
4. RNA is much shorter than the DNA molecule, because DNA carries many genes whereas RNA carries information from only one gene.

Three types of RNA are involved in protein synthesis: **messenger RNA (mRNA)**, **ribosomal RNA (rRNA)**, and **transfer RNA (tRNA)**.

Transcription is similar to DNA replication, with a few notable exceptions. Concept Table 10.1 outlines the main features of transcription and how it differs from replication.

Concept Table 10.1   Transcription—Significant features, and how it differs from replication

1. Replication and transcription result in a new molecule whose base sequence has been dictated by DNA.
2. During transcription ribonucleotides pair with deoxyribonucleotides of DNA. RNA polymerase joins together the ribonucleotides.
3. In transcription only one strand of the DNA molecule is transcribed.
4. Only a short portion of the DNA molecule, usually a gene, is transcribed.

Continues

---

5. Many copies of an RNA molecule may be transcribed, but a gene is copied only once during replication.

6. When transcription is completed, the RNA separates from the DNA molecule and moves from the nucleus to the main body of the cell; the two DNA strands then rejoin.

Translation

The gene's message, carried on RNA, becomes a polypeptide chain via the process of translation. Translation takes place on ribosomes, which are located outside the cell nucleus (Chapter 3). Here the three different types of RNA play specific roles; Concept Table 10.2 describes how these RNA molecules participate in translation.

Concept Table 10.2   Translation and the roles of RNA

RNA	Function
mRNA	Carries the genetic information, as a sequence of **codons**, from the gene in the nucleus to **ribosomes** in the cell cytoplasm.
tRNA	Single strands of RNA about 75 bases long. Each tRNA molecule corresponds to a specific amino acid, and so different molecules have different base sequences. On one end tRNA has a sequence of three bases, together called an <u>anticodon</u>, that are complementary to three bases on an mRNA molecule (**codon**). On the other end tRNA carries an amino acid. During translation tRNA collects its specific amino acid and transports it to a particular site on an mRNA molecule; the site is determined by codon-anticodon pairing.
rRNA	Serves as the site for polypeptide synthesis. Four rRNA molecules aggregate together and become wrapped up in proteins to form a **ribosome**. During translation, ribosomes hold tRNA and mRNA in position so amino acids carried by tRNAs can be joined into a polypeptide chain; ribosomes also are associated with enzymes that catalyze the linking of the amino acids.

Protein synthesis is one of the cell's major functions, because proteins perform most cell and body activities. Protein synthesis is costly, because it uses large amounts of energy, but this cost can be viewed as an investment towards the individual's survival. Scientists recognize three phases of protein synthesis, and the main features of each phase are outlined in Concept Table 10.3.

Concept Table 10.3   The three phases of protein synthesis

Phase	Significant Features
Initiation	mRNA is threaded through a groove in a ribosome. tRNA associates with mRNA, by codon-anticodon pairing, and with the ribosome to form a multimolecular complex.
Elongation	The ribosome moves along the chain of mRNA, with the appropriate tRNA bearing an amino acid becoming attached at each step. Enzymes associated with the ribosomes join the amino acids carried by a sequence of tRNAs; each tRNA is then ejected from the complex. In this way the amino acid (polypeptide chain) grows.
Termination	Growth of the polypeptide chain stops when the last amino acid has been added.

■ **A Note on the Genetic Code**   The base sequence AUG is the start codon, which signals the starting point of translation. UAA, UAG, and UGA are stop codons; any one of these terminates translation.

Gene Mutation: A Change in Base Sequence

A mutation is a change in the sequence of nucleotide bases in DNA. Mutations generally have a major and negative effect on an individual. Concept Table 10.4 outlines the different forms of mutations, and their effects and origins.

Concept Table 10.4   Mutations

General Categories

Chromosomal	Affect large regions of a chromosome or the entire chromosome and therefore affect many genes
Gene mutations	Affect individual genes

Types of Gene Mutations

Base substitution	A nucleotide base pair is replaced by another.
Insertion	One or more nucleotide base pairs are inserted into a DNA molecule.
Deletion	One or more nucleotide base pairs are removed or lost from a DNA molecule.
Rearrangement	Base pairs in a DNA molecule change position in the molecule. *Example:* an inversion in base order.

Effects of Gene Mutations

Interference	Mutations that interfere or prevent transcription, mRNA transport, or protein synthesis

Continues

Concept Table 10.4 Mutations (continued)

Structural Mutations that change the amino acid sequence and thereby change the protein. There are three main types of structural mutations:

1. **Missense**—nucleotide substitution causes one amino acid to replace another.

2. **Nonsense**—an amino acid codon is changed into a stop codon, thus terminating translation at that point

3. **Frameshift**—insertion or deletion of one or more base pairs, which changes the **reading frame** (the group of codons read as a unit)

Origins of Mutations

1. Spontaneous errors arising during DNA replication.

2. Physical or chemical agents (<u>mutagens</u>) that cause changes in DNA structure; *examples*: ultraviolet light and nicotine. <u>Carcinogens</u> are substances that cause cancer by inducing mutations.

Regulation of Gene Activity

Through a process of gene regulation, each cell in an organism controls the type and amount of protein produced at a particular time. There are five levels at which genes can be regulated, and both prokaryotes and eukaryotes can use any of the five. Concept Table 10.5 outlines these levels.

Concept Table 10.5 Levels of gene regulation

Level	Mechanism
Transcriptional	Regulation of the amount of mRNA transcribed
Posttranscriptional	Translation is blocked or permitted, depending on whether certain mRNAs are modified. Such modifications are needed before the mRNAs can attach to ribosomes
Translational	Regulation of the rate of mRNA translation by preventing mRNA from reaching ribosomes, or by limiting the growth of the amino acid chain
Posttranslational	A requirement that some proteins must be modified after translation in order to function
Regulation of protein activity	The efficiency of a protein is regulated by factors in its cellular environment

Gene Regulation in Prokaryotes

Most prokaryotic cells can respond very quickly to changes in their environment (by producing proteins to fit their situation) through regulation of gene activity at three main levels. Concept Table 10.6 explores the prokaryotic system of gene regulation.

Concept Table 10.6   Gene regulation in prokaryotes

Transcriptional level control	Controls the amount of protein manufactured
Simultaneous transcription and translation	Increases the speed of response to stimuli
Short-lived mRNA	Allows for fast response to changing environments

The **operon** system is one type of transcriptional regulation found in prokaryotes. It consists of a group of genes transcribed together in response to a set of factors that control the transcription process. This topic is described in detail on page 169 of your text.

Gene Regulation in Eukaryotes

While each cell in your body contains the identical genetic information, all cells do not perform the same functions. This obvious fact implies that certain genes are active only in specific cells, and that there must be some control over which genes are active, when they become active, and how much of a given protein they produce. The exact mechanisms of such finely tuned gene control in eukaryotes are not yet well understood. Most control comes at the transcriptional level, though not through an operon system. Instead, eukaryotes have **activators**, proteins that bind to DNA and stimulate transcription. Prokaryotes and eukaryotes also differ in gene structure and genome organization; related genes are usually next to each other in prokaryotes, but tend to be scattered throughout the eukaryotic genome. Eukaryotes have **introns** and **exons**. Introns are nucleotide sequences occurring in a gene that are transcribed but not translated into protein; exons are the sequences that are transcribed and translated. This arrangement is not found in prokaryotes.

Thought Provokers

1. Define the term mutation and then indicate the causes of and different types of mutations that may occur in prokaryotic cells. Finally, discuss the consequences of each type of mutation.

2. Prepare a Concept Table that compares and contrasts the similarities and differences in prokaryotes and eukaryotes of the universal genetic theme: DNA → RNA → protein.

Self-Test

For each statement or question choose the best response and mark your choice in the space provided. For some items you will select your responses from a *Key*.

Questions 1–5: Using the *Key*, indicate the most appropriate nitrogen base pairing for the base in the numbered item.

a. adenine   **c.** cytosine   **e.** uracil
b. guanine   **d.** thymine

_____ 1. In DNA, guanine pairs with this.

_____ 2. In RNA, guanine pairs with this.

_____ 3. In DNA, adenine pairs with this.

_____ 4. In RNA, adenine pairs with this.

_____ 5. In DNA, cytosine pairs with this.

Questions 6–15: In the following items more than one answer from the *Key* may apply. Give *all* the correct answers.

a. DNA   **c.** t- or sRNA   **e.** protein
b. mRNA   **d.** rRNA

_____ **6.** Contains ribose

_____ **7.** Contains phosphate

_____ **8.** Carries amino acids to ribosome sites

_____ **9.** Contains the codon

_____ **10.** Carries the anticodon

_____ **11.** Ribosomes are made of this.

_____ **12.** A portion of the molecule reads AGGCCTGCTAATCG.

_____ **13.** The beginning of the molecule always codes for methionine.

_____ **14.** The molecule that contains a few cloverleaf or hairpin configurations.

_____ **15.** RNA that can only be made in the presence of RNA polymerase

Questions 16–20: Using the *Key*, indicate for each event described which level of gene regulation is probably functioning.

a. transcriptional   **c.** translational
b. posttranscriptional   **d.** posttranslational

_____ **16.** RNA is made but cannot leave the nucleus.

_____ **17.** Sugar molecules are added to a protein molecule and the protein becomes functional.

_____ **18.** m-RNA cannot bind to the ribosome.

_____ **19.** A repressor is interacting with DNA.

_____ **20.** Polypeptide chain growth stops at 50% elongation.

Questions 21–28: The following questions relate to gene regulation in *E. coli*, a prokaryote. Choose the appropriate answer from the *Key*.

a. operator   **c.** structural gene   **ab.** repressor
b. regulator   **d.** promoter   **ac.** operon
                     e. inducer

_____ **21.** The role of lactose in the system

_____ **22.** What gives rise to the repressor

_____ **23.** What the repressor binds to

_____ **24.** The B-galactosidase gene is considered a(n) _____.

_____ **25.** Genes y and a are this type.

_____ **26.** The whole system shown in the *Key* is best summarized by this term.

_____ **27.** Where RNA polymerase first binds

_____ **28.** What inactivates the repressor

Questions 29–39: Two items, A and B, are compared relative to a numbered concept. If A is larger or greater than B, mark A in the space provided; if B is greater than A, mark B; if both items are essentially equivalent, mark C.

_____ **29.** Size of the genome   **a.** prokaryotes   **b.** eukaryotes

_____ **30.** Presence of plasmids   **a.** prokaryotes   **b.** eukaryotes

_____ **31.** Number of introns   **a.** prokaryotes   **b.** eukaryotes

_____ **32.** Number of different nitrogen bases   **a.** DNA   **b.** RNA

_____ **33.** Size of molecule   **a.** DNA   **b.** RNA

_____ **34.** Types or kinds of   **a.** DNA   **b.** RNA

_____ **35.** Number of chains in hemoglobin molecule   **a.** alpha   **b.** beta

_____ **36.** Number of strands   **a.** RNA   **b.** DNA

_____ **37.** Number of codons in the basic genetic code   **a.** prokaryotes   **b.** eukaryotes

_____ **38.** Ability to digest lactose   **a.** Caucasians   **b.** most other races

_____ **39.** Spatial and temporal regulation of genes   **a.** *E. coli*   **b.** humans

Questions 40–45: Using the *Key*, mark whether the following items, relating to the disease thalassemia, are True or False.

a. True   **b.** False

_____ **40.** Thalassemia typically is a hereditary disease.

_____ **41.** The defect involves the plasma membrane of red blood cells.

_____ **42.** The disease can be detected via analysis of the blood.

_____ **43.** Signs of the disease include an enlarged spleen and enlarged bones.

_____ **44.** Thalassemia can be cured by chemical treatment at birth.

_____ **45.** Transfusion is one method of treatment.

Key for questions 46–50

a. DNA replication   **c.** transcription   **e.** plasmids
b. translation   **d.** tRNA

_____ **46.** "TATA" and "CAT" boxes are closely associated with regulation of this.

_____ **47.** The mushroom poisoning of Caesar was related to interference in _____ by the chemical toxin in the mushroom.

_____ **48.** Twenty different forms of this are necessary for protein synthesis.

_____ **49.** RNA polymerase is responsible for this process.

_____ **50.** DNA polymerase is responsible for this process.

Special Practice: How Genes Work

The following problems will help you master the material in this chapter on gene function. Solutions are in the Answer Key at the end of the book.

1. What peptide would the messenger RNA below encode? (Consult the genetics code in text Figure 10.7.)

A-U-G-U-U-U-U-U-A-U-A-A-C-G

2. A deletion mutation occurs in the gene that encodes the mRNA listed in Problem 1 so that the new message has only four U's in a row instead of the original five.

A U G U U U U A U A A

This mutation shifts the reading frame of the message. What will be the new amino acid sequence?

3. You find a mutant bacterium that makes lactose-digesting enzymes whether or not lactose is present (i.e., it is constitutive). You determine that the mutation is in the gene that encodes the repressor protein. How might the mutation work?

a. The mutation changes the operator so that it will not bind to the repressor.
b. The mutation changes the promoter so that it will not bind to the RNA polymerase.
c. The mutation changes the repressor so that it will not bind to lactose.
d. The mutation changes the repressor so it can never bind to the operator.

4. A geneticist studying the lactose operon discovers a mutation that destroys the operator. What will be the phenotype of this mutation?

a. The mutant will make lactose-digesting enzymes only when lactose is present.
b. The mutant will make lactose-digesting enzymes only when lactose is absent.
c. The mutant will make lactose-digesting enzymes whether lactose is present or not (i.e., all the time).
d. The mutant will NOT make lactose-digesting enzymes at any time, whether lactose is present or absent.
e. None of the above.

5. Consider the following sequence of bases, which represents the <u>noncoding</u> strand of DNA around a particular gene in a human chromosome. The "ˇ" marks the start of transcription.

5′ČTATATTTAGĊGCGATCGGCĊTTTACGTCCCŤGTCTĂTACTĂTGGCAAGATĂACGAATAAAĊ3′

a. What would be the sequence of the coding strand in this region?
b. What would be the sequence of the mRNA from this gene?
c. Translation nearly always begins with the codon 5′AUG3′. What amino acid does this encode? (Check text Figure 10.7.)
d. Which codon will stop translation?
e. What will be the sequence of the protein made by this gene?

6. What is the <u>anticodon</u> for the tRNA bearing the amino acid Trp?

    a. 3′UGG5′   **c.** 3′UAG5′   **e.** 3′TGG5′
    b. 3′ACC5′   **d.** 3′AUA5′

7. Which of the following is more likely to represent a strand of RNA instead of a single strand of DNA?

    a. 5′-A-A-G-G-T-G-3′

    b. 5′-A-A-C-C-T-C-3′

    c. 5′-A-A-U-U-A-G-3′

    d. 5′-T-A-A-A-G-G-3′

    e. Not enough information available to make a choice

Key Terms from the Text Chapter

activator *text page 242*

chromosomal mutation *233*

codon *229*

elongation *233*

exon *244*

gene regulation *237*

genetic code *228*

initiation *233*

intron *244*

messenger RNA (mRNA)
  226

operon *238*

protein synthesis *231*

reading frame *230*

repressor *240*

ribosomal RNA (rRNA) *226*

ribosome *231*

termination *233*

transcription *226*

transfer RNA (tRNA) *226*

translation *226*

Concept Figure: Information Flow in the Cell

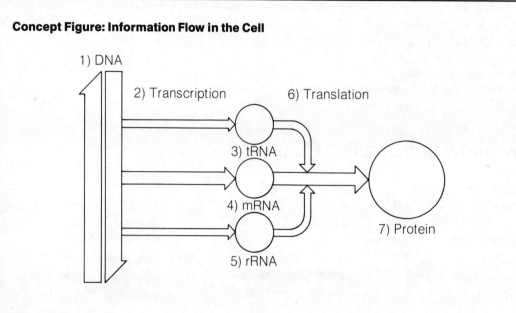

1) DNA

2) Transcription

6) Translation

3) tRNA

4) mRNA

5) rRNA

7) Protein

Exercise

Using the drawing as a guide, complete the chart by filling in the appropriate number.

Event	Process/Molecule
Point at which most eukaryote gene regulation takes place	_____
Stretches q nucleotides that encode RNA	_____
Conversion of RNA message into amino acid sequence	_____
Includes an anticodon sequence	_____
Carries information to make a protein	_____
Carries an amino acid attached by a covalent bond	_____
Component of ribosomes	_____
Where mutations occur	_____
A polypeptide	_____
Occurs in the cytoplasm	_____
Occurs in the nucleus	_____

11

Genetic Recombination and Recombinant DNA Research

CHAPTER IN BRIEF

Perspective and Review

Genetic recombination occurs in nature, producing novel gene arrangements and at times acting as an evolutionary force. However, such natural recombination is a random process. In the early 1970s the development of genetic engineering techniques gave geneticists the ability to copy this natural process under controlled conditions. Geneticists can now isolate individual genes and recombine them not only with genes from the same species, but with genes from different organisms. Recombinant DNA technology has begun to pay off as large quantities of once rare or expensive drugs can now be produced at much lower cost, and yields of economically important plants and animals can be improved.

The advantages of this technology in alleviating human suffering are obvious, but they do not come without a price. Genetic engineering has raised many new moral and ethical problems for humans. For example, how much should we tinker with human sex cells to produce the sort of children we want? Should genetically engineered organisms be released into the environment? Such controversial issues will need to be addressed as the technology advances.

Recombination in Nature

<u>Genetic recombination</u> is the term biologists use to describe a new arrangement of genes on a DNA molecule. During reproduction, genetic recombination occurs in all organisms; for example, during meiosis, crossing over produces new gene arrangements and combinations. Occasionally such recombination can produce a totally new phenotype by forming new gene arrangements on chromosomes.

There are two important features of recombination: (1) In general recombination only occurs between homologous sequences of DNA (homologous chromosomes), which ensures that genes are not lost or gained; and (2) recombination can occur at any point along a chromosome.

Recombination can have an evolutionary effect. If a new phenotype for a trait produced by recombination enjoys an advantage over other existing phenotypes, then the affected organism may reproduce more successfully, and the frequency of the new phenotype will increase in the population. Recombinations occur more often than do mutations, and it is not surprising that species that have a high recombination frequency have greater potential to evolve adaptations to new conditions and thus to survive as the world around them changes.

The Power of Recombinant DNA Research

Recombination in nature is a slow process. However since the advent of **recombinant DNA technology** (genetic engineering), geneticists can now isolate genes and design and construct new gene combinations very quickly. Geneticists use special molecular tools to make recombinant DNA in laboratories. Concept Table 11.1 describes these tools.

Concept Table 11.1   Molecular tools of recombinant DNA technology

Restriction enzymes	Enzymes that occur naturally in microorganisms. Each enzyme recognizes a specific DNA sequence of a few base pairs, and cuts the DNA at a consistent point at or near this *recognition site*; cleavage leaves a few unpaired bases sticking out from the cut ends. Called *sticky ends*, these ends will pair with complementary bases from any gene.
DNA ligase	"Molecular glue." It is a protein that joins the sticky ends to complementary ends by strong covalent bonds.
Plasmids	Small circular pieces of DNA replicated in bacterial cells. A bacterium cell may contain many copies of a plasmid. Plasmids can carry foreign genes into bacteria, where the genes can be replicated.

Using the tools of recombinant DNA technology, geneticists can now isolate a particular gene and make many copies of that gene—a technique called <u>cloning</u>. Concept Table 11.2 presents the main steps geneticists today use to clone a gene, focusing on the human growth hormone (HGH) gene as an example.

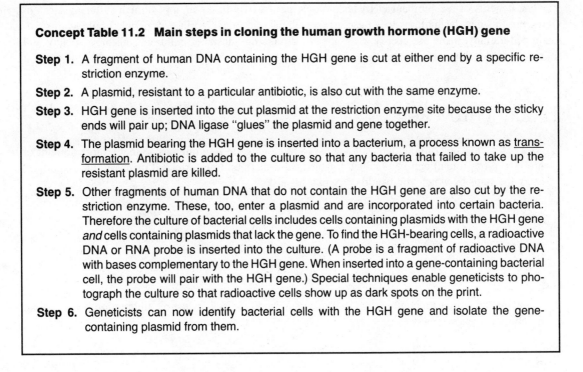

Concept Table 11.2 Main steps in cloning the human growth hormone (HGH) gene

Step 1. A fragment of human DNA containing the HGH gene is cut at either end by a specific restriction enzyme.

Step 2. A plasmid, resistant to a particular antibiotic, is also cut with the same enzyme.

Step 3. HGH gene is inserted into the cut plasmid at the restriction enzyme site because the sticky ends will pair up; DNA ligase "glues" the plasmid and gene together.

Step 4. The plasmid bearing the HGH gene is inserted into a bacterium, a process known as <u>transformation</u>. Antibiotic is added to the culture so that any bacteria that failed to take up the resistant plasmid are killed.

Step 5. Other fragments of human DNA that do not contain the HGH gene are also cut by the restriction enzyme. These, too, enter a plasmid and are incorporated into certain bacteria. Therefore the culture of bacterial cells includes cells containing plasmids with the HGH gene *and* cells containing plasmids that lack the gene. To find the HGH-bearing cells, a radioactive DNA or RNA probe is inserted into the culture. (A probe is a fragment of radioactive DNA with bases complementary to the HGH gene. When inserted into a gene-containing bacterial cell, the probe will pair with the HGH gene.) Special techniques enable geneticists to photograph the culture so that radioactive cells show up as dark spots on the print.

Step 6. Geneticists can now identify bacterial cells with the HGH gene and isolate the gene-containing plasmid from them.

Promises and Problems in Recombinant DNA Research

Concept Table 11.3 outlines three main ways in which humans exploit recombinant DNA technology for their own uses.

Concept Table 11.3 Human exploitation of recombinant DNA technology

Mass-production of proteins
This use applies mainly to areas of medical technology. Drug production via genetic engineering can increase the supply and lower the cost of certain essential drugs such as insulin and growth hormone.

Improvement of plant and animal stocks
Rather than relying on nature to produce a new mutation or recombination to improve yields, it is now possible to insert genes into plants and animals that, for example, increase plant resistance to drought or improve milk production in cows.

Human gene therapy
Perhaps the most exciting and controversial area of recombinant DNA research; currently more theoretical than practical. There are two main types:

1. *Somatic cell therapy*
Involves inserting a needed gene into an individual who lacks the gene in order to correct a deficiency. This type of therapy affects only the individual; the person still carries the defective gene and can pass it on to her or his children.

2. *Germ line gene therapy*
Involves inserting genes into the sex cells. Hence, not only is the individual affected but so too are all potential descendents. For technical reasons this therapy is not yet a viable option. It is also controversial and raises many ethical questions.

The benefits of recombinant DNA technology, particularly in the area of human suffering, are obvious, but this new technology does raise serious ethical questions. While few people argue against somatic cell therapy, many are uneasy at the idea of producing "designer children." Clearly, society will soon need to develop guidelines in these areas.

Thought Provokers

1. As a researcher in a biology lab, you are asked to clone gene Y in humans so that a large amount of product Y (a protein) can be obtained for medical use. In outline form and using simple sentences, show the steps by which you would carry out this task.

2. Compare and contrast recombination as it occurs normally in cells when recombination is carried out in laboratory experiments.

3. Give at least three reasons why genetic engineering is important.

4. Describe at least three problems that can occur during or after a genetic engineering experiment that result in a failed experiment.

Self-Test

For each statement or question choose the best response and mark your choice in the space provided. For some items you will select your response from a *Key*.

Key for questions 1–3, relating to genetic recombination.

a. True   **b.** False

_____ 1. Recombination can occur in living organisms and between DNA molecules in test tubes with no living organisms.

_____ **2.** Recombinant DNA is mutated DNA.

_____ **3.** DNA from a eukaryote cannot be recombined with that of a prokaryote.

Key for questions 4–7
a. True   **b.** False

Transposons:

_____ **4.** Can cause changes in prokaryotic genomes.

_____ **5.** Can cause changes in eukaryotic genomes.

_____ **6.** Help to stabilize genomes.

_____ **7.** Are composed of RNA.

_____ **8.** Normally, recombination occurs during:
  a. mitosis   **c.** both A and B
  b. meiosis   **d.** neither A nor B

_____ **9.** When recombination takes place it typically involves:
  a. all chromosomes indiscriminately
  b. homologous chromosomes only
  c. heterologous chromosomes only
  d. heterozygous alleles
  e. homozygous alleles

Questions 10–12: Using the *Key*, indicate which types of recombination are possible.
a. Possible   **b.** Impossible

_____ **10.** Eukaryotic to eukaryotic DNA

_____ **11.** Prokaryotic to prokaryotic DNA

_____ **12.** Eukaryotic to prokaryotic DNA

_____ **13.** For the human genome the number of possible recombinants for heterozygotes is:
  a. not calculable   **d.** $2^{50,000}$
  b. 2^n **e.** $\log 10 \times 2^{46}$
  c. 2^{46}

Key for questions 14–18
a. A substance produced via genetic engineering
b. A substance not produced by genetic engineering

_____ **14.** Insulin

_____ **15.** Estrogens

_____ **16.** Human growth factor

_____ **17.** Interferon

_____ **18.** Tissue plasminogen activator

_____ **19.** Approximately 93% of the human diet is supplied by how many different kinds of plants?

    a. 3   **c.** 30   **e.** 75

    b. 10   **d.** 50

_____ **20.** "Jumping genes" were discovered by whom, and in what?

    a. Hershey and Chase, in phage

    b. Watson and Crick, in DNA

    c. Beadle and Tatum, in _Neurospora_

    d. McClintock, in corn

    e. Griffith, in _Pneumococcus_

Special Practice: Genetic Recombination and Genetic Engineering

The following problems will help you master some important principles relating to gene recombination and recombinant DNA research. Solutions are in the Answer Key at the end of the book.

1. A person is heterozygous for four different genes. How many different kinds of gametes will form in this person's gonads after meiosis?

2. The restriction enzyme called BamHI (pronounced "bam H one") recognizes the sequence 5'GGATCC3' and cleaves it between the two G's. How many restriction fragments will result when the DNA below is digested by BamHI, and what will be their size?

5′TCGAATTGGATCCGCGCTACTGTACGGCTCGTACGTGGATCCCCGGTCAGGATCCAACTTAAGACT3′
3′AGCTTAACCTAGGCGCGATGACATGCCGAGCATGCACCTAGGGGCCAGTCCTAGGTTGAATTCTGA5′

3. The restriction enzyme BglII (pronounced "bagel two") recognizes the sequence 5′AGATCT3′ and cleaves it after the first A, and the enzyme EcoR1 recognizes the sequence 5′GAATTC3′ and cleaves it after the first G. Will the ends left by either of these two enzymes form "sticky ends" with DNA fragments cut by BamHI?

4. The human genetic disease muscular dystrophy is caused by a mutation that disrupts the structure of a muscle protein and hence the ability of muscles to work. Would you expect the strategy in text Figure 11.11 for somatic cell gene therapy involving transforming blood cells with the normal gene that prevents muscular dystrophy to be effective? Support your choice.

Key Terms from the Text Chapter

clone   _text page 254_

DNA ligase _253_

electrophoresis _253_

gene therapy _257_

recombinant DNA technology   _248_

restriction enzyme _253_

transposon _251_

Human Genetics

Perspective and Review

Most human traits are polygenic: that is, more than one gene controls a particular characteristic. Others follow simple Mendelian laws of inheritance. This fact enabled early geneticists to determine whether certain genes were dominant or recessive, sex-linked or autosomal, by analyzing family pedigrees—ordered histories of family members through time. This process depended on families' keeping good records, which wasn't always done. Hence, reliable case studies were often difficult to find.

In the last two or three decades, however, new techniques have greatly improved our ability to study human genetics. The first such development, karyotyping, has allowed geneticists to look at the number and structure of chromosomes. This led in turn to the discovery of genetic causes for many diseases. More recently, the exciting developments of cell hybridization and RFLP have allowed geneticists to map the positions of different human genes. Thanks to these new tools it is now possible to detect many genetic defects in unborn children and to detect heterozygote carriers of genetic diseases. Genetic counselors can now advise a couple on their chances of producing a genetically defective child.

How Traditional Techniques Reveal Thousands of Human Genetic Conditions

More than 3,000 human characteristics are inherited according to Mendelian principles; these traits include color blindness and baldness.

Humans make difficult subjects for genetic analysis. They have a long life cycle, produce few offspring, and do not choose mates on the basis of whether they fit a particular study. Consequently, geneticists have often had to rely on pedigree analysis to follow traits in humans. A **pedigree** is an orderly diagram showing relationship, sex, genotype, and phenotype of all family members through numerous generations. By following the rules derived from Mendelian principles, it is possible to determine from a pedigree whether a trait is dominant or recessive, sex-linked, or carried on an autosome. Table 12.1 in your text presents examples of human conditions inherited in a Mendelian fashion. Concept Table 12.1 describes three of these conditions.

Concept Table 12.1   Three human traits inherited according to Mendelian principles

Trait	Significant Features
Phenylketonuria (PKU)	*Description:* Inability to break down phenylalanine into tyrosine. Results in a buildup of phenylalanine, which causes abnormal nerve cell development in the brain. *Genetics:* Caused by a recessive allele on an autosome; heterozygotes, having one normal and one PKU gene, do not show the condition but carry the defective gene and can pass it on to their children.
Duchenne muscular dystrophy (DMD)	*Description:* Degenerative muscle condition occurring in males. *Genetics:* Caused by a recessive allele on the X chromosome; usually passed on to sons by mothers who are heterozygous carriers (human females have two X chromosomes; males have an X and a Y).
Huntington's disease	*Description:* Symptoms arise between the ages of 35 and 50; there is progressive degeneration and death of nerve cells, with accompanying intellectual deterioration and jerky movements. *Genetics:* Caused by a dominant autosomal gene.

Karyotyping is the use of special dyes and labeling techniques to get a picture of an organism's set of chromosomes. This technique enables geneticists to study the effects of changes in chromosome structure or number. Not surprisingly, humans are highly sensitive to changes in chromosome structure and number and also to movement of genes within the genome. A change in chromosome number is responsible for Down syndrome; the affected individual has three copies of chromosome 21 (trisomy 21). **Chromosome translocation** arises when part of a chromosome spontaneously moves to a new location on another chromosome. Burkitt's lymphoma is a cancer caused by translocation of a region of chromosome 8 to chromosome 14 in white blood cells. Some individuals have the **fragile X syndrome**—the X chromosome breaks easily at a specific point, an event that has been implicated in some cases of mental retardation.

The New Genetics: Recent Revolution in the Mapping of Human Genes

Beginning in the 1970s two new techniques were developed that have allowed geneticists to map human genes. These are <u>somatic cell hybridization</u> and the use of RFLPs. Both techniques have been called the "new genetics."

■ **Somatic Cell Hybridization** The technique of somatic (non-sex) cell hybridization allows geneticists to combine a human cell and a mouse cell into a single cell with two nuclei. The fused cell is known as a **somatic cell hybrid**. As this cell continues to divide, the human chromosomes are gradually lost from the cell until eventually all that remains are cells with mouse chromosomes. Because the human chromosomes are lost gradually, a researcher can accumulate a bank of fused cells containing different human chromosomes. For example, a researcher looking for the gene that produces PKU may find that only a hybrid cell lacking human chromosome 12 cannot produce PKU. The scientist then knows that the gene for PKU is located on chromosome 12. This technique can be performed using cells from any two organisms; one set of chromosomes will always be lost.

■ **RFLPs** Discovered in the 1980s, RFLPs have become the basis for a popular technique for studying chromosomes. While homologous chromosomes have similar base sequences, in different people the sequence will occasionally differ in a base pair. If this variant region is excised with a restriction enzyme that recognizes one of the sequences, the result will be fragments of DNA of different length from each person. These differences are called **restriction fragment length polymorphisms (RFLPs)**. If all individuals affected by the same genetic condition have the same length RFLP, then this fragment is likely to contain the defective gene.

Helping People with Genetic Diseases

Different genetic diseases become evident at different stages in a person's life cycle. The earliest possible diagnosis is crucial to preventing damage and to prescribing treatment. Following are the three main types of therapy available to cope with gene-based conditions.

■ **Physiological Therapy** This therapy treats the effects of the defective gene by intervening in an individual's metabolic or other body functions. *Example:* PKU sufferers need to follow a special diet to prevent buildup of phenylketones.

■ **Protein Therapy** This treatment involves giving patients the protein they cannot make because they carry a gene defective for that protein. *Example:* diabetics receive injections of the protein insulin.

■ **Gene Therapy** Ongoing research may one day enable geneticists to replace defective genes with appropriately functioning ones.

Preventing New Cases of Genetic Disease

■ **Prenatal Diagnosis** Doctors and scientists can now detect the presence of genetic defects in unborn children by using one of two main procedures. In **amniocentesis**, the physician samples the amniotic fluid surrounding the fetus, which also contains some fetal cells; these cells are then grown in culture and tested for defects. In **chorionic villus sampling**, a physician removes fetal cells from the placenta, and the cell's chromosomes are studied and RFLPs analyzed.

■ **Detecting Carriers** Newly developed sensitive biochemical analyses have enabled geneticists to detect heterozygote **carriers** of defective genes; previously geneticists had to rely on pedigree studies to predict carriers.

Thought Provoker

1. Explain how harmful recessive genes and harmful dominant genes can pass from generation to generation without disappearing. Use examples as supporting evidence and include several explanations for this phenomenon.

Self-Test

For each statement or question choose the best response and mark your choice in the space provided. For some items you will select your response from a *Key*.

Key for questions 1–10

a. True   **b.** False

_____ 1. Phenylalanine hydrolase converts tyrosine to phenylalanine.

_____ 2. Phenylketones are normal constituents of urine.

_____ 3. It is possible to diagnose some human diseases by studying cell karyotypes.

_____ 4. Many human traits are polygenic.

_____ 5. Individuals who are heterozygous for many or most traits are less apt to show inherited diseases than are individuals who are homozygous recessive for many traits.

_____ 6. In fragile X syndrome, the entire chromosome disintegrates.

_____ 7. Scientists have made somatic hybrids of mouse and human cells.

_____ 8. Albinism in humans is due to an autosomal dominant gene.

_____ 9. The high frequency of albinism among the Hopi Indians is related to the superior nature of this gene.

_____ 10. Amniocentesis provides cells for karyotyping.

Questions 11–20: Use the *Key* to indicate the genetic character of each of the following conditions in humans.

a. (X) sex-linked trait
b. autosomal dominant
c. autosomal recessive
d. chromosomal nondisjunction

_____ **11.** phenylketonuria

_____ **12.** pattern baldness

_____ **13.** Down syndrome

_____ **14.** Duchenne muscular dystrophy

_____ **15.** Turner syndrome

_____ **16.** Klinefelter syndrome

_____ **17.** Huntington's disease

_____ **18.** hemophilia

_____ **19.** trisomy 21

_____ **20.** albinism

_____ **21.** If you saw the genetic notation 8/14, what event would you say has occurred?

    a. translocation   **c.** nondisjunction   **e.** transformation
    b. mutation   **d.** conjugation

_____ **22.** Which procedure is needed to do a karyotype on a fetus?

    a. transfusion   **c.** transplant   **e.** incubation
    b. hemodialysis **d.** amniocentesis

_____ **23.** Aspartame might be harmful to persons with:

    a. hemophilia   **c.** phenylketonuria   **e.** muscular dystrophy
    b. diabetes   **d.** albinism

Key for questions 24–27

a. True   **b.** False

The myc gene:

_____ **24.** Is an example of an oncogene.

_____ **25.** Is inactivated when moved from its normal position.

_____ **26.** Occurs in the germ line rather than the somatic cell line.

_____ **27.** Can be regulated by neighboring genes.

Questions 28–32: Use the *Key* to identify each statement or series of symptoms with a particular genetic condition.

a. Duchenne's muscular dystrophy
b. Klinefelter syndrome
c. Huntington's disease
d. PKU

e. Turner syndrome
ab. Down syndrome
ac. XYY genotype

_____ **28.** Males: breast development, tall, sterility, low IQ.

_____ 29. Nerve cells degenerate, person develops jerky movements.

_____ 30. Prison populations apparently show an inordinate number of males with this characteristic.

_____ 31. Severe mental retardation occurs if the disease is not detected and arrested soon after birth.

_____ 32. A single extra somatic chromosome is responsible for this condition.

_____ 33. Which human cell listed below would have 92 chromosomes?

    a. somatic cell hybrid   **c.** egg   **e.** tetraploid liver cell
    b. sperm   **d.** mature red blood cells

Key for questions 34–37 (relating to RFLPs technology)
a. True   **b.** False

_____ 34. The procedure used for RFLPs works on both RNA and DNA.

_____ 35. An endonuclease is required.

_____ 36. The nucleic acids are cut into exactly similar pieces when this procedure is used.

_____ 37. It is possible to identify some normal and abnormal genes using this technique.

_____ 38. The "P" in RFLP stands for:

    a. paternal   **c.** phenomenon   **e.** polymorphism
    b. pseudonym   **d.** placenta

_____ 39. Which individual would _not_ show a Barr body?

    a. calico cat   **d.** woman
    b. person with Turner syndrome   **e.** all of the foregoing
    c. person with Klinefelter syndrome

_____ 40. It is possible to use genetic principles and methods to solve crimes:

    a. in some cases
    b. never, because we still lack the technology
    c. never, because it is illegal
    d. in virtually every case
    e. Scientists have not tried it yet.

Special Practice: Human Genetics

The following problems will help you master important principles of human genetics. Solutions are in the Answer Key at the end of the book.

1. A woman is heterozygous for the hemophilia mutation, and her husband is normal.
    a. What proportion of her sons will be affected, on average?
    b. What proportion of her daughters will be carriers, on average?
    c. What proportion of her daughters will have the disease, on average?

2. A woman's mother had the disease PKU, and her father was colorblind. She marries a man who has normal color vision but who is heterozygous for the PKU allele. What proportions of sons and daughters might this couple expect to be affected by these two genetic conditions?

3. Human cells are fused with mouse tissue culture cells to form hybrid cells. As the hybrid cells proliferate, they gradually lose human chromosomes more or less at random. From these cells, several clones missing different human chromosomes are established. A somatic cell geneticist analyzes four of these lines, determining which human chromosomes are present and whether hexoseaminidase, an enzyme lacking in those with Tay-Sachs disease, is present. From the data below, on which chromosome does the gene for this enzyme lie?

Cell line	A	B	C	D
Chromosomes present	1, 12, 21	2, 15, X	7, 12, 15	9, 21, 22
Human enzyme present?	No	Yes	Yes	No

4. A genetic counselor collected the following data from a family that has some members afflicted with Huntington's disease. The mother and older son have the disease, but the father and younger son do not. The family's daughter is now wrestling with the decision to have children or not, knowing that if she has the mutant allele, her children have a 50% chance of inheriting the disease. A phlebotomist collects blood cells from family members, and a molecular geneticist digests the cells' DNA with the restriction enzyme BamHI. The geneticist separates the DNA fragments by electrophoresis and, with a probe that recognizes both the mutant and normal Huntington's gene, visualizes the DNA fragments with the following results.

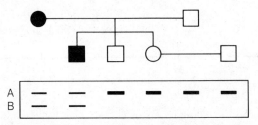

By observing the pattern of restriction fragments, how would you counsel the daughter concerning her risk of passing Huntington's disease to her children?

5. A husband and wife are both heterozygous for the albinism allele. They have six children, all of them normal, and the woman is once again pregnant. What is the probability that this next child will have albinism?

Key Terms from the Text Chapter

albinism *text page 265*
amniocentesis *276*
autosomal dominant *265*
autosomal recessive *265*
carrier *265*
chorionic villus sampling *277*

chromosome translocation *267*
fragile X syndrome *268*
Klinefelter syndrome *266*
oncogene *268*
pedigree *262*

restriction fragment length polymorphism (RFLP) *272*
single active X *271*
somatic cell hybrid *270*
Turner syndrome *266*
X-linked *262*

Exercise

Match each genetic term on the left with the best related phrase on the right.

somatic cell genetics	parts exchange; a cause of cancer
fragile X syndrome	a dominant normal allele
pedigree	oncogene
carrier	homologous DNA sequences that differ in a single base pair
RFLPs	mating body cells for gene mapping
Klinefelter and Turner syndromes	noticeable in early childhood
myc	changes in chromosome number
most genetic traits	a leading cause of mental retardation
chromosome translocation	X-linked trait
sexual phenotype	a geneticist begins with this
chorionic villus sampling	replacement of defective genes
gene therapy	involves RFLP analysis of fetal cells

13

Reproduction and Development: The Start of a New Generation

Perspective and Review

Organisms have many different mating and reproductive strategies to ensure that fertilization occurs. Once the sperm has fertilized an egg the process of embryonic development begins. Early embryonic development is divided into three stages: cleavage, gastrulation, and neurulation. By the end of the blastula stage the future role of each cell has been determined. Subsequent development is divided into morphogenesis and differentiation: The embryo takes shape, and its different organs start to function. Growth usually continues until adulthood. However, special cells, called stem cells, retain the ability to divide and so can replace old or dead cells when needed. Stem cells that continue to divide but do not differentiate become cancer cells.

Gonads give rise to egg and sperm cells by the processes of **oogenesis** and **spermatogenesis**, respectively. Gonads themselves develop from the germ layer in the fertilized egg.

Mating and Fertilization: Getting Egg and Sperm Together

Most animal species have evolved some mating behavior that ensures that males and females are together at the appropriate time for fertilization of the egg by a sperm. Concept Table 13.1 describes some important features associated with mating and fertilization.

Concept Table 13.1   Concepts associated with mating and fertilization

Mate recognition	Signals, often visual or olfactory, emitted by one sex of a species that elicit sexual response in the opposite sex.
Synchronized production	Eggs and sperm must be mature at the same time; many species have synchronized production and release of gametes so that these events occur at certain times of day or in particular seasons.
External fertilization	Aquatic organisms, such as fish, release egg and sperm into the water. Thus, fertilization takes place outside the female's body.
Internal fertilization	Typical of terrestrial organisms. The male deposits sperm in the female's body by the process of copulation; this ensures a supply of sperm when the egg is mature.

Fertilization is the fusion of an egg and sperm cell to form a diploid **zygote**; it triggers the process of embryonic development. Both egg and sperm cells are designed for their respective roles and so differ considerably in size and shape. The **ovum**, or egg, is the largest cell of the body; as well as carrying the mother's DNA, it must protect and nourish the developing embryo and direct its early development. In contrast, the sperm is one of the smallest body cells, and its streamlined shape and flagella allow it to swim rapidly to the egg and carry out its function of fertilization.

Patterns of Early Embryonic Development

Three developmental stages transform the zygote into a recognizable **embryo**; cleavage, gastrulation, and neurulation. Concept Table 13.2 outlines the main features of each stage.

Concept Table 13.2   Early embryonic development: Three stages

Stage	Main features
Cleavage	The zygote undergoes rapid mitotic divisions to form a solid ball of cells, the **morula**, which subsequently becomes a hollow ball of hundreds of cells, the **blastula** (cells are called **blastomeres**). A cell's location in the blastula determines its ultimate function.
Gastrulation	The blastula becomes an embryo with three cell layers. **Ectoderm** (outer layer) gives rise to skin and nervous tissue; **mesoderm** (middle layer) becomes muscle, bone, blood, reproductive and excretory organs; **endoderm** (inner layer) becomes the inner lining of the gut and organs arising from it.
Neurulation	The **neural tube** is formed by rolling up of ectodermal cells. These cells give rise to the brain and spinal column.

Organogenesis: Development of Body Organs

After neurulation, the embryo starts to take shape as its various organs develop. This process, known as **organogenesis**, involves two main steps, which are outlined in Concept Table 13.3.

Concept Table 13.3   Organogenesis

Stage	Main features
Morphogenesis	Process leading to formation of the body's organs; involves certain cells changing shape, dividing rapidly, dying, or migrating to a new location.
Differentiation	Development of specialized cell types, such as nerve and muscle cells, that begin to carry out their specific functions.

Development Continues Throughout Life

All animals continue to grow and develop after birth, but different organs grow at different rates. Most organs stop growing at adulthood. **Stem cells** are cells that retain the ability to divide throughout life, producing replacements for worn-out cells such as skin and red blood cells. Two types of substances regulate cell division so that growth occurs only when needed: growth factors stimulate **growth**, and **chalones** inhibit it. When this regulatory system malfunctions, cancer can result. Tumors, a group of continually dividing cells, come in two forms: **benign** tumor cells remain in a fixed location; **malignant** (cancerous) cells grow and migrate throughout the body (**metastasize**). Cancer cells are stem cells that fail to differentiate and continue to divide. They proliferate because certain genes, called oncogenes, are switched on, producing proteins that act as growth factors to stimulate cell division.

The Formation of New Gametes: The Developmental Cycle Begins Anew

Gametogenesis is the formation of <u>gametes</u>—that is, egg and sperm cells. The **germ plasm** is a small group of cells in the developing ovum which give rise to the gonads: testes in males and ovaries in females. In the testes, stem cells continually produce millions of sperm, a process known as **spermatogenesis**. Many fewer eggs are produced in the ovaries (via **oogenesis**). During its development from an immature **oocyte** to a mature egg cell, the ovum receives yolk proteins that migrate to the ovary from different parts of the body. In certain animals, such as lizards, an unfertilized egg can develop into a new individual, a process known as **parthenogenesis**.

Thought Provokers

1. Compare and contrast normal cell growth and development with tumor growth and development.

2. Name eight key events in development, and indicate one normal and one abnormal feature that may occur at each stage listed.

Self-Test

For each statement or question choose the best response and mark your choice in the space provided. For some items you will select your response from a *Key*.

Questions 1–20: Using the *Key*, rate two items, A and B, on the following characteristics.
a. A is greater than B   **c.** Both items are approximately the same
b. B is greater than A

_____ 1.	size	**a.** egg	**b.** sperm
_____ 2.	extent/range/frequency of internal fertilization	**a.** aquatic animals	**b.** land animals
_____ 3.	size of egg	**a.** humans	**b.** fishes
_____ 4.	amount of yolk in ovum	**a.** humans	**b.** fishes
_____ 5.	frequency of metastases	**a.** benign tumors	**b.** malignant tumors
_____ 6.	colorfulness of bird or fish	**a.** females	**b.** males

_____ 7. strength of pheromones   **a.** humans   **b.** moths

_____ 8. degree of differentiation   **a.** gastrula cells   **b.** blastula cells

_____ 9. head/body size in   **a.** child   **b.** adult

_____ 10. growth throughout life   **a.** humans   **b.** lobsters

_____ 11. ability to continue to divide   **a.** stem cells   **b.** brain cells

_____ 12. cell growth   **a.** with chalones   **b.** without chalones

_____ 13. cytochemical skeleton   **a.** normal cells   **b.** cancer cells

_____ 14. rate of cell aging   **a.** mice   **b.** humans

_____ 15. copulation   **a.** fishes   **b.** frogs

_____ 16. gray crescent   **a.** unfertilized egg   **b.** fertilized egg

_____ 17. size of placenta   **a.** birds   **b.** humans

_____ 18. degree of gut formation   **a.** blastula   **b.** gastrula

_____ 19. incidence of parthenogenesis   **a.** humans   **b.** insects

_____ 20. importance of notochord   **a.** insects   **b.** vertebrates

Questions 21–30: Use the _Key_ to indicate the origin of the tissue in the numbered item.

a. ectoderm   **b.** endoderm   **c.** mesoderm

_____ 21. muscles

_____ 22. blood

_____ 23. skin

_____ 24. gut lining

_____ 25. nervous system

_____ 26. connective tissue

_____ 27. bones

_____ 28. lungs

_____ 29. liver

_____ 30. eye

Key for questions 31–40

a. True   **b.** False

_____ 31. The notochord represents mesodermal tissue.

_____ 32. Normal cells tend to be rounder than cancer cells, which tend to be flattened.

_____ 33. Cleft palate is due to a defect during neurulation.

_____ 34. Follicle cells produce the hormone estrogen.

_____ **35.** Retroviruses are DNA viruses that can make RNA.

_____ **36.** High-fat and low-fiber diets increase the risk of cancer.

_____ **37.** Oncogenes frequently are derived from mutated or normal genes in animals.

_____ **38.** Proto-oncogenes are associated with growth factors in cells.

_____ **39.** Crystallin is a protein that forms part of the spinal cord.

_____ **40.** The germ plasm is a region especially devoted to the formation of somatic tissue.

Key Terms from the Text Chapter

benign *text page* 298
blastocoel 286
blastocyst 286
blastodisc 286
blastomere 286
blastula 286
chalone 298
cleavage 284
committed 291
copulation 283
determination 291
determined 291
development 280
developmental determinant 286
differentiated cell 293
differentiation 292
ectoderm 289
embryo 280

endoderm 289
external fertilization 282
follicle cell 303
gametogenesis 301
gastrulation 288
germ layer 289
germ plasm 301
gray crescent 287
growth 295
inner cell mass 286
internal fertilization 283
malignant 298
mate 282
mesoderm 289
metastasize 298
morphogenesis 292
morula 286
neural crest 282
neural tube 290

neurulation 290
notochord 291
oocyte 303
oogenesis 303
organogenesis 292
oviduct 303
ovum 283
parthenogenesis 304
placenta 286
primary embryonic induction 291
proto-oncogene 299
spermatogenesis 302
stem cell 296
transformed 298
trophoblast 286
yolk 283

Exercise: Stages of Development

1. Complete this table on the main stages of development. Try to do this without consulting your text.

Stage	Events/Principal Features
a. Cleavage	_____
	_____
	_____
	_____
	_____
	_____
b. Gastrulation	_____
	_____
	_____
	_____
	_____
c. Neurulation	_____
	_____
	_____
	_____
	_____

2. What developmental milestone occurs after the normal completion of early development?

_____

14

The Human Life Cycle

CHAPTER IN BRIEF

Perspective and Review

Humans have primary sexual characteristics, encompassing the gonads and their associated tubes and glands. Beginning at puberty, male testes constantly produce sperm. Females also start producing mature eggs at puberty, but generally only one egg ripens every 28 days. The cycle of egg maturation and release is known as the menstrual cycle and is directed by a number of interacting hormones. Humans have the ability to influence fertilization in the form of birth control to prevent pregnancy, or to seek infertility treatment to increase its probability. In vitro (test-tube) fertilization and implantation of human embryos in the uterus has been a recent advance in the treatment of infertility.

Once a human egg has been fertilized it takes about 260 days until the baby is born. After eight weeks all the organs have formed, and the embryo is called a fetus. From this point onward, the main activity of the fetus is growth. During this time the mother's body provides the fetus with food and oxygen through the placenta. The fetus stimulates its own birth by causing the mother's body to produce hormones that induce uterine contractions and widening of the cervix (labor).

The human life cycle is divided into four main periods: infancy, childhood, puberty, and adulthood. At about 30 years, humans begin the aging process.

Male and Female Reproductive Systems

Humans have primary and secondary sexual characteristics. Secondary characteristics are features such as breasts in females and facial hair in males; primary characteristics are the reproductive organs. These organs are divided into two groups: (1) Primary reproductive organs—the **ovaries** of females and the **testes** of males, and (2) accessory reproductive organs—the glands and ducts associated with the gonads. Concept Tables 14.1 and 14.2 summarize the main features of the male and female reproductive systems, respectively.

Concept Table 14.1   Male reproductive system

Function	Production and transport of sperm to the egg.
Primary Organs	
Testes	A pair of testes are located in the **scrotum**; each testis consists of **seminiferous tubules** containing three types of cells. **Spermatogenic cells** develop into sperm; **supporting (Sertoli) cells** nourish developing sperm; and **interstitial (Leydig) cells** produce hormones.
Accessory Organs	
Epididymis	Tube on top of each testis in which sperm mature
Vas deferens	Muscular tube that carries sperm from the epididymis to the ejaculatory duct
Ejaculatory duct	Carries sperm and **seminal fluid** to the urethra
Urethra	Duct that transports sperm to outside the body
Penis	Organ that transfers sperm to the female
Accessory Glands	
Seminal vesicle	Source of secretions that provide nutrients, regulate pH, and stimulate vaginal muscle contractions

Continues

Concept Table 14.1 Male reproductive system (continued)

Prostate gland	Secretes an alkaline fluid; sperm, plus secretions from prostate gland and seminal vesicle, constitute **semen**
Bulbourethral gland	Mucus-secreting gland at the base of the penis
Sperm Production	Four male hormones interact to control sperm production: **testosterone, luteinizing hormone (LH), follicle-stimulating hormone (FSH),** and **releasing hormone**

Concept Table 14.2 Female reproductive system

Function	Produce ova (eggs), nourish and protect the developing embryo and give birth.
Primary Organs	
Ovaries	A pair of almond-shaped organs containing **oocytes** (immature egg cells), and **follicular cells** that surround and support the oocytes; an oocyte together with its follicular cells is known as a **follicle.**
Accessory Organs	
Oviduct (fallopian tube)	Cilia-lined tube that transports the egg to the uterus
Uterus (womb)	Pear-shaped sac where the embryo develops
Cervix	Narrow opening connecting the uterus to the vagina
Vagina	Muscular tube that receives the penis and serves as the birth canal
Clitoris	Tissue sensitive to sexual stimulation
Bartholin's gland	Secretes a lubricating fluid

Cyclic egg maturation and preparation of the uterus for pregnancy is controlled by hormones. The cycle, known as the **menstrual cycle**, takes about 28 days in humans. Concept Table 14.3 summarizes the main events of this cycle. Study Figure 14.9 of your text to see how different organs and hormones in the body interact in the menstrual cycle.

Concept Table 14.3 The menstrual cycle

1. Menstrual flow commences. **Estrogen** and **progesterone** levels are low.
2. Low levels of these hormones stimulate the brain to release luteinizing hormone (LH) and follicle-stimulating hormone (FSH).
3. LH and FSH stimulate the development of one follicle, the egg matures, and the follicle cells secrete estrogen.
4. Estrogen causes the uterus lining (**endometrium**) to thicken and its blood supply to increase in preparation for implantation of a fertilized egg.

Continues

Concept Table 14.3   The menstrual cycle (continued)

5. **Ovulation** occurs (about day 14). The follicle ruptures and the egg is released into the oviduct; the remaining follicle cells become known as the **corpus luteum**.

6. If fertilization takes place, hormones produced by the corpus luteum maintain the early stages of the pregnancy. If fertilization does not occur, the corpus luteum disintegrates and the lining of the uterus is shed (menstrual flow). The cycle begins again.

Sperm Meets Egg—or Doesn't: Fertilization, Birth Control, and Infertility

There are two main research areas in human fertility: birth control and overcoming infertility. Table 14.3 in your text details many of the contraceptive methods currently used by humans to prevent pregnancy. In addition to preventing pregnancy, scientists have developed techniques to help infertile couples conceive, including **in vitro fertilization** (test-tube babies).

Pregnancy, Human Development, and Birth

Concept Table 14.4 outlines some of the main features of human embryonic development.

Concept Table 14.4   Human development

Stage	Significant Features
Implantation	The human embryo implants in the wall of the uterus when it is about six days old and has reached the **blastocyst** stage.
Early development	**Trophoblast** cells develop into the chorion, a fluid-filled sac surrounding the embryo that later develops into the **placenta**. In addition to providing nutrients, the placenta releases the hormone **human chorionic gonadotropin (hCG)**, which prevents a new menstrual cycle. Ectoderm and endoderm form around the eighth day, when the **amniotic cavity** and **umbilical cord** begin to develop.
Gastrulation	Occurs about the third week. The mesoderm forms.
Neurulation	Also starts during the third week, and is followed rapidly by organogenesis.
Fetus	By the end of eight weeks all the rudimentary organs are present and the embryo is known as a fetus. The sex organs are still indistinguishable as either male or female. If the fetus is a boy, genes on the Y chromosome will produce proteins that cause the organs to develop into male structures.

The approximately nine months of human pregnancy are divided into three trimesters (periods of three months). Most development takes place during the first trimester, and most growth during the remaining two.

At about 260 days the fetus produces a substance that stimulates the mother's body to produce prostaglandins and oxytocin, hormones that induce uterine muscle contraction and widening of the cervix. These involuntary contractions together with voluntary abdominal contractions from the mother push the baby out.

Growth, Maturation, and Aging: Development Continues

Concept Table 14.5 describes the main stages in the human life cycle. Study Figure 14.17 in your text for a more comprehensive description of developments at each stage.

Concept Table 14.5 Stages in the human life cycle	
Stage	**Significant developments**
Infancy	0–2 years
Childhood	2–12 years: Most physical and mental development take place during this and the preceding stage; 70% of total height and weight are achieved.
Puberty	11–13 years in females; 13–15 in males. Maturation of reproductive organs and development of secondary sexual characteristics occur.
Adulthood	Aging begins at about 30 years, and entails a gradual decrease in cell functional level. Around age 50, women cease to menstruate (**menopause**), and males may lose **potency**. **Senescence** starts sometime after 60.

Two hypotheses have been proposed to account for aging. The genetic clock hypothesis suggests that "aging genes" determine when our organs will wear out. The wear-and-tear hypothesis proposes that random errors in DNA accumulate over time, and interfere with each cell's ability to function.

Life span is the maximum potential age individuals of a species live—over 100 years for humans. **Life expectancy** is the maximum probable age an individual will reach—78 years for women, and 71 for men.

Thought Provokers

1. Starting at the origin point of a male gamete and of a female gamete, compare and contrast the pathways that each gamete follows in its transit through the reproductive tract of the human male and female, respectively. Next, indicate in what ways the sex hormone regulatory systems in human males and females are similar and in what ways they differ.

2. List all the approaches to birth control and then list the three most effective and least dangerous methods of birth control. Indicate 5 to 6 additional but less effective birth control methods.

Self-Test

For each statement or question choose the best response and mark your choice in the space provided. For some items you will select your response from a *Key*.

Questions 1–13: Using the *Key*, indicate for each statement the most appropriate hormone *or* hormones.

a. FSH	**d.** releasing hormone	**ae.** estrogen
b. LH	**e.** testosterone	**bd.** progesterone
c. HCG		

_____ 1. Produced by the human embryo to assure its survival in utero

_____ 2. Hormones released by the pituitary

_____ 3. Hormone that determines maleness

_____ 4. Produced by the hypothalamus

_____ 5. Hormones produced by the ovary

_____ 6. Hormone produced by the Leydig interstitial cells

_____ 7. Acts primarily on the egg follicle

_____ 8. Stimulates the Leydig cells directly

_____ 9. Stimulates development of the spermatogenic cells

_____ 10. Secreted by the follicle cells

_____ 11. High levels of this hormone indicate that the egg is mature and ready for release.

_____ 12. Hormones produced by the corpus luteum

_____ 13. The best early indicator of pregnancy

_____ 14. The chemical gossypol is used to:
   a. increase egg production in females.
   b. stop egg production in females.
   c. increase sperm production in males.
   d. stop sperm production in males.
   e. prevent the embryo from anchoring to the uterus.

Key for questions 15–25
a. True   **b.** False

_____ 15. The chorion develops from the trophoblast.

_____ 16. The placenta eventually produces the hormones estrogen and progesterone.

_____ 17. At the site of the placenta there is an exchange of red blood cells between the mother and the embryo to provide oxygen and nutrients to the embryo and to remove wastes.

_____ 18. At the blastula stage the embryo is composed of three main cell layers.

_____ 19. At the gastrula stage the embryo has four distinct cell layers.

_____ 20. Somites give rise to muscle and the spine.

_____ 21. Somites are derived from the endoderm tissues.

_____ 22. The organs and tissue systems of an embryo and fetus are fully formed by about three months.

_____ 23. In the absence of any particular additional signal, human primordial gonads will develop as female genitalia.

_____ 24. "Progeria" is a term used to describe some of the last stages in normal embryonic growth.

_____ 25. Prior to birth, the pituitary produces prostaglandins and the uterus produces oxytocin.

Questions 26–30: Match each _Key_ response with the condition that results when it is present as a fetus develops.

a. thalidomide   **c.** alcohol   **e.** tobacco smoking
b. German measles   **d.** diethylstilbestrol

_____ 26. Mental retardation, facial anomalies, emotional abnormalities, cleft palate, underdeveloped heart

_____ 27. Cervical cancer during adolescence

_____ 28. Damage to eyes, ears, heart and brain

_____ 29. Miscarriage and low birth weight

_____ 30. Abnormal limb development

For questions 31–36, match the conditions listed in the _Key_ with the following statements relating to sexually transmitted diseases (STDs).

a. herpes type-II   **c.** syphilis   **e.** papillomavirus
b. gonorrhea   **d.** chlamydia   **ab.** AIDS

_____ 31. The most common venereal disease

_____ 32. Wart lesions appear on the genitalia. This agent may also precipitate cervical cancer.

_____ 33. Causes painful ulcers on the genitalia; not treatable with antibiotics; lasts an entire lifetime; related to cold sores or fever blisters

_____ 34. Treatable by antibiotics, but if left untreated may cause heart and nervous system damage

_____ 35. The second most common venereal disease

_____ 36. The newest and most deadly of STDs; may be acquired via heterosexual or homosexual activity

_____ 37. The main effect of an IUD is to prevent:

      a. insemination   **c.** hormone secretion   **e.** implantation
      b. erection   **d.** ovulation

_____ **38.** Currently, test-tube babies are called such because they are:

    a. fertilized in a test tube.

    b. fertilized and allowed to develop in a test tube.

    c. removed from the mother and grown to maturity in the tube.

    d. preserved in the tube.

    e. given medicine and undergo surgery in a test tube.

Key Terms from the Text Chapter

cervix   *text page 312*

chorion   *317*

corpus luteum   *313*

endometrium   *312*

epididymis   *308*

follicle   *311*

in vitro fertilization   *306*

life expectancy   *327*

life span   *327*

menstrual cycle   *312*

ovary   *311*

ovulation   *312*

penis   *309*

prostate gland   *308*

scrotum   *308*

semen   *309*

seminal vesicle   *308*

seminiferous tubule   *308*

senescence   *326*

testis   *308*

testosterone   *310*

urethra   *309*

uterus   *312*

vagina   *312*

vas deferens   *308*

Exercise

Male | **Female**

1. Draw simple cycle diagrams that show, for human males and females, respectively, how hormones control sperm release and egg production. Begin at the top of each circle with releasing hormone (RH) made in the hypothalamus. Include labels that show all the important hormones, and the events they trigger, in each cycle.

Life's Origins and Diversity on Our Planet

Perspective and Review

From the origin of the universe life slowly evolved on the planet Earth. Earth's unique position relative to the sun and its size and geological composition and activity allowed our unique organic form of life to evolve. This process involved a number of important steps, from the origin and accumulation of organic compounds to the emergence of functioning cells.

By studying fossils scientists have been able to piece together much of the history of life on Earth and the effect different life forms have had on the planet. In addition, geologists have discovered that the major land masses on Earth are constantly moving, and this in turn has had an impact on developing life forms.

Today, scientists classify all living organisms into groups, based on similar structures, using the binomial system of nomenclature. Although previously only plant and animal kingdoms were recognized, most biologists now identify five kingdoms.

Earth as a Stage for Life/The Unseen Drama: From Molecules to Cells

Scientists believe that the universe originated about 18 million years ago. From that time our planet and life on our planet have evolved into the forms we see today. Concept Table 15.1 summarizes the main events in the evolution of life; the first three stages deal with the origin of Earth and organic molecules and the remaining five with the emergence of living cells.

Concept Table 15.1 From the origin of the universe to the origin of life	
Formation of stars	Big bang—a giant explosion that most astronomers believe created all matter in the universe
Formation of planets	Gravity pulls clouds of gas and dust together to form planets; Earth was formed about 4.6 billion years ago (byo).
Organic molecules accumulate	The origin of organic molecules remains a mystery, but three hypotheses have been proposed: (1) They were present from the beginning on Earth. (2) They arrived on Earth via a collision with carbonaceous meteorites. (3) Natural energy converted atmospheric gases to organic compounds.
Polymer formation	There are two main ways by which polymers could have formed. (1) Amino acids formed polymers after exposure to extreme environmental conditions. (2) Inorganic clays acted as substrates and catalysts in polymerization.
Self-replication evolves	Self-replicating RNA formed as one of the first polymers.
Molecular interactions occur	How RNA became linked to genes and how the genetic code developed are still a mystery.
Cell-like compartments form	Spheres of polypeptides and phospholipids may have enclosed self-replicating molecules to form protocells.
Cell-like activities emerge	Protocells developed metabolic pathways; earliest cells were anaerobic and may have been either **heterotrophs** or **chemoautotrophs**.

Earth and Life Coevolve: Diversity of Habitats and Species

Evidence suggests that life has existed on Earth for about 3.8 billion years. During the first 3 billion years, known as the age of microbes, microscopic organisms had a major impact on the physical Earth and subsequent life forms. Concept Table 15.2 outlines the significant features in the evolution of life forms.

There are several important points to note: Early life originated in anoxic conditions, and atmospheric oxygen and a corresponding tolerance to oxygen by organisms evolved later; also, the first multicellular organisms evolved in the seas, and movement onto land was a later development. Study Table 15.1 in your text for a detailed picture of how the emergence of different life forms affected the future course of our planet.

Concept Table 15.2   Evolution of life forms

Time	Significant Features
3.8 bya	First life evolves as anaerobic cells.
3.5 bya	**Autotrophs** present on earth.
2.8 bya	Photosynthesis results in oxygen being given off into the atmosphere and seas.
2 bya	Organisms evolve oxygen tolerance; oxygen buildup in the atmosphere results in formation of an ozone layer.
1.4 bya	Eukaryotic cells emerge; read text page 341 for a description of the **endosymbiotic theory** of eukaryotic evolution.
670 mya	Age of microbes ends and **metazoans** appear, mainly soft-bodied marine organisms.
550 mya	Hard-shelled animals such as clams evolve; global cycles develop.
400 mya	Atmosphere fully formed; large fish in seas and primitive land plants exist.
200 mya–present	Amphibians, reptiles, birds, mammals, and modern plants emerge.

All the continental land masses lie on crustal plates, which are being constantly formed at <u>rifts</u> and destroyed in deep ocean trenches. Building, movement, and destruction of plates is known as **plate tectonics**. Geologists divide the Earth into four major time spans termed <u>geological eras</u>: Proterozoic (570 mya–4.6 bya); Paleozoic (240–570 mya); Mesozoic (65–240 mya); Cenozoic (present–65 mya). Each era is further subdivided into a number of <u>geological periods</u>. During the Paleozoic, the Earth had only one large continent, Pangaea; during the Cenozoic, plate tectonics resulted in the present continental structure. Movement of continental land masses carried organisms to new locations on the globe. Study Figure 15.11 in your text for a detailed description of the evolution of life and land masses on earth.

The Science of Taxonomy: Cataloging Life's Diversity

Taxonomy is the study of classification. Scientists classify all living organisms into groups that share similar structural features. This technique employs the **binomial system of nomenclature**, developed by Linnaeus. Each organism receives two names, its first name, or **genus**, and its second, or **species**, name. A species is a group of organisms sharing similar traits; a genus consists of groups of similar species related by descent from a common ancestor. There are five ascending levels of <u>taxonomic groups</u> above the genus level: **family**, **order**, **class**, **phylum**, and **kingdom**.

Previously, only two kingdoms were recognized—plants and animals. Today, many biologists recognize five: **Monera**, **Protista**, **Fungi**, **Plantae**, and **Animalia**. Some biologists prefer to use a 4 or 6 kingdomed classification. Study figures 15.2 and 15.3 in your text to see the evolutionary trees of humans and other organisms.

Thought Provokers

1. Prepare your own simplified (but logical) evolutionary outline to summarize how a first living cell might have originated from elemental matter. Your outline should include 10–20 steps.

2. Explain why large organisms are not likely to be anaerobic. In your answer, compare aerobe features with those of a known anaerobe.

Self-Test

For each statement or question choose the best response and mark your choice in the space provided. For some items you will select your response from a *Key*.

_____ 1. Methanogens are:

   a. aerobic   **c.** eukaryotes   **e.** plants
   b. anaerobic   **d.** protists

_____ 2. Methanogens are:

   a. heterotrophs   **c.** saprophytes   **e.** parasites
   b. photosynthesizers   **d.** chemoautotrophs

_____ 3. Methanogens have been shown to:

   a. fix methane   **c.** have no RNA   **e.** no longer exist
   b. fix carbon   **d.** lack DNA

Key for questions 4–8
a. Not more than .5 billion years   **d.** 4–5 billion years
b. 1 billion years   **e.** 18 billion years
c. 2–3 billion years

_____ 4. The age of the universe

_____ 5. The age of the Earth

_____ 6. Life first formed on the Earth after approximately this time interval had elapsed.

_____ 7. Large animals and plants appeared on Earth about this long ago.

_____ 8. The Cenozoic, Mesozoic, and most of the Paleozoic eras

_____ 9. The primitive Earth's atmosphere may have contained all but one of the following:

   a. HCN   **c.** CO_2 **e.** O_2
   b. CO   **d.** H_2

_____ **10.** From the foregoing list of compounds, which is critical to the formation of amino acids and nucleotides but not for carbohydrates or lipids?

_____ **11.** Which *two* molecules are the primary constituents of stars?

    a. CO   **c.** H_2 **e.** HCOOH
    b. CO_2 **d.** helium gas

_____ **12.** Carbonaceous chondrites are a kind of:

    a. meteorite   **c.** fossil animal   **e.** fossil bacterium
    b. star   **d.** fossil plant

_____ **13.** Carbonaceous chondrites are of major interest because they have been shown to contain:

    a. carbon   **c.** gases   **e.** nucleotide bases
    b. heavy metals   **d.** amino acids

_____ **14.** Which of the following was probably the first self-replicating molecule?

    a. RNA   **c.** proteins   **e.** sugars
    b. DNA   **d.** amino acids

_____ **15.** Stromatolites have been shown to contain a type of

    a. fern   **c.** amoeba   **e.** cyanobacterium
    b. mollusk   **d.** bone

_____ **16.** The deposit of large amounts of iron in lakes has been ascribed to the action of:

    a. carbon   **c.** other minerals   **e.** acids
    b. hydrogen   **d.** oxygen

_____ **17.** Which of the following is not considered a possible endosymbiont of eukaryotic cells?

    a. polypeptides   **c.** chloroplasts   **e.** mitochondria
    b. nuclei   **d.** flagella

_____ **18.** Chert rocks are rich in:

    a. anthracite   **c.** iron   **e.** quartz
    b. basalt   **d.** sulfur

_____ **19.** Rifts of the crustal plates are:

    a. cracks or junctures   **d.** seabottom currents
    b. deep valleys   **e.** of unknown character
    c. mountains

Key for questions 20–25

a. Paleozoic   **c.** Cenozoic
b. Mesozoic   **d.** Precambrian

_____ **20.** The most recent geologic period

_____ **21.** The first life probably came about during this period.

_____ **22.** The era when Pangaea formed

_____ **23.** The era when Pangaea broke apart

_____ **24.** Bacteria probably originated during this period.

_____ **25.** The period during which dinosaurs, birds, mammals, and flowering plants arose

_____ **26.** The person who created the binomial system of nomenclature was:

        a. Schleiden   **c.** Darwin   **e.** Linnaeus

        b. Schwann   **d.** Mendel

Key for questions 27–28

a. Family   **c.** Class   **e.** Genus

b. Order   **d.** Species

_____ **27.** The grouping(s) used in the binomial system of classification.

_____ **28.** The broadest and the narrowest groupings of organisms.

Key for questions 29–35

a. Animalia   **c.** Fungi   **e.** Protista

b. Plantae   **d.** Monera

_____ **29.** Single-celled eukaryotes

_____ **30.** Molds and yeasts

_____ **31.** Contains the most primitive life forms

_____ **32.** Complex multicellular heterotrophs

_____ **33.** Organisms with the simplest kind of DNA

_____ **34.** Autotrophic eukaryotes

_____ **35.** Prokaryotes

Key Terms from the Text Chapter

Animalia *text page 346*

Archaebacteria *346*

binomial system of
   nomenclature *345*

chemoautotroph *332*

class *345*

endosymbiotic theory *341*

family *345*

Fungi *346*

genus *345*

kingdom *345*

Monera *346*

order *345*

phylum *345*

Plantae *346*

plate tectonics *345*

Protista *346*

species *345*

taxonomy *333*

Concept Figure: Origin of Life on Earth

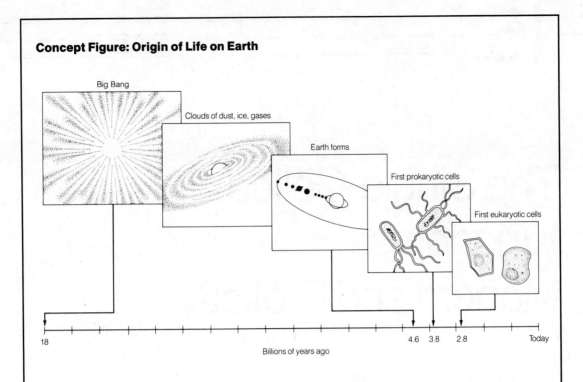

Billions of years ago

Exercise

1. Using the drawing as a guide, fill in the chart. Your task is to list, for each stage in the origin of life on Earth, events or characteristics that laid a foundation for the following stage. For the final stage, mention one or more features of early eukaryotic cells that made evolution of more complex forms possible.

Stage	Events/Characteristics Important for Next Stage
Big bang:	
Clouds of gas, dust, ice:	
Early Earth:	
Prokaryotic cells:	
Eukaryotic cells:	

16

The Single-Celled Kingdoms: Monera and Protista

CHAPTER IN BRIEF

Perspective and Review

All unicellular organisms are classified into two kingdoms, the Monera and Protista. These cells abound in a wide range of habitats for two main reasons: They are highly successful at obtaining nutrients, and their rapid reproduction rate allows for swift adaptation to environmental conditions.

The Monera are prokaryotes, which include the bacteria. An ancient form of one moneran group, the chlorophyll-containing cyanobacteria, may have been incorporated into a eukaryotic cell to become the first chloroplast. Although classified as nonliving, viruses, viroids, and prions are often considered with the Monera. The eukaryotic Protista comprise fungal, plant, and animal-like forms. Protists may have evolved as primitive bacteria were incorporated into large ancestral cells.

Both the Monera and Protista are of tremendous ecological and medical importance. Decomposers release nutrients from dead organic matter and make it available to plants. Cyanobacteria release oxygen, and cycle elements such as carbon and nitrogen. Radiolarian shells are major components of limestone and other rock formations. Many species cause diseases in plants and animals, including humans; some, such as the gut bacteria that aid digestion and prevent disease, are beneficial. Finally, many of these single-celled organisms have become invaluable tools in genetic engineering.

Monera: The Prokaryotic Kingdom

The Monera are single-celled prokaryotes, which include bacteria and related organisms. Approximately 2,500 species have been described, and are classified into three main divisions:

1. **Archaebacteria**   Possibly the most ancient group of living organisms, this division includes the methane producers, halophiles (salt-tolerant bacteria), and thermophiles (acid- and heat-resistant bacteria).

2. **Cyanobacteria**   Representatives of this group are found in most environments. They are the only prokaryotes with chlorophyll *a* and often form aggregations that show a primitive form of division of labor between cells.

3. **Schizophyta**   A diverse group, described in detail in Table 16.1 of your text (p. 358). Most disease-causing bacteria, as well as the beneficial nitrogen-fixing forms, belong in this division.

Concept Table 16.1 summarizes the characteristic features of the Monera.

Concept Table 16.1   General characteristics of the kingdom Monera

Cell Structure	Outer cell wall composed of peptidoglycans. There is an inner plasma membrane and a single circular chromosome. Cytoplasm is noncompartmentalized, and there are no membrane-enclosed organelles. Cell shapes include **cocci**, **bacilli**, **spirilla**, and **vibrios**. Shape is often used as a basis of classification.
Nutrition	Majority are heterotrophic **saprobes**, though some are **parasites** (disease-causing forms) or **symbionts** (cellulose-digesting bacteria in herbivores). A few groups are autotrophs (the photosynthesizing blue-greens and the chemoautotrophic methane producers).
Reproduction	Usually by binary fission.
Genetic Recombination	1. Direct exchange by **conjugation**—transfer of genetic material from one cell to another through sex pili.
	2. Indirect via **transduction** or **transformation**. Table 16.1 in your text describes all three forms.
Behavior	Many monerans have cilia or flagellae, which allow simple locomotion; many will respond to certain stimuli by exhibiting **phototaxis** (response to light), **chemotaxis** (response to chemicals), or **magnetotaxis** (response to gravitational fields).

Viruses, **viroids**, and **prions** are noncellular microparasites that depend on living cells for their existence. As a group they are not considered to be alive, although they probably resemble the ancestors of living cells. Viruses are fragments of DNA or RNA surrounded by a **capsid** (protein coat). They infect cells by injecting their DNA; once inside the host, viral genes override the cell's own genes and direct the cell to produce copies of the viral DNA. Eventually the host cell bursts, releasing the new capsids to infect other cells. Viroids are plant parasites composed only of RNA molecules. Prions appear to have no genetic material and consist only of proteins. Prions have been implicated in nerve and brain diseases.

The Protists: Single-Celled Eukaryotes

Protists comprise 35,000 species of free-living unicellular eukaryotes. They are larger than prokaryotes, are compartmentalized, and contain organelles. The Protista is divided into three sections: **protozoa**, **phytoplankton**, and slime molds. Concept Table 16.2 outlines the main features of the phyla or divisions within each section.

Concept Table 16.2   The Protista: Classification and general characteristics

Section protozoa	Heterotrophic animallike protists divided into four phyla based on mode of locomotion.
Phylum/Division	
Mastigophora	Most primitive, move by flagellae. Most are parasites or symbionts; includes *Trypanosoma*, which causes sleeping sickness.
Sarcodina	Move by pseudopodia, cellular projections also used in feeding; marine forms, such as the Foraminifera, have external shells; includes *Amoeba*.
Sporozoa	Internal parasites having a nonmotile spore stage; includes the malaria-causing *Plasmodium vivax*.
Ciliophora	Aquatic forms that swim and feed using cilia; contain several organelles, a polyploid macronucleus, and a diploid micronucleus; includes *Didinium*.
Section phytoplankton	Marine and freshwater cells that contain chlorophyll and photosynthesize; many individuals move by flagellae.
Phylum/Division	
Euglenoids	Gliding, spindle-shaped cells with a light receptor (**stigma**).
Dinoflagellates	Cells have two flagellae, chlorophylls *a* and *c*, and carotenoids; members of this group are responsible for **red tides**.
Diatoms and **golden-brown algae**	Most abundant group; may be nonmotile, amoeboid, or flagellated; individuals encased in silicon shells and contain chlorophylls *a* and *c*, and fucoxanthin.
Section slime molds	Funguslike group; secrete enzymes to break down organic matter, which is later digested.
True slime molds	A mass of cells called a *plasmodium*, which consists of a single cytoplasm with many diploid nuclei. Reproductive structures called **fruiting bodies** form when food is scarce, and produce **spores** that can disperse to new sites.
Cellular slime molds	Single-celled amoebalike forms; cells aggregate in unfavorable conditions and move to new locations.

Thought Provokers

1. For each type of organism listed, indicate: (1) the features characteristic of organisms in that group; (2) one genus or species of the group that, from a human perspective, has a specific beneficial or harmful effect. If there are both harmful and beneficial representatives of a group, name one of each.

   a. mastigophoran
   b. sporozoan

   c. bacterium
   d. virus

2. Compare and contrast the modes of nutrition of the different groups of monerans. Give specific organisms and food sources.

Self-Test

For each statement or question choose the best response and mark your choice in the space provided. For some items you will select your reponse from a *Key*.

_____ 1. An important component of the wall of bacteria is:

   a. cellulose   **c.** starch   **e.** lipopolysaccharide
   b. chitin   **d.** peptidoglycan

_____ 2. A structure in bacteria that is resistant to chemicals and heat is:

   a. the nucleoid   **c.** a plastid   **e.** endospore
   b. a ribosome   **d.** the dictyosome

_____ 3. A typical intestinal bacterium such as *E. coli* may divide as often as once every:

   a. minute   **c.** hour   **e.** few seconds
   b. 15–20 minutes   **d.** day

_____ 4. Organisms that exhibit magnetotaxis use which compound in the process?

   a. Fe_3O_4 **c.** MgO_2 **e.** CH_4
   b. Ca_3PO_4 **d.** Ca_2OH

Key for questions 5–8

a. a sexual process   **b.** not a sexual process

_____ 5. transduction

_____ 6. transformation

_____ 7. binary fission

_____ 8. conjugation

Key for questions 9–18, which relate to various types of prokaryotes

a. archaebacteria   **c.** cyanobacteria   **e.** none of these
b. schizophyta   **d.** all of these

_____ **9.** Have heterocysts.

_____ **10.** Are typical halophilic organisms.

_____ **11.** Are bacteria.

_____ **12.** Contain bacteriochlorophyll.

_____ **13.** Contain ribosomes.

_____ **14.** Contain chlorophyll *a*.

_____ **15.** Taxon for a methanobacterium.

_____ **16.** Grouping for spirochetes and mycoplasmas.

_____ **17.** Gliding and sheathed prokaryotes.

_____ **18.** The most primitive group (choose A, B, or C).

_____ **19.** The morphology/form of the organism that causes syphilis is:

    a. spirochete   **b.** bacillus   **c.** coccus   **d.** not known

_____ **20.** Bacteria that lack a cell wall are:

    a. sheathed   **c.** spirochetes   **e.** rickettsias
    b. prosthecate   **d.** mycoplasmas

_____ **21.** Of the organisms listed in question 20, which may be transmitted by fleas, ticks, or lice and cause typhus and spotted fevers?

Key for questions 22–24

a. True   **b.** False

_____ **22.** All bacteria contain DNA and RNA.

_____ **23.** A nitrogen-fixing organism can convert NH_3 and NH_4^+ to N_2 (nitrogen gas).

_____ **24.** *Clostridium botulinum* can live and grow in the absence of oxygen.

Key for questions 25–37. Read the numbered statement or concept and choose the best response from the *Key*, which lists potential disease agents.

a. virus   **b.** bacterium   **c.** prion   **d.** viroid

_____ **25.** An infectious agent composed of nucleic acid only

_____ **26.** Agent of common dysentery of humans

_____ **27.** Cause of the common cold

_____ **28.** Organism responsible for genital and oral herpes

_____ **29.** Organism responsible for botulism

_____ **30.** Infective agents that have no nucleic acid

_____ **31.** Scrapie and kuru diseases are attributed to this type of organism.

_____ **32.** Some of these organisms can be treated with penicillin.

_____ **33.** Agent that causes leprosy

_____ **34.** Cause of diphtheria

_____ **35.** Organisms that have capsids

_____ **36.** Acyclovir or interferon may be used to treat infections caused by this type of organism.

_____ **37.** Cause of Creutzfeldt-Jakob disease and possibly Alzheimer's disease.

Key for questions 38–40, which refer to protists.
a. True   **b.** False

_____ **38.** Are all eukaryotic organisms.

_____ **39.** Contain both RNA and DNA.

_____ **40.** Are closely related to the Monera.

Key for questions 41–52
a. Mastigophora   **b.** Sarcodina   **c.** Sporozoa   **d.** Ciliophora

_____ **41.** The phylum with organisms whose cells have a macronucleus and a micronucleus.

_____ **42.** Flagellated protozoans belong to this group.

_____ **43.** An organism in this phylum causes illness in approximately 300 million people, and kills 2–4 million, each year.

_____ **44.** _Blepharisma_ and _Didinium_ are in this group.

_____ **45.** Includes organisms that move exclusively by pseudopodia.

_____ **46.** Species in this phylum are transmitted by tse-tse flies to cattle and humans.

_____ **47.** The terms <u>trophozoite</u>, <u>schizont</u>, and <u>gametocyte</u> are applicable to organisms in this group.

_____ **48.** Includes amoeboid protozoans.

_____ **49.** The phylum of the agent of malaria.

_____ **50.** Includes radiolarians and foraminiferans.

_____ **51.** The agent of African sleeping sickness is in this taxon.

_____ **52.** The taxon for trichonympha, a wood-digesting protozoan.

_____ **53.** Malaria is more dangerous now than it was in the past because:
   a. Humans are more susceptible now.
   b. There are now more and new vectors for the disease.
   c. The parasite and the vector have become symbiotic.
   d. The parasite and the vector have become resistant to certain chemicals.
   e. The parasite and the vector have been cultivated in laboratories and they have escaped in large numbers.

_____ **54.** In organisms that have a macronucleus and a micronucleus, the macronucleus functions primarily in:

    a. metabolism   **b.** heredity   **c.** both A and B   **d.** neither A nor B

_____ **55.** In the organisms described in question 54, the micronucleus functions primarily in:

    a. metabolism   **b.** heredity   **c.** both A and B   **d.** neither A nor B

Key for questions 56–65, which concern plantlike Protists.

a. euglenoids   **c.** golden-brown algae and diatoms   **e.** None of these
b. dinoflagellates   **d.** A, B, and C

_____ **56.** Have holes, channels, and patterns in the cell wall.

_____ **57.** Produce deadly neurotoxins.

_____ **58.** Contain chlorophyll *a*.

_____ **59.** Have shells of silicon.

_____ **60.** Have a stigma or eyespot.

_____ **61.** Swim by means of two flagellae.

_____ **62.** Responsible for "red tides."

_____ **63.** Contain fucoxanthin.

_____ **64.** Have valves and may look like a pill box.

_____ **65.** Are a major reason why shellfish are not eaten during warm-weather months.

Key Terms from the Text Chapter

archaebacteria *text page 358*   parasite *355*   spore *356*
capsid *360*   pathogenic *354*   symbiont *355*
ciliate *364*   phytoplankton *366*   viroid *362*
cyanobacteria *359*   prion *362*   virus *360*
eubacterium *359*   protozoan *363*
fruiting body *367*   saprobe *355*

17

Plants and Fungi: Decomposers and Producers

Perspective and Review

Biologists believe that fungi and land plants evolved from single-celled ancestors. Fossil evidence shows that fungi were living on land between 450 million and 500 million years ago. As fungi are closely associated with plants it is thought that fungi may have helped plants make the transition from the marine to a terrestrial environment.

The transition to land presented many new problems for plants: the need to avoid desiccation while allowing gas exchange to occur; the need for support structures; the need to absorb and internally transport water and minerals from the soil; and the need to reproduce without shedding gametes into water. As plants evolved from the early bryozoans to angiosperms, each group developed new structures to deal with these challenges.

Three main trends are obvious in the evolution of land plants: the development of a vascular system, which helped solve the problems of support and transport; seed production to improve dispersal and survival of offspring; and increasing dominance of the diploid sporophyte phase. The angiosperms, or flowering plants, show the greatest advances in all three areas.

An Overview of the Kingdom Fungi: The Great Decomposers

The kingdom Fungi contains about 100,000 species, including mushrooms and molds. While most are saprobes, decomposing dead organic matter, about 5,000 species are plant parasites. Fungi can be distinguished from other kingdoms by their mode of nutrition and their unique physical structure. Concept Table 17.1 outlines some of the main fungal characteristics.

Concept Table 17.1   Main features of the Fungi

Nutrition	Fungi are heterotrophs. They secrete enzymes that break down organic matter, which is then absorbed through the cell membrane, a process termed <u>extracellular digestion</u>.
Structure	The body consists of tubular filaments called **hyphae** that are packed together to form a **mycelium**. Each hypha has chitinous, perforated cell walls through which cytoplasm moves between cells.
Reproduction	Asexual reproduction is the most common form. Fragments of hyphae give rise to new individuals; hyphal cells can divide or bud; or a fungus can produce asexual **spores** that disperse, divide mitotically, and develop into new fungi. Hyphae and asexual spores are haploid. Sexual reproduction can also

Continues

occur, when part of the mycelium differentiates into a gamete-producing structure of one **mating type** (called either + or –). Gametes from a + and a – strain fuse to form a diploid zygote, which undergoes meiosis and produces spores that grow into mycelia. Figure 17.4 in your text illustrates the general life cycle of fungi.

Fungal–Plant Interactions

An important feature of fungi is their close association with plants. Biologists have divided these associations into three main groups.

Mycorrhizae are symbiotic associations between plant roots and fungi. Fungi growing either outside or inside plant root cells send out hyphae that increase the plant's supply of nutrients and water.

Lichens are mutualistic associations (both species benefit) between ascomycete fungi and algae. The alga receives protection and water from the fungus, while the fungus is nourished by the photosynthetic products of the alga.

A third type of interaction is **parasitic**: About 5,000 fungal species attack plants and are the main causes of plant diseases.

A Survey of Saprobes and Parasites: The Major Fungal Classes

Fungi are divided into five classes, based on their spore-producing structures. Concept Table 17.2 outlines the significant features of each class.

Concept Table 17.2   Major classes of the Fungi

Class	Significant features
Oomycetes	Includes saprobes and parasitic forms living in damp areas. They form mobile **zoospores**, which disperse by swimming.
Zygomycetes	Filamentous fungi that produce thick-walled **zygospores**. Members of this group form the most important mycorrhizal associations.
Ascomycetes	Includes both saprobes and parasites. Spores are produced in a sac, or **ascus**, borne on an **ascocarp**; includes yeasts.
Basidiomycetes	Mushrooms and toadstools are in this class, which produces **basidiospores** in club-shaped **basidia**. Their complex life cycle is fully described and illustrated in Figure 17.9 in your text.
Deuteromycetes	(Fungi Imperfecti) These are fungi such as *Penicillium* that only reproduce asexually, producing spores called **conidia**.

An Overview of the Plant Kingdom: Alternation of Generations and a Trend Toward Life on Land

Plants are multicellular autotrophs that photosynthesize. Like the fungi, plants also alternate haploid and diploid phases, but in plants both phases are multicellular. The haploid phase, or **gametophyte**, produces male and female gametes. The diploid phase, or **sporophyte**, produces male and/or female spores by meiosis. Plants in which the haploid phase dominates, such as algae, are called <u>haplotonic</u>; those such as mosses, in which both phases are conspicuous, are termed <u>haplodiplontic</u>; the majority of plants have a dominant diploid phase and are said to be <u>diplontic</u>. Plants are classified into five main groups: algae, bryophytes, ferns, gymnosperms, and angiosperms. Algae are the most primitive, and angiosperms are the most advanced and recently evolved group.

Algae: Ancestral Plants That Remained Aquatic

Most algae are multicellular aquatic organisms with simple reproductive structures. They evolved from photosynthetic protists around 600 million years ago. Biologists divide the algae into three main groups. Concept Table 17.3 outlines the main features of these groups.

Concept Table 17.3   Classification of the algae

Division	Significant features
Rhodophyta (red algae)	This group can live at great water depths due to the presence of phycoerythrins, pigments that absorb blue-green light. They can reproduce either asexually by fragmentation or sexually. The gametophyte phase dominates.
Phaeophyta (brown algae)	This group includes the large **kelps**. The pigment fucoxanthin colors the algae and allows them to collect blue and violet wavelengths of light that penetrate to medium depths where the plants live. Most brown algae have leaflike **fronds** to trap sunlight, a supporting **stipe**, and an anchoring **holdfast**. The diploid sporophyte is dominant in kelps, while in smaller species the gametophyte is the major phase.
Chlorophyta (green algae)	This group comprises single-celled species and species that form multicellular aggregations. Confined to shallow areas, this group contains chlorophylls *a* and *b* and carotenoid pigments and is considered the ancestor of land plants. Some forms, such as *Ulva*, are haplodiplontic.

Simple Land Plants: Still Tied to Water

During the Devonian period plants made the transition to land. Two main groups were involved in this phase: The **bryophytes**, or mosses, and the **lower vascular plants**, such as ferns. Both these groups still depend on water to reproduce. Concept Table 17.4 outlines the main features of each group.

Concept Table 17.4   Bryophytes and lower vascular plants

Bryophytes	The mosses, liverworts, and hornworts. All are small plants with a waterproof coating to prevent desiccation and perforated leaves to allow gas exchange. **Rhizoids** act as anchors but do not function in absorption or transportation. Bryophytes are haplodiplontic; an **antheridium** produces sperm, and an **archegonium** produces eggs. Fertilization results in **sporangia**, the diploid sporophyte stage. Sporangia in turn produce haploid spores that germinate into gametophytes. Table 17.7 in your text illustrates the generalized life cycle of a moss.
Lower vascular plants	Ferns, horsetails, and their relatives. The first plants to evolve an internal vascular system to transport oxygen, minerals, and products of photosynthesis. All lack true roots, but have horizontal **rhizomes** from which leafy, erect structures grow. In horsetails these parts are true **stems**. Stems and leaves die and are replaced annually via **vegetative reproduction**. The fern sporophyte has spore-producing **sori**. Spores develop into tiny gametophytes. Figure 17.9 in your text describes the fern life cycle.

Gymnosperms: Conquerors of Dry Land

Gymnosperms, which include the conifers, evolved during the Mesozoic. The evolution of pollen, seeds, and a more dominant diploid phase all contributed to the success of this group on land. Gametophytes (eggs and pollen) are housed on the sporophyte plant, and pollen is air-transported to the egg so that fertilization does not depend on water. The embryo develops inside an **ovule** and becomes encased in a seed. Gymnosperms are heterosporous: Male gametophytes develop from **microspores**, and females form the larger **megaspores**. Biologists recognize four main subdivisions: cycads, a small group of tropical, palmlike plants; ginkgos; gnetophytes; and conifers. Conifers are distinguished by their narrow, needle-like leaves and woody cones. The leaves are covered by a waterproof *cuticle*. Figure 17.23 in your text illustrates the life cycle of a pine.

Angiosperms, the Flowering Plants: A Modern Success Story

During the Cenozoic, **angiosperms**—the flowering plants—became the dominant land plants. The group is divided into two subclasses, monocots and dicots; Table 17.2 in your text summarizes their main features. The key to angiosperm success lay partly in the evolution of broad leaves for trapping sunlight, but more importantly in the evolution of their characteristic reproductive structures and strategies. Concept Table 17.5 describes the main features of angiosperm reproduction.

1. The haploid phase is completely dependent on the dominant diploid sporophyte. Male and female flowers are produced.

2. The male flower part, or **stamen**, consists of the **anther**, where <u>microspore mother cells</u> give rise to male gametophytes (pollen grains), and a stalk, or **filament**.

3. Within the female flower the **ovary** houses and protects **ovules**, which contain <u>megaspore mother cells</u>. The **stigma** acts as a sticky trap or receptacle for pollen, which is transported to the ovary via the **style**.

4. When pollen reaches the stigma two sperm nuclei migrate to the ovary, where **double fertilization** occurs. One sperm nucleus fuses with the egg to form a zygote, and a second fuses with two other nuclei in the ovary to form the **endosperm**, a nutritive tissue for the developing embryo. The ovary subsequently develops into a **fruit**. Figure 17.25 in your text presents a detailed view of the angiosperm life cycle.

Coevolution

Most flowering plants depend on animal **pollinators**, such as bees and butterflies, to carry pollen from male to female reproductive structures. In return, the pollinators obtain food, such as nectar. This mutual dependence is the result of **coevolution**, natural selection for interdependence between plant and pollinator, based on enhanced reproductive success for both.

Thought Provokers

1. Compare and contrast plants and fungi in relation to structure, life cycle, and mode of nutrition.

2. Compare and contrast mycorrhizae and lichens and indicate the special features associated with each.

Self-Test

For each statement or question choose the best response and mark your choice in the space provided. For some items you will select your response from a *Key*.

Key for questions 1–5

a. True　　　　**b.** False

———— **1.** Some fungi are autotrophs.

_____ 2. Some fungi are photosynthetic.

_____ 3. Some fungi are saprobes.

_____ 4. Some fungi are parasitic.

_____ 5. Fungi are prokaryotic organisms.

_____ 6. In fungi the most common mode of reproduction is:

    a. asexual   **c.** not known   **e.** difficult to determine

    b. sexual   **d.** obscure

_____ 7. If + and − strains of a particular fungus are in proximity, what usually happens?

    a. They combine and destroy each other.

    b. They repel each other.

    c. They mate.

    d. They are induced to form more vegetative hyphae.

    e. They divide and form haploid cells.

_____ 8. The association between the roots of higher plants and fungi is best described as:

    a. autotrophic   **c.** coincidental   **e.** symbiotic

    b. bacteriostatic   **d.** detrimental

_____ 9. A lichen is a combination of

    a. tree roots and algae

    b. an alga and a fungus

    c. tree roots and bacteria

    d. bacteria and fungi

    e. algae and bacteria

Key for questions 10–19: Choose the best response to complete each statement, using the following _Key_, which lists the major fungal classes.

a. ascomycetes   **c.** oomycetes   **e.** zygomycetes

b. basidiomycetes   **d.** deuteromycetes

_____ 10. _Rhizopus_ is the most ecologically important species of the class _____.

_____ 11. A fungus of the class _____ caused the Irish potato blight.

_____ 12. _____ form dark, thick-walled sexual spores.

_____ 13. Most yeasts are members of _____.

_____ 14. _____ lack a sexual stage.

_____ 15. _Claviceps_, powdery mildews, truffles, and morels are members of the _____.

_____ 16. _____ are known as the "club fungi."

_____ 17. _____ produce sexual spores in sacs.

_____ 18. Examination of _____ reveals that they have gills.

_____ 19. Puffballs, bracket fungi, smut fungi, and field mushrooms are _____.

_____ 20. A potent cancer-causing biochemical produced by fungi is:

    a. actidione   **c.** acridine   **e.** penicillin

    b. acriflavin   **d.** aflatoxin

_____ **21.** All organisms in the plant kindgom are (mark *all* letters that are correct):

  a. multicellular   **c.** autotrophic   **e.** eukaryotes
  b. heterotrophic   **d.** photosynthetic

Key for questions 22–27, which relate to either the gametophyte or the sporophyte phase of the plant life cycle.

a. gametophyte   **b.** sporophyte

_____ **22.** the diploid phase

_____ **23.** phase in which meiosis occurs

_____ **24.** plant phase that is the product of meiosis

_____ **25.** a haploid plant

_____ **26.** a plant that produces gametes

_____ **27.** the phase formed when gametes fuse

_____ **28.** What percentage of the Earth's surface is covered with water?

  a. 25   **b.** 50   **c.** 60   **d.** 75   **e.** 90

_____ **29.** Algae contribute to what percentage of all photosynthesis that occurs on Earth?

  a. 25   **b.** 50   **c.** 60   **d.** 75   **e.** 90

Key for questions 30–40, which relate to algae.

a. red algae   **c.** green algae   **e.** none of these
b. brown algae   **d.** all of these

_____ **30.** Can photosynthesize.

_____ **31.** sargassum and other kelps

_____ **32.** multicellular plants

_____ **33.** Produce sporophytes and gametophytes.

_____ **34.** Contain chlorophylls *a* and *b* and carotenoids.

_____ **35.** Useful products are agar and carrageenan.

_____ **36.** *Ulva* and *Chlamydomonas*

_____ **37.** the algal group found in the deepest parts of the ocean

_____ **38.** possibly the direct ancestors of land plants

_____ **39.** Have fronds, stipe, and holdfast.

_____ **40.** All species contain phycoerythrins.

Key for questions 41–51, which relate to bryophytes.

a. True   **b.** False

_____ **41.** Have sporophytes attached to gametophytes.

_____ **42.** Produce roots.

_____ **43.** Have an internal vascular system.

_____ **44.** Require water for reproduction.

_____ **45.** Contain chlorophyll.

_____ **46.** Probably gave rise to the club mosses.

_____ **47.** Some have gametophytes shaped like a street lamp.

_____ **48.** Are found in ocean habitats.

_____ **49.** Produce eggs in antheridia and sperm in archegonia.

_____ **50.** Are simpler than ferns and more complex than algae.

_____ **51.** Include mosses, liverworts, and hornworts.

_____ **52.** The lower vascular plants include all but which one of the following?

    a. ferns   **c.** lycopods   **e.** club mosses
    b. horsetails   **d.** liverworts

_____ **53.** Compared to earlier ferns, those alive today are:

    a. similar, but smaller   **c.** asexual only   **e.** lacking in chlorophyll
    b. much larger   **d.** sexual only

_____ **54.** The situation in today's ferns described in question 53 can be ascribed to:

    a. asexual reproduction   **d.** mutation
    b. failure of sporophytes to survive   **e.** all of these
    c. failure of gametophytes to survive

Key for questions 55–60

a. ferns   **c.** lycopods   **e.** none of these
b. horsetails   **d.** all of these

_____ **55.** Possess rhizomes.

_____ **56.** Produce true roots.

_____ **57.** Are photosynthetic.

_____ **58.** Sporophyte phase is most conspicuous.

_____ **59.** Produce sori.

_____ **60.** Typically have fronds.

Key for questions 61–65, which relate to gymnosperms.

a. True   **b.** False

_____ **61.** Produce pollen and eggs.

_____ **62.** Fertilization is dependent on water.

_____ **63.** The gametophyte is larger and more prominent than the sporophyte.

_____ **64.** Include conifers.

_____ **65.** Usually are deciduous.

_____ **66.** Which one of the following statements is <u>not</u> true of gingko?

    a. It is a tree with fan-shaped leaves.
    b. It is deciduous.
    c. It is resistant to pollution.
    d. Females can produce a smell like rancid butter.
    e. Male and female reproductive structures are on the same plant.

_____ **67.** Which one of the following is <u>not</u> true of _Welwitchsia_?

    a. It requires much water.
    b. It is a gnetophyte.
    c. It grows low to the ground and has long, twisting leaves.
    d. It produces cones.
    e. It looks like an overgrown turnip.

_____ **68.** Which one of the following pairings includes a tree that is <u>not</u> an evergreen?

    a. yew-hemlock   **c.** sequoia-fir   **e.** pine-cedar
    b. larch-spruce   **d.** maple-birch

_____ **69.** The hard, woody cones of conifers are:

    a. male   **b.** female

Key for questions 70–75

a. True   **b.** False

_____ **70.** Angiosperms have seeds enclosed in an ovary.

_____ **71.** There evidently has been a coevolution of certain birds, insects, and mammals with angiosperms.

_____ **72.** Angiosperms appeared prior to gymnosperms in the history of the developing Earth.

_____ **73.** The endosperm of angiosperms is triploid, not diploid.

_____ **74.** A fruit is really a ripened seed.

_____ **75.** The sporophyte is more developed than the gametophyte in angiosperms, and the stigma, style, and ovary are female structures in angiosperms.

Key Terms from the Text Chapter

angiosperm _text page 388_	kelp _381_	seed _386_
anther _384, 389_	lichen _373_	sporangium _378, 384_
bryophyte _382_	lower vascular plant _382_	spore _373_
coevolution _391_	megaspore _386_	stem _385_
deciduous _387_	microspore _386_	stigma _389_
double fertilization _390_	mycelium _372_	style _389_
endosperm _390_	mycorrhiza _373_	vascular plant _382, 385_
fruit _390_	ovule _387_	vegetative reproduction _385_
gymnosperm _386_	pollen tube _388_	
hypha _372_	pollinator _390_	

Concept Figure: Plant Evolution

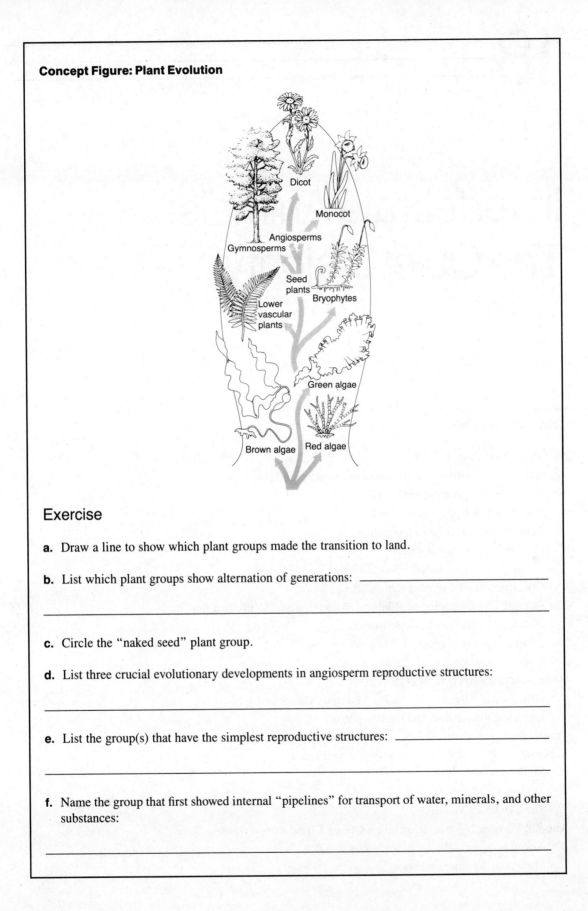

Exercise

a. Draw a line to show which plant groups made the transition to land.

b. List which plant groups show alternation of generations: _____

_____

c. Circle the "naked seed" plant group.

d. List three crucial evolutionary developments in angiosperm reproductive structures:

_____

e. List the group(s) that have the simplest reproductive structures: _____

_____

f. Name the group that first showed internal "pipelines" for transport of water, minerals, and other substances:

_____

18

Invertebrate Animals: The Quiet Majority

CHAPTER IN BRIEF

Perspective and Review

Animals are <u>multicellular heterotrophs</u>, mobile for at least part of their life cycle. Animal reproduction is primarily sexual, and unlike plants, animals do not have alternation of generations; most species are diploid and produce haploid gametes. At least 35–37 phyla evolved in the kingdom Animalia. Most of these are marine and 95% are **invertebrates**.

Except for sponges, the diverse cells in an animal's body are organized into <u>tissues</u> and <u>organs</u>. As invertebrates evolved from ancestral protists, five important anatomical trends shaped animals' anatomy and physiology: a trend away from radial symmetry and toward bilateral symmetry; a trend toward cephalization (development of a head region); development of a more complex, elongate body with two openings and a gut; a trend toward a fluid-filled cavity, or <u>coelom</u>: and a trend toward segmentation. These trends resulted in major reorganization of the animal body, changes that have been maintained and elaborated in all subsequent forms.

Animals and Evolution: An Overview of the Animal Kingdom

The kingdom Animalia has a long evolutionary history, one that is well understood because animals have left a more complete fossil record than most members of other kingdoms. The earliest animal fossils date from 700 million years ago. Since their emergence as multicellular heterotrophs, animals have radiated into a variety of diverse forms adapted for many habitats. Sponges and cnidarians diverged early on from the main evolutionary branch. Figure 18.3 in your text illustrates the evolutionary relationships of the main animal groups.

Sponges: The Simplest Animals

Sponges make up the phylum Porifera, which contains about 5,000 species, most of them marine. Sponges are <u>sessile</u> filter-feeders that strain fine food particles from the surrounding water. They have an asymmetrical, saclike body in which an opening, or <u>osculum</u>, leads to a <u>central cavity</u>. The body wall is bilayered, and the inner wall is lined by <u>choanocytes</u>, flagellated cells that draw water in through pores in the body wall and expel it out through the osculum. <u>Amoebocytes</u> in the choanocytes digest and distribute food. <u>Spongin</u> fibers and <u>spicules</u> of calcium or silica support and protect the sponge. Sponges lack specialized tissues, and waste excretion takes place through pores or directly across cell membranes. Sponges reproduce either asexually by budding or sexually.

Cnidarians: The Radial Animals

The phylum Cnidaria includes the familiar corals and jellyfish. This group evolved radial symmetry and tissues. Concept Table 18.1 summarizes the main **cnidarian** features.

Concept Table 18.1   The phylum Cnidaria

Body plan	Two types: the **polyp**, a hollow cylinder with a whorl of tentacles around the mouth (*Example:* sea anemone), and the **medusa**, an inverted umbrella shape with tentacles and mouth pointing downwards (*Example:* jellyfish).
Body wall	Three layers; an outer **epidermis**, a jellylike middle layer, or **mesoglea**, and an inner **gastrodermis**. **Nematocysts**, stinging capsules in the epidermis, inject prey with a paralyzing toxin and are also used in defense.
Digestion	Food is taken into the **coelenteron**, or **gastrovascular cavity**; digestion is **extracellular**.
Responses	A network of **nerve cells** detects stimuli and activates responses.
Reproduction	*Asexual*: by budding; some cnidarians, such as corals, form large colonies by budding. *Sexual*: Gametes fuse to form ciliated **planula** larva, which settles into a polyp. In adults with a medusa form, the polyp that develops from a planula differentiates into a **strobila**, which resembles a stack of saucers, each "saucer" becoming a medusa. Figure 18.8 in your text illustrates the complex medusan life cycle.

Flatworms: The Beginning of Bilateral Symmetry and Cephalization

The phylum Platyhelminthes consists of both free-living and parasitic flatworms. Parasitic forms, such as flukes and tapeworms, are major causes of diseases in livestock and humans. Concept Table 18.2 summarizes some of the advances and features of this phylum.

Concept Table 18.2   The phylum Platyhelminthes

Body plan	Five major advances: **bilateral symmetry** and **cephalization**; three cellular tissue layers (epidermis, mesoderm and endodermis); true **organs** (two or more tissues functioning as a unit) and **organ systems** (sets of organs with related functions).
Organ systems/Functions	
Digestion	An eversible **pharynx** used in feeding, and a branched **intestine** lined with absorptive cells but that has only one opening.
Excretion	A network of tubules adjacent to ciliated **flame cells** that drive water out through pores.
Muscle	Layers of contractile muscles below the epidermis together with cilia; function in locomotion.

Continues

Nervous	A brain, **nerve cords**, lateral nerves, and light-sensitive eye spots.
Reproduction	Hermaphroditic, with cross-fertilization (reciprocal exchange of gametes with another individual) typical.

Roundworms: Advances in Digestion

The roundworm phylum Nematoda includes many important decomposers but also many species that are parasitic on plants and animals. Nematodes show bilateral symmetry, cephalization, and three tissue layers. They have also evolved a digestive tract, with a mouth and anus, and a **pseudocoelom**—a fluid-filled space between the inner and outer tissue layers that acts as a **hydroskeleton**. All other more complex animals have evolved a true cavity or coelom, a space within the mesoderm. The development of a coelom was a major advance in animal body architecture; in addition to acting as a hydroskeleton, it allowed the development of a closed circulatory system and provided a fluid-filled cavity in which organs could be suspended. Figure 18.11 in your text illustrates the evolution of the coelom.

Protostomes and Deuterostomes: Two Roads Diverge

Zoologists believe that shortly after the evolution of bilateral symmetry, animals branched into two main lineages: protostomes and deuterostomes. **Protostomes**, which include mollusks, annelids, and arthropods, show spiral cleavage, and the mouth develops as the first opening from or near the blastopore. **Deuterostomes** include **echinoderms** and chordates, have radial cleavage, and the anus arises from the blastopore. There are also other differences in embryonic timing and determination.

Mollusks: Soft-Bodied Animals of Water and Land

At least 100,000 species make up the phylum Mollusca, a group of soft-bodied animals that includes oysters, clams, and octopuses. The **mollusks** exhibit major advances in circulatory, respiratory, and nervous systems. The phylum is divided into three classes. Concept Table 18.3 describes the main characteristics of this group.

Concept Table 18.3   The phylum Mollusca

Body plan	Body divided into a locomotory muscular **foot**; a head, a **visceral mass** containing internal organs; and a **mantle**, tissue folds covering the visceral mass that secretes the shell. **Gills** are suspended in the **mantle cavity**.
Systems	An **open circulatory system** including a heart that pumps blood in vessels and open spaces; gas exchange takes place in blood vessels in the gills. Except for bivalves, mollusks have a rasping tongue, or **radula**. Sexual reproduction results in a mobile ciliated **trochophore** larva.

Continues

Concept Table 18.3   The phylum Mollusca (continued)

Classification (three classes)	**Gastropoda:** Sea slugs (**nudibranchs**) and slugs, which have lost their shells, and the more characteristic snails, identified by a coiled shell and **torsion**—a twisting of the body during development. Land snails have air-breathing lungs and leave **slime trails** secreted by **slime glands**. **Bivalva: Filter-feeding** clams and oysters. The body is enclosed in two shells (valves). **Cephalopoda:** Includes octopuses and squids; efficient and large predators that possess a well-developed brain. The foot is modified into 8–10 arms and terminates in a **siphon**; the mantle is adapted for swimming.

Annelid Worms: Segmentation and a Closed Circulatory System

The phylum Annelida comprises the segmented worms. This is the first group to possess all five evolutionary trends: bilateral symmetry, cephalization, a gut tube, a coelom, and segmentation. Concept Table 18.4 summarizes the phylum's main features.

Concept Table 18.4   The phylum Annelida

Structure	Segmented body with **septae** dividing adjacent segments. Each segment contains two excretory **nephridia**, nerve cells, and a fluid-filled region of the coelom surrounded by circular and longitudinal muscles. **Setae** and muscles are used in locomotion.
Digestion	A gut with a **crop** for storing food, and a **gizzard** for grinding food.
Circulation	**Closed circulatory system**; blood flows only in vessels and transports nutrients and wastes.
Reproduction	Sexually reproducing marine annelids produce trochophore larvae. Earthworms and leeches are hermaphroditic.
Classification (three classes)	**Polychaeta:** predominantly marine; include fanworms. **Oligochaeta:** Includes earthworms and most terrestrial species. **Hirudina:** Freshwater forms, including leeches.

Arthropods: The Joint-Legged Majority

The largest animal group on Earth, the phylum Arthropoda, includes forms as diverse as fossil trilobites, crabs, and butterflies. The group is characterized by an external skeleton, modified segments, an acute sensory system, and rapid movement and metabolism made possible by special respiratory structures. Concept Table 18.5 describes the main features of this group.

Concept Table 18.5   The phylum Arthropoda

External structure	An **exoskeleton**, an outer hard, chitinous, waterproof cuticle that protects soft body parts and prevents desiccation. Exoskeleton **joints** allow movement. Arthropods grow by **molting**, periodic shedding of the exoskeleton.
Body structure	Segments usually fused into specialized regions such as a **head**, **thorax**, and **abdomen**. Appendages are modified for specialized functions, such as **mouthparts** for feeding.
Respiration	A well-developed system consisting of **tracheae** in insects, **book lungs** in spiders, and gills in aquatic forms.
Sensory structures	Most have sensory antennae; in terrestrial forms these detect **pheromones**. Compound eyes detect movement and often color.
Classification	Arthropods are divided into three subphyla and seven classes; the five major classes are: **Crustacea:** Mostly aquatic; includes barnacles, crabs, and lobsters. The calcareous exoskeleton is known as a **carapace**. Two main body regions, a **cephalothorax** and posterior **abdomen**. **Arachnida:** Includes scorpions, **spiders**, and mites. No antennae and usually six pairs of legs. The first pair form poison-bearing **chelicerae**, and the second grasping **pedipalps**. Spiders have web-spinning **spinnerets** on the abdomen. **Chilopoda:** Centipedes, predatory flattened animals with **poison claws** on the first body segment. **Diplopoda:** Millipedes; feed on decaying organic matter. **Insecta:** The largest and most successful arthropod group; extremely diverse and mainly terrestrial. Three body regions and elaborate mouthparts. Often the embryo develops from a voracious larva to a transitional **pupa** and undergoes **metamorphosis** into the adult form (example: butterflies). **Social insects** include bees, ants, and termites.

Echinoderms: The First Endoskeletons

The echinodermata were the first deuterostomes. This group shows an odd mixture of apparent evolutionary regressions and developments. The adult body is radially symmetrical. A nerve ring around the mouth gives rise to nerve cords, but there is no brain, excretory, or respiratory system. Echinoderms reproduce sexually and also have the ability to regenerate lost body parts. Echinoderms also show two new features: an internal calcareous **endoskeleton**, and a coelom that forms a **water vascular system** that in turn acts as a hydraulic pressure locomotory system. The five living classes are: Asteroidea, sea stars; Crinoidea, sea lilies; Ophiuroidea, brittle stars; Echinoidea, sea urchins and sand dollars; and Holothuroidea, sea cucumbers.

Thought Provokers

1. Starting with the Porifera, briefly describe the distinguishing features and evolutionary advances of each of the phyla presented in this chapter. Write no more than three to four sentences on each phylum.

2. Briefly discuss each of the following terms or paired expressions. Give an example or illustration of each.

    a. deuterostomes/protostomes

    b. open circulatory system/closed circulatory system

    c. cephalization

    d. exoskeleton/endoskeleton

Self-Test

For each statement or question choose the best response and mark your choice in the space provided. For some items you will select your response from a *Key*.

_____ **1.** The earliest fossil remains suggest that the first animals beyond the Protista were:

    a. unable to reproduce sexually   **d.** insects
    b. unable to reproduce asexually   **e.** soft-bodied
    c. very large

_____ **2.** The first invertebrate animals date back how many million years?

    a. 120   **b.** 250   **c.** 500   **d.** 700   **e.** 1,000

_____ **3.** The lower animals seem to be the direct descendents of:

    a. monerans
    b. protists
    c. plants
    d. vertebrates
    e. nothing; they were the first organisms

Key for questions 4–20: Match each term or statement with a phylum from the *Key*.

a. Arthropoda	**d.** Porifera	**ac.** Annelida
b. Cnidaria	**e.** Platyhelminthes	**ad.** Mollusca
c. Chordata	**ab.** Nematoda	**ae.** Echinodermata

_____ **4.** the first group to have a true mesoderm with living cells

_____ **5.** animals with nematocysts

_____ **6.** choanocytes are typical of this group

_____ **7.** polyps and medusas

_____ **8.** includes tapeworms and flukes

_____ **9.** includes free-living and plant and animal parasites

_____ **10.** a foot, a head, and a visceral mass

_____ **11.** a head, thorax, joints, and chitin exoskeleton

_____ **12.** A pseudocoelom together with a mouth and an anus are first seen in this group.

_____ **13.** first creatures with gills

_____ **14.** organisms that lack a nervous system

_____ **15.** gastropods and cephalopods

_____ **16.** first true cephalization

_____ **17.** deuterostomes

_____ **18.** the most intelligent creatures without backbones

_____ **19.** animals with septa, nephridia, and setae

_____ **20.** "jointed feet"

Questions 21–23. Select a response from the *Key* to indicate the mechanism of movement.

a. flagella   **b.** cilia   **c.** pseudopodia

_____ **21.** planaria

_____ **22.** planulae

_____ **23.** choanocytes

Key for questions 24–45

a. True   **b.** False

Sponges:

_____ **24.** have choanocytes and amebocytes that can ingest food.

_____ **25.** have a distinct mouth and an anus.

_____ **26.** can reproduce asexually.

_____ **27.** have flagellated cells called amebocytes.

_____ **28.** produce spongin, a complex polysaccharide.

Cnidarians:

_____ **29.** possess a digestive cavity called the coelenteron.

_____ **30.** have nematocysts that contain enzymes for the digestion of food.

_____ **31.** can regenerate lost body parts or produce whole organisms from body pieces.

_____ **32.** can bud.

_____ **33.** form strobila, which are sex cells, or gametes.

Flatworms (Platyhelminthes):

_____ **34.** are bilaterally symmetrical.

_____ **35.** are cephalized.

_____ **36.** have a mouth and an anus.

_____ **37.** are hermaphroditic.

_____ **38.** possess primitive lungs.

_____ **39.** have a body shape designed to facilitate speed during locomotion.

_____ **40.** have a muscular system.

Nematodes:

_____ **41.** are the most abundant animals on Earth.

_____ **42.** are highly resistant to extremes of heat, cold, radiation, and chemicals.

_____ **43.** are cephalized and show bilateral symmetry.

_____ **44.** have three tissue layers.

_____ **45.** include organisms that cause trichinosis, ascariasis, hookworm disease, and elephantiasis.

_____ **46.** Which of the following is <u>not</u> true of protostomes and deuterostomes?
   a. Protostomes include mollusks, annelids, and arthropods.
   b. Echinoderms are deuterostomes.
   c. Chordates are deuterostomes.
   d. Protostomes have a spiral cleavage pattern, and deuterostomes have a radial cleavage pattern.
   e. The first indentation in both protostomes and deuterostomes forms a mouth.

Key for questions 47–72
a. True   **b.** False

In the phylum Mollusca:

_____ **47.** Shells, if formed, are composed of calcium chloride.

_____ **48.** The radula is a reproductive organ.

_____ **49.** Torsion in snails results in the anus and gills being positioned at the posterior, or tail, of the organism.

_____ **50.** Shells are absent in slugs and nudibranchs.

_____ **51.** There is a closed circulatory system and a heart.

_____ **52.** Bivalves include oysters, clams, mussels, and scallops.

_____ **53.** Gills may be present for gas exchange and filter feeding.

_____ **54.** Members include the squid, octopus, and nautilus.

Regarding annelids:

_____ **55.** Polychaeta and Oligochaeta are types of annelids.

_____ **56.** All are segmented roundworms.

_____ **57.** There is an excretory system composed of flame cells.

_____ **58.** An open circulatory system is present.

_____ **59.** Annelid worms have a stomach with a small and large intestine.

_____ **60.** There are several hearts.

Arthropods:

_____ **61.** include the most species of any animal group.

_____ **62.** produce cuticles of chitin.

_____ **63.** have an abdomen.

_____ **64.** have book lungs, gills, and tracheae as respiratory structures.

_____ **65.** Centipedes have two pair of legs per segment; millipedes have one pair of legs per segment.

_____ **66.** Crustaceans include the shrimp, crabs, lobsters, and barnacles.

_____ **67.** The exoskeleton of crustaceans is hardened with silica.

_____ **68.** A change called metamorphosis occurs within a structure called the larva.

Echinoderms:

_____ **69.** have an internal skeleton.

_____ **70.** locomote by means of flagellae and cilia.

_____ **71.** include star fish, sea cucumbers, sea lilies, and sea urchins.

_____ **72.** show bilateral symmetry in adults.

_____ **73.** Antennae of insects are used for what primary purpose?

    a. locomotion   **c.** sensing   **e.** communicating
    b. digestion   **d.** reproduction

_____ **74.** Mollusk gills are located in the:

    a. head   **b.** mantle   **c.** foot   **d.** viscera   **e.** tail

Key for questions 75–82. Match the numbered statement with the best response from the _Key_.

a. setae	**d.** radula	**ab.** mantle
b. chelicerae	**e.** clitellum	**ac.** trochophore
c. tracheae		**ad.** pedipalps

_____ **75.** a highly mobile, fringed larva

_____ **76.** poison fangs of spiders

_____ **77.** hard, toothlike structure used for scraping up food

_____ **78.** bristles found in roundworms

_____ **79.** modified legs for holding prey

_____ **80.** air passages in insects

_____ **81.** fold of tissue over the viscera that can excrete inorganic salts for shells

_____ **82.** a mucus- and chitin-secreting structure in certain worms.

Key Terms from the Text Chapter

abdomen   *text page 410*

animal   *394*

bilateral symmetry   *401*

bivalve   *407*

book lung   *411*

cephalization   *401*

cephalopod   *407*

cephalothorax   *412*

closed circulatory system   *409*

cnidarian   *399*

deuterostome   *405*

echinoderm   *397*

endoskeleton   *414*

exoskeleton   *409*

filter feeder   *407*

flatworm   *401*

gastropod   *406*

hydroskeleton   *404*

insect   *413*

invertebrate   *394*

medusa   *399*

metamorphosis   *413*

mollusk   *405*

molt   *410*

nerve cord   *403*

open circulatory system   *406*

polyp   *399*

protostome   *405*

pseudocoelom   *403*

pupa   *413*

roundworm   *403*

segmentation   *408*

segmented worm   *408*

social insect   *413*

spider   *412*

sponge   *396*

thorax   *410*

vertebrate   *394*

water vascular system   *414*

Concept Figure: The Invertebrate Animals

Exercise

Test your memory by filling in at least two examples of each invertebrate group listed in the table. Underline the phyla that show bilateral symmetry. Circle those in which a true coelom is present. Star the phylum that includes the most diverse aggregate of animal species. Finally, under "Notable features," list at least two *other* distinguishing features for each phylum.

Phylum	Examples	Number of species	Notable features
Porifera		5,000	
Cnidaria		10,000	
Platyhelminthes		10,000	
Nematoda		12,000	
Mollusca		120,000	
Annelida		5,000	
Arthropoda		1,000,000	
Echinodermata		6,000	

19

Vertebrates and Their Relatives

CHAPTER IN BRIEF

The Rise of *Homo sapiens*

    Homo habilis

    Homo erectus

    Homo sapiens

    The Agricultural Revolution

Perspective and Review

The phylum Chordata comprises 5% of the animal kingdom and arose from an aquatic invertebrate ancestor. Apart from two small marine groups, **vertebrates**—animals with backbones—are the dominate chordates. As they evolved, **chordates** developed a broad range of physical and behavioral adaptations. Specializations for particular environments and conditions led to adaptive radiation, the evolution of a variety of forms from a single ancestral type. Although human evolution has resulted in a number of unique physical traits and capabilities, it has been guided by the same principles that govern the emergence of all species.

The Chordates, Including the Simple Tunicates and Lancelets

About 45,000 species make up the phylum Chordata, including fish, amphibians, reptiles, birds, and mammals. Five main evolutionary advances, summarized in Concept Table 19.1, characterize the phylum. These adaptations allowed chordates to grow large and develop greater nervous control and intelligence. Figure 19.4 in your text illustrates how each chordate group expanded on these innovations.

Concept Table 19.1   Major features and classification of the phylum Chordata

Adaptations

1. A dorsal **notocord**, a supporting rod that runs the length of the animal. In tunicates the notocord is present only in the embryo; the vertebral column replaces the notocord in vertebrates.
2. A tube of nervous tissue, the **nerve cord** or **spinal cord**, which runs above the notocord.
3. **Gill slits** (openings in the pharynx). In most reptiles, birds, and mammals these are present only in the embryo.
4. A tail that extends beyond the anus is present during some part of the life cycle.
5. Muscle blocks (myotomes), modified body segments.

Classification (three chordate subphyla):

1. **Urochordata.**   Filter-feeding **tunicates**. The adult secretes a **tunic** that encloses a food-straining **pharynx**. The tadpolelike larva has a notocord and nerve cord in its tail, which disappears at metamorphosis.
2. **Cephalochordata.   Lancelets.** Small, fishlike marine animals that have all the chordate characteristics throughout their lives.
3. **Vertebrata.**   The vertebrates. Includes fish, amphibians, reptiles, birds, and mammals.

Fishes: The Earliest Vertebrates

The first vertebrates to evolve were filter-feeding **fishes** that arose in the Paleozoic era. Concept Table 19.2 describes the evolution of fishes in the order in which each group appeared.

Concept Table 19.2 Evolution of fishes

Agnathans	Jawless fishes. Characterized by a **bony skeleton** that included gill supports and a **skull**, and a muscular system for pumping water. Only two groups survive, the parasitic **lampreys** and the scavenging **hagfish**. Both have cartilage in place of bone.
Placoderms	The first jawed fishes, which arose from the agnathans about 425 million years ago. They possessed three main innovations that were further developed in later vertebrates: hinged **jaws**, **vertebrae**, and **fins**.
Chondrichthyes	Sharks, rays, and skates. All have a cartilaginous skeleton.
Osteichthyes	Bony fishes. There are two main groups: **Lobe-finned fish** are air breathing and have muscular lobes for "walking." Presentday representatives are the lungfishes and coelacanths. **Teleosts**, or **spiny-finned fishes**, are the largest vertebrate group. Teleosts have spiny fins and swim bladders that allow them to adjust buoyancy.

Amphibians: First Vertebrates to Live on Land

The first **amphibians** evolved between 345 million and 400 million years ago. The group includes frogs, toads, and salamanders. Three important features characterize amphibians: (1) front and hind limbs with powerful muscles, (2) air-breathing lungs for gas exchange (although the moist amphibian skin also serves as a site for gas exchange), and (3) partial separation of oxygenated and unoxygenated blood in the heart. Although amphibians are terrestrial, they still depend on water to prevent desiccation and for reproduction. Eggs are laid in water, where the larvae develop.

Reptiles: Conquerors of the Continents

The key to successful terrestrial life for vertebrates was the development of ways to avoid desiccation and dependence on water for reproduction. **Reptiles**, which include snakes and crocodiles, evolved a number of adaptations to overcome these problems, and as a result underwent a great adaptive radiation that spanned 150 million years until the mass extinction at the end of the Cretaceous. Concept Table 19.3 summarizes the important adaptations and some key events in reptile evolution.

Concept Table 19.3   Reptile evolution

Adaptations

1. A dry, scaly skin to prevent desiccation.
2. Large **lungs** and an expandable rib cage. A heart and circulatory system with more complete separation of oxygenated and unoxygenated blood, so that more oxygen can reach the tissues.
3. Copulatory organs in males to deliver sperm directly into the female's body.
4. **Amniote** eggs, which bathe the embryo in water, provide it with food, and have a leathery shell to prevent desiccation.

Evolution

Cotylosaurs were the first reptiles, giving rise to the thecodonts (**dinosaurs**) and the therapsids, the group ancestral to mammals.

Birds: Airborne Vertebrates

A highly successful group, **birds** have radiated into a class comprising 8,600 species specialized for diverse modes of life. The main trends evident in bird evolution are largely adaptations for flight. Concept Table 19.4 summarizes these features.

Concept Table 19.4   Evolutionary adaptations of birds

Skeletal adaptations

1. **Feathers**. Lightweight structures composed of dead cells containing keratin. Flight feathers are made more aerodynamic by interlocking **barbules**. Down feathers provide insulation.
2. Hollow, lightweight **bones**. The **sternum** is enlarged to anchor the powerful flight muscles. Legs are reduced and can be folded under the body.

Physiological adaptations

1. **Homeothermy** (**warm-bloodedness**); they maintain a constant internal temperature, which allows for constant ATP production during cellular respiration. (All "lower" animals are **poikilothermic**, or **cold blooded**: Their body temperature fluctuates along with that of the external environment.)
2. Connected **air sacs** and lungs to increase gas exchange and complete separation of oxygenated and unoxygenated blood.

Mammals: Rulers of the Cenozoic

From an evolutionary standpoint **mammals** have been a tremendously successful group. They have undergone such a rapid radiation into 5,000 modern species that the present era (the Cenozoic) is known as the Age of Mammals. Concept Table 19.5 describes the main features that have contributed to the success of mammals and summarizes the three main mammalian groups.

Adaptations

1. **Body hair** or **fur** at some point in the life cycle.
2. Female **mammary glands** that produce **milk**, a fat- and protein-rich fluid, for their young. Most mammals also have a placenta to support the embryo.

Specializations

Mammals are efficient homeotherms due to their metabolism, insulating hair or blubber, and behavioral modifications such as migration and hibernation. Limbs and teeth are often highly specialized. Mammals have a well-developed nervous system, which reaches its highest level in primates and cetaceans (whales and porpoises). Most mammals show extended parental care.

Classification (Three main groups):

1. **Monotremes**. The most primitive, and the only egg-laying mammals; the duck-billed platypus and the spiny anteater are the only two living forms.
2. **Marsupials**. Includes kangaroos and opossums; young are born early in development and complete development in a pouch.
3. **Placentals**. Most modern mammals, including mice, dogs, bats, and humans.

Evolution of Primates: Our Own Taxonomic Order

The **primates** arose about 6 million years ago as a branch from the chimpanzee lineage. Primitive primates evolved two important specializations for living in trees: the **opposable thumb** and acute vision. These and later specializations formed the basis for a number of human physical traits. Primate characteristics include **stereoscopic vision**, increased brain size, an upright gait, teeth modified for omnivory, and reproductive modifications that include the production of small litters. Offspring are born helpless and require extensive parental care, an investment that pays off in increased survivorship of young. Zoologists recognize two suborders; the prosimians, small, primitive tree-dwellers, which include lemurs and tarsiers; and the **arthropoids**, which include Old and New World monkeys, apes, and humans. Apes, gorillas, and chimpanzees most resemble humans and are termed **hominoids**.

The Rise of *Homo sapiens*

Concept Table 19.6 outlines the evolution of **hominids** leading to the emergence of humans (**Homo sapiens**).

Early hominids	The earliest hominids, *Australopithecus afarensis*, emerged in Africa about five million years ago (mya). Individuals had small brains but were fully upright. Less than 1.3 meters tall, they lived on the ground and were herbivorous.
Homo habilis	First appeared in Africa about 2 mya. Possessed a more developed brain and were larger than their predecessors. They ate meat and were the first primates to use tools.

Continues

Concept Table 19.6   Hominid evolution (continued)

Homo erectus	Originated in Africa about 1.7 mya and migrated throughout Eurasia. Members of this species were taller, and parts of the brain may have undergone internal reorganization. They made more complex tools. Cooperative cooking, hunting, and food sharing may have developed and been maintained by **cultural transmission**.
Homo sapiens	This species appeared 500,000 years ago and is character-ized by larger brains, reduced teeth, and enlarged rear **skulls**. There are two groups of *H. sapiens*: An archaic group in-cluded Neanderthals; the second, modern, group included the now-extinct Cro-Magnons, which arose in Africa and re-placed the Neanderthals. About 10,000 years ago the agri-cultural revolution began, which led to an accumulation of knowledge passed down through generations, a process known as cultural evolution.

Thought Provokers

1. Consider the probable and possible primate origins of *Homo sapiens*, and briefly describe the physical and other features of human ancestors. Use appropriate names, times, and examples.

2. Trace the ascending pathway of evolutionary development in vertebrates, starting with the simplest and progressing to the most developed. Use pertinent examples in your explanation.

Self-Test

For each statement or question choose the best response and mark your choice in the space provided. For some items you will select your answer from a *Key*.

Key for questions 1–25

a. amphibians	**d.** mammals	**ac.** lancelets
b. birds	**e.** fishes	**ad.** two or more of these
c. reptiles	**ab.** tunicates	**ae.** none of these

_____ **1.** Have thickened skins and amniotic eggs

_____ **2.** Include apodes

_____ **3.** Characteristically have lightweight bones and a specially developed sternum

_____ **4.** Include Tyrannosaurus and Brontosaurus

_____ **5.** Produce milk

_____ **6.** the Urochordata

_____ **7.** the earliest vertebrates

_____ **8.** Archaeopteryx

_____ **9.** dolphins and porpoises

_____ **10.** the first homeotherms

_____ **11.** Have gill slits

_____ **12.** primates

_____ **13.** Cephalochordata

_____ **14.** Have air sacs and lungs

_____ **15.** Can live on land and in water

_____ **16.** whales

_____ **17.** Are cold-blooded creatures

_____ **18.** Notochords, present in larvae, disappear in adults

_____ **19.** The first group on the evolutionary scale with a four-chambered heart

_____ **20.** toads and salamanders

_____ **21.** Dryopithecus, Ramapithecus, and Sivapithecus

_____ **22.** warm-blooded creatures

_____ **23.** Have barbules

_____ **24.** Show the highest level of nervous system development

_____ **25.** Include teleosts

_____ **26.** Which one of the following statements is <u>not</u> true? Bats:

    a. include more species than all other mammals.
    b. include some blood-suckers.
    c. are vertebrates.
    d. are the only mammals that fly.
    e. navigate by means of infrared radiation.

_____ **27.** Your text reasons that dinosaurs were extinguished by:

    a. a major fire   **c.** a virulent disease   **e.** a number of possibilities
    b. an ice age   **d.** a meteor strike

_____ **28.** All but one of the following reflect the highest degrees of animal intelligence. Which one does not?

    a. drawing pictures
    b. making and using tools
    c. burying the dead with mementos or gifts
    d. communicating by sign and verbal signals
    e. capturing prey and taking prisoners

_____ **29.** Muscle blocks are most closely associated with the term:

    a. myotomes   **c.** cephalization   **e.** gastrointestinal
    b. bilateral symmetry   **d.** cardiovascular

Key for questions 30–50

a. True   **b.** False

_____ **30.** Tunicates and lancelets lack vertebrae.

_____ **31.** Tunicates and lancelets are chordates.

_____ **32.** Notochords run about halfway down the length of animals that possess this structure.

_____ **33.** Gill slits are considered part of the anterior gut.

_____ **34.** Sometime during their development, all chordates have a tail.

_____ **35.** The most primitive chordates are filter-feeders.

_____ **36.** Lampreys and hagfishes are jawless parasitic fishes whose earlier, now-extinct relatives were agnathans.

_____ **37.** Chondrichthyes have much cartilage in their bodies.

_____ **38.** Amphibians appeared and began to diversify during the age of flowering plants.

_____ **39.** Many amphibians use swallowing movements to pump air to the lungs.

_____ **40.** Poikilothermic animals are warm-blooded.

_____ **41.** Mammals were the rulers of the Mesozoic age.

_____ **42.** Monotremes and marsupials are special types of placental mammals.

_____ **43.** Lemurs and tarsiers are tree-dwelling mammals.

_____ **44.** Lemurs and tarsiers are members of the Anthropoidea.

_____ **45.** Aye-ayes, sifakas, pottos, and lorises are prosimians.

_____ **46.** Old World monkeys are more closely related to humans than are New World monkeys.

_____ **47.** Primates characteristically have teeth that are typical of carnivores.

_____ **48.** DNA analyses show that humans are more closely related to chimpanzees than to gorillas.

_____ **49.** Major development and evolution of primates occurred in the past 20 million years.

_____ **50.** *Homo habilis* was more advanced than *Homo erectus*.

_____ **51.** Which statement is correct about agnathan fishes?

    a. Very few species of that group are alive today.

    b. They had powerful jaws.

    c. They had a cartilage covering for the brain.

    d. Gill slits were used for feeding.

    e. The fish were unusual in that they lacked bones.

_____ **52.** All but one of the following were characteristic of placoderms. Which one was not?

    a. They lived over 800 million years ago.

    b. They had hinged jaws.

    c. They developed the first fins.

    d. They developed the first vertebrae.

    e. They had a notochord and spinal cord.

Key Terms from the Text Chapter

air sac   *text page 429*

amphibian   *426*

Australopithecus   437

bipedalism   *438*

bird   *429*

chordate   *419*

cultural transmission   *439*

dinosaur   *428*

fin   *424*

fish   *422*

gill slit   *421*

hominid   *437*

hominoid   *435*

Homo sapiens   439

jaw   *423*

lamprey   *423*

lancelet   *420*

lung   *424*

mammal   *431*

mammary gland   *431*

marsupial   *431*

monotreme   *431*

opposable thumb   *434*

primate   *433*

reptile   *427*

skull   *422*

spinal cord   *420*

stereoscopic vision   *436*

tail   *421*

teleost   *425*

tunicate   *420*

vertebrate   *419*

warm-blooded   *429*

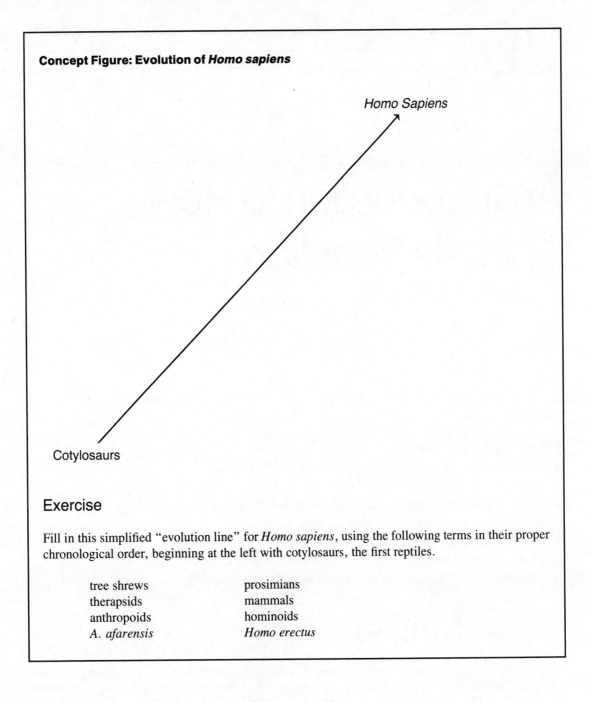

Concept Figure: Evolution of *Homo sapiens*

Homo Sapiens

Cotylosaurs

Exercise

Fill in this simplified "evolution line" for *Homo sapiens*, using the following terms in their proper chronological order, beginning at the left with cotylosaurs, the first reptiles.

tree shrews	prosimians
therapsids	mammals
anthropoids	hominoids
A. afarensis	*Homo erectus*

20

An Introduction to How Animals Function

CHAPTER IN BRIEF

Perspective and Review

Animals live in fluctuating environments. However, in order to survive an animal must keep its life processes, such as respiration, running at a constant rate regardless of external conditions. **Homeostasis**, the maintenance of internal constancy, is therefore a central problem facing all animals. In order to survive in their various habitats, animals have evolved **anatomical** (structural) and **physiological** (ways in which structures function) adaptations. These adaptations, which arose by natural selection, allow different organisms to exploit their environments in different ways.

Staying Alive: Problems, Solutions and the Role of Physical Size

All cells and organisms must exchange materials with the external environment. For example, cells must take in oxygen and must expel waste products of metabolism. This exchange of materials at the cellular level takes place by diffusion. Unicellular organisms have organelles that carry out life-supporting processes. Each cell in multicellular organisms must also accomplish the same processes, but relatively few of these cells are in direct contact with the external environment. To overcome this logistical problem, multicellular organisms have systems of tubes that connect the interior of the animal with the external world. These systems—for digestion, respiration, and excretion—provide sites where diffusion between body fluids (such as blood) and tube contents can take place. Substances diffuse from tubes into body fluids, and vice versa; body fluids in turn are transported around the body, coming into contact with individual cells so that materials diffuse into cells and waste products are returned to the tube.

In order to carry out the various tasks that enable an animal to stay alive, body cells are organized into discrete functional groups. There are four levels of organization, described in Concept Table 20.1.

Concept Table 20.1   Hierarchy of cellular organization

Tissue	A group of cells that perform the same function. There are four main animal tissues: **epithelial tissue** covers body surfaces; **connective tissue** binds and supports other tissues and organs; **nervous tissue** transmits electrical impulses; and **muscle tissue** facilitates movement. Figures 20.6 and 20.7 in your text describe epithelial and connective tissue.
Organ	A group of two or more tissues that operate as a unit to perform a particular function. Example: the stomach.
Organ system	Two or more organs that serve a common function. *Example:* the digestive system, which includes the mouth, stomach, intestines, and enzyme-secreting organs and which together process food.
Organism	The collective organ systems.

Animal Adaptations: Form and Function Suit the Environment

Animal adaptations have evolved to suit the environments in which animals live. For example, whales have a streamlined shape ideal for swimming; predatory cats have powerful muscles that enable them to hunt, and sharp canine teeth to tear the flesh of their victims. Desert animals have large appendages that radiate heat, and have evolved physiological mechanisms for conserving, and in some cases producing, water.

Homeostasis: Keeping the Cellular Environment Constant

Physiological systems constantly adjust to changes in the external environment. As a result, body cells are maintained in a condition in which they can function efficiently. Concept Table 10.2 describes **feedback loops**, the physiological strategies that permit animals to maintain homeostasis.

Concept Table 20.2   Feedback loops: strategies for homeostasis

Feedback loop	A physiological circuit consisting of a *receptor*, which senses environmental conditions, an *integrator*, which evaluates situations and makes decisions, and an *effector*, to execute commands. Example: nerves (receptors) detect an empty stomach; they signal the brain (integrator), which interprets the signal as hunger and in turn signals muscles (effectors) that enable the animal to move in search of food.
Negative feedback loop	A system that resists change by detecting stimuli and activating mechanisms that act in the opposite direction to the stimulus.
Positive feedback loop	A system in which an initial stimulus triggers a response, which in turn acts as a stimulus for a further response.

Endotherms (animals that maintain a constant internal temperature) have a number of additional mechanisms to help maintain homeostasis. Whales have a thick insulating layer of fat (blubber), an anatomical mechanism for controlling heat loss. Species of birds and whales migrate to warmer climates in winter—a behavioral adaptation. Feedback loops enable animals, including humans, to respond to changes in temperature by reducing blood flow to the extremities in cold conditions and by increasing the flow to radiate excess heat when the body becomes overheated.

Ectotherms (animals whose internal temperature fluctuates with the environment) generally have behavioral mechanisms for maintaining temperature homeostasis. For example, lizards warm up by orienting themselves in a way that maximizes the amount of sun shining on their bodies. Some ectoderms also have physiological adaptations; certain freshwater fish have two sets of enzymes, each set functional at different temperatures.

Thought Provokers

1. Explain negative and positive feedback systems and give at least one example of each. Explain why feedback loops are important.

2. Define homeostasis, name two physiological parameters involved, and explain what can happen if homeostasis is disrupted.

Self-Test

For each statement or question choose the best response and mark your choice in the space provided. For some items you will select your response from a *Key*.

_____ 1. Which one term best fits the concept of homeostasis?
- **a.** difference
- **b.** equilibrium
- **c.** storage
- **d.** depletion
- **e.** fluctuation

_____ 2. Homeostatic mechanisms fundamentally operate via their effects on:
- **a.** body fluids
- **b.** muscles
- **c.** bone
- **d.** the brain
- **e.** the liver and intestines

_____ 3. Which choice shows the correct order in terms of increasing complexity?
- **a.** tissues, organs, cells
- **b.** tissues, cells, organs
- **c.** organs, tissues, cells
- **d.** cells, tissues, organs
- **e.** cells, organs, tissues

_____ 4. Which <u>two</u> of the following does a large animal <u>not</u> need for proper functioning?
- **a.** structural support
- **b.** a nervous system
- **c.** vision
- **d.** the ability to think
- **e.** an endocrine system

Key for questions 5–10
- **a.** True
- **b.** False

_____ 5. Homeostatic systems require receptors, integrators, and effectors.

_____ 6. Diffusion is the means of materials transport for very small, flat animals.

_____ 7. The endocrine system acts just as fast as the nervous system to coordinate and integrate the functions of organ systems.

_____ 8. Specialized anatomical adaptations allow different organisms to exploit their environments in different ways.

_____ 9. A rabbit's ears radiate excess internal heat.

_____ 10. Physiological systems adjust to environmental conditions at specific times of the day.

Questions 11–13. Using the *Key*, indicate the type of feedback loop that operates in or characterizes each of the following situations.
- **a.** Positive feedback loop
- **b.** Negative feedback loop

_____ 11. response to a brief chilling of the human body

_____ 12. oxytocin and uterine responses

_____ 13. screeching microphone feedback

_____ 14. Which of the following is <u>not</u> true with regard to temperature regulation?
- **a.** Ectotherms regulate temperature in much the same way as do endotherms.
- **b.** The hypothalamus acts as the body's thermostat in humans and in blue whales.
- **c.** Temperature is just one of several parameters involved in homeostasis.
- **d.** Both hypo- and hyperthermia can be fatal.
- **e.** "Set point" is a genetically determined ideal temperature for body-cell activity.

_____ **15.** Which one of the following is not characteristic of a fever?

    a. It may occur as a response to infections by microbes.

    b. It is controlled by the thalamus.

    c. It causes pyrogens to be released from white blood cells.

    d. It results when the body's metabolic rate increases.

    e. It may result in death.

Key Terms from the Text Chapter

anatomy *text page 445*

connective tissue *448*

epithelial tissue *448*

feedback loop *452*

homeostasis *445*

muscle tissue *448*

organ *448*

organism *448*

organ system *448*

physiology *445*

tissue *448*

Concept Figure: Feedback Loops

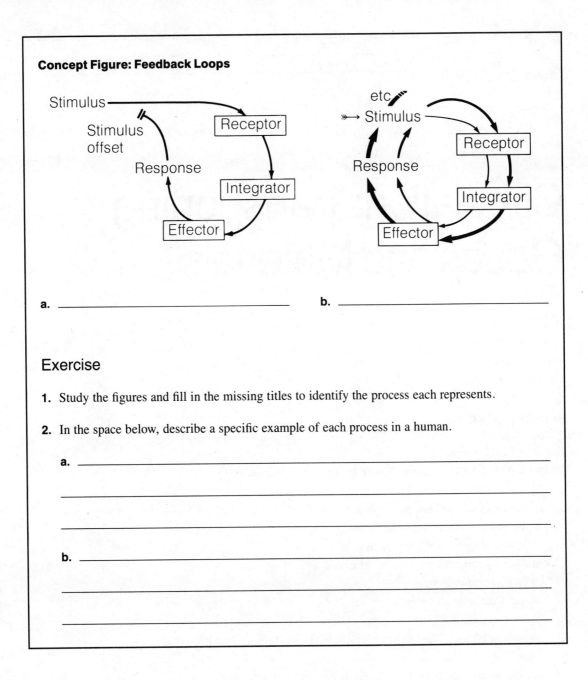

a. _____   b. _____

Exercise

1. Study the figures and fill in the missing titles to identify the process each represents.

2. In the space below, describe a specific example of each process in a human.

   a. _____

   _____

   _____

   b. _____

   _____

   _____

21

Circulation: Transporting Gases and Materials

Perspective and Review

The **circulatory system** consists of a heart and blood vessels that transport blood to the tissues. Its main function is to transport oxygen and nutrients to the cells and to remove waste products. However, the system performs a number of additional functions: It is important in the body's defense against foreign invaders such as bacteria; it helps regulate body temperature and pH; and it carries substances that repair cuts and leaks in the system.

Invertebrates have a simple circulatory system, while that of vertebrates is more complex. As the vertebrate circulatory system evolved it developed two important features that are most refined in mammals: increased separation of oxygenated and deoxygenated blood, resulting in more efficient transport of oxygen to the cells; and a tendency towards a high pressure system. This adaptation allows blood to be pumped a greater distance from the heart, which in turn enables animals to grow to larger size.

Blood: A Multipurpose Liquid for Internal Transport

Blood has both liquid and solid components. Concept Table 21.1 describes the composition of blood and the functions of its various elements.

Concept Table 21.1 Blood composition

Plasma	Liquid portion of blood, consisting mostly of water. It transports blood cells and particles, and contains three important proteins: globulins (which include antibodies) and albumen, both important in the body's defense system; and fibrinogen, a clotting protein.
Leukocytes (white blood cells)	Important components of the body's defense mechanism, they are divided into five classes: **neutrophils** and **monocytes**, which engulf foreign particles; **eosinophils**, which break down foreign proteins and blood clots; **basophils**, which produce histamine and release an anticlotting substance; and **lymphocytes**, which are involved in the immune response.
Erythrocytes (red blood cells)	Most common type of blood cell; small, circular, biconcave discs without nuclei that carry oxygen and carbon dioxide. The cells die after about 120 days; a negative feedback loop involving the hormone erythropoietin controls their replacement.
Thrombocytes (platelets)	Cell fragments involved in blood clotting.

Circulatory Systems: Strategies for Material Transport

Two basic types of circulatory systems occur in the animal kingdom. The more primitive open circulatory system occurs in most invertebrates, including mollusks and arthropods. There is usually a simple two-chambered heart, and hemolymph (a blood equivalent) is carried partially in blood vessels but also percolates freely through the tissues. Many of these animals possess a separate gas exchange system. Segmented worms and vertebrates have a closed circulatory system. Blood flows only in blood vessels and transports oxygen in addition to nutrients and waste products. Concept Table 21.2 outlines the main evolutionary advances in the circulatory systems of different vertebrate classes.

Concept Table 21.2   Vertebrate circulatory systems

Fish	Simple loop structure: A two-chambered heart consisting of an **atrium** that receives deoxygenated blood from the body, and a **ventricle** that receives blood from the atrium and pumps that blood to the gills. Gas exchange occurs in the gills, and oxygenated blood then flows to the body.
Amphibians	Three-chambered heart with two atria, one that receives oxygenated blood from the lungs and another that receives deoxygenated blood from the body. Both empty into a single ventricle, so some mixing of bloods occurs.
Reptiles	Certain reptiles, such as crocodiles, have a septum, or partition, that partially divides the single ventricle, thus reducing mixing of oxygenated and deoxygenated blood.
Birds and mammals	A high-pressure two-loop system with a four-chambered heart (an upper, smaller atrium and lower ventricle on each side). The two-loop arrangement ensures complete separation of oxygenated and deoxygenated blood. In the **pulmonary circulation** loop deoxygenated blood is pumped from the right ventricle to the lungs, where gas exchange occurs, and oxygenated blood is returned to the left side of the heart. The **systemic circulation** then pumps this blood to the rest of the body.

Circulation in Humans and Other Mammals: The Life-Sustaining Double Loop

The pumping heart and the network of blood vessels that allow the cells to carry on essential life processes is well developed in mammals. Concept Table 21.3 describes the structure and functioning of the mammalian circulatory system.

Concept Table 21.3   Structure and functioning of the mammalian circulatory system

Arteries	Large muscular vessels that carry blood from the heart; muscular contractions in arteries maintain blood pressure.
Arterioles	Smaller vessels that branch from arteries. They have a less-developed muscle layer.
Capillaries	Microscopic vessels forming networks, or **capillary beds**, that permeate the tissues. Capillary walls are just one cell thick, so diffusion can occur across their cell membranes. Arterioles branch into capillaries, from which oxygen and other

Continues

Concept Table 21.3   Structure and functioning of the mammalian circulatory system (continued)

	substances enter tissues. Deoxygenated blood and wastes from the tissues diffuse first into capillaries and are transported to **venules**, small vessels that connect into veins.
Veins	Large, thin-walled vessels that carry deoxygenated blood to the heart. A series of **valves** prevents backflow of blood in the veins.
Heart and circulation	Two veins, the **superior and inferior venae cavae**, carry deoxygenated blood to the right atrium in the heart, from where it is pumped to the right ventricle. This ventricle pumps blood to the lungs via the **pulmonary artery**. Reoxygenated blood flows back to the left atrium via the pulmonary vein and from there to the left ventricle. Contraction of the ventricle forces blood into the **aorta**, the main artery of the systemic circulation. A series of valves prevents backflow of blood in the heart. Note that the pulmonary artery is the only artery to carry deoxygenated blood and the pulmonary vein is the only vein transporting oxygenated blood.

Heartbeat

Special pacemaker cells control heartbeat. Those near the **sinoatrial (SA) node** control atrial contractions, while those near the **atrioventricular node** control ventricle contractions. The term **cardiac cycle** describes the contraction of atria or ventricles (**systole** phase) and subsequent relaxation of these muscles (**diastole** phase).

Blood Distribution and Clotting

If blood is required in a particular part of the body, **vasoconstriction** (contraction of blood vessels) in other parts of the body shunts blood to that region. At the same time, **vasodilation**—widening of the vessel's internal spaces—occurs in the area requiring more blood.

When a vessel is cut, clotting occurs to stop blood loss. Clotting is a complex sequence of events controlled by substances in the plasma. Concept Table 21.4 summarizes the main steps in blood clotting.

Concept Table 21.4   Main steps in blood clotting

1. Vasoconstriction reduces blood flow to the region of tissue damage.
2. Platelets release *serotonin*, which maintains the vasoconstriction.
3. Platelets in the region of the wound stick to each other and form a plug.
4. **Coagulation**—formation of a blood clot—occurs: Injured cells from damaged tissue release an "activator," which stimulates the conversion of **prothrombin** into **thrombin**. Thrombin in turn stimulates the transformation of **fibrinogen** into tough, insoluble threads of **fibrin**. These threads form a mesh that traps red blood cells, producing a clot.

The Lymphatic System: The Second Circulatory System

Because the circulatory system functions under high pressure, some fluids escape into the body tissues. To prevent buildup of tissue fluid, a second system, the **lymphatic system**, collects the fluid (known as **lymph**) and returns it to the circulatory system. Lymph vessels also carry debris and bacteria, which are ultimately destroyed by lymphocytes in structures known as **lymph nodes**. The thymus, an important organ involved in immunity, and the spleen, which filters blood and stores white blood cells, are both considered components of the lymphatic system.

Thought Provokers

1. As animals become more complex their circulatory systems also become more complex. Briefly describe the increasing degrees of circulatory system complexity, from amoebae to humans. Include at least six different evolutionary innovations.

2. Modern medicine has clarified some of the important factors associated with atherosclerosis and heart disease. Develop a brief essay-discussion with the following terms, and define each term as it relates to current concepts in medicine. Terms: atherosclerosis, heart disease, cholesterol, LDL, HDL, receptors, diet, metabolism, exercise.

Self-Test

For each statement or question choose the best response and mark your choice in the space provided. For some items, you will select your response from a *Key*.

_____ 1. The rete mirabile is a:
   a. type of red blood cell
   b. type of white blood cell
   c. series of large blood vessels
   d. series of small blood vessels
   e. part of the lymphatic system

_____ 2. The number of liters of blood in the human body is about:
   a. 2   b. 3   c. 5   d. 7   e. 10

_____ 3. A liter is slightly greater than a:
   a. pint   b. quart   c. gallon   d. ounce   e. milliliter

a. plasma   **c.** fibrinogen   **e.** platelets
b. serum   **d.** fibrin

_____ **4.** term for the actual clot protein

_____ **5.** the fluid portion that remains after blood clots

_____ **6.** cell fragments that are important in blood clotting

_____ **7.** the fluid portion of blood prior to clotting

_____ **8.** essential protein necessary to form a clot

Key for questions 9–12

a. True   **b.** False

Human red blood cells:

_____ **9.** when mature, lack a nucleus

_____ **10.** live approximately one year before dying

_____ **11.** are spherical in shape

_____ **12.** typically contain mitochondria and an endoplasmic reticulum at maturity

_____ **13.** With regard to erythropoietin, mark <u>all</u> true statements.

    a. Is produced by the liver and the kidney.
    b. Results in the manufacture of more red blood cells.
    c. Is not produced when the oxygen supply is high.
    d. Is an enzyme.
    e. Stimulates cellular activity in the bone marrow.

Key for questions 14–16

a. Cell is phagocytic   **b.** Cell is not phagocytic

_____ **14.** lymphocyte

_____ **15.** monocyte

_____ **16.** neutrophil

Questions 17–21. Match the numbered statement with the <u>best</u> answer from the *Key*, which lists various cell types.

a. neutrophil   **c.** lymphocyte   **e.** eosinophil
b. basophil   **d.** monocyte   **ab.** thrombocyte

_____ **17.** another name for platelets

_____ **18.** histamine-producing cells

_____ **19.** antibody-producing cells

_____ **20.** used to break down blood clots and foreign proteins

_____ **21.** the most common and active phagocytic cell in the body

_____ **22.** Arthropods and mollusks have a circulatory medium termed:

    a. hemolymph   **c.** cytoglobin   **e.** erythrocytin

    b. hemoglobin   **d.** erthropoietin

Questions 23–29. Match the numbered statement with the best response from the _Key_.

a. amphibians/reptiles   **c.** segmented worms   **e.** mammals

b. birds   **d.** fish   **ab.** none of these

_____ **23.** have an open circulatory system

_____ **24.** have a two-chambered heart

_____ **25.** the first animals to show a closed circulatory system

_____ **26.** first to evolve a four-chambered heart

_____ **27.** have the most complicated or advanced heart

_____ **28.** possess three-chambered hearts

_____ **29.** animals that show lung-loop circulation systems (choose all responses that apply)

_____ **30.** The maximum desirable gas/nutrient diffusion distance between the circulatory site and body cells is approximately one:

    a. micrometer   **c.** centimeter   **e.** meter

    b. millimeter   **d.** decimeter

Questions 31–39 involve a comparison between arteries and veins. If the numbered statement is greater or larger in arteries, mark A; if the statement is greater or larger in veins, mark B.

_____ **31.** thickness of the vessel wall

_____ **32.** diameter of the lumen

_____ **33.** number of valves present

_____ **34.** pressure in the vessel

_____ **35.** amount of blood-borne oxygen carried in the vessel

_____ **36.** vessel type that clinicians usually employ to measure blood pressure

_____ **37.** vessels that retain or contain the most blood

_____ **38.** vessel type in which leg muscle activity can be important for improving blood circulation

_____ **39.** vessel system from which the right atrium receives blood

Questions 40–43. Blood coming into the heart from the general body circulation will pass through the valves of the heart in a definite order. Using the _Key_, supply the valve sequence.

a. aortic semilunar   **c.** atrioventricular

b. pulmonary semilunar   **d.** ventricular multiphasic

_____ **40.** Blood first entering the heart will pass what valve?

_____ **41.** This same blood will next pass what valve?

_____ **42.** The next valve that blood encounters during circulation is which?

_____ **43.** Finally, blood will pass this valve.

_____ **44.** The initial electrical impulse of a new heartbeat begins where?

    a. atrioventricular node   **b.** sinoatrial node

_____ **45.** Where are the pacemaker cells located?

    a. atrioventricular node   **b.** sinoatrial node

_____ **46.** The resting phase of a heartbeat occurs:

    a. during diastole   **c.** during both phases

    b. during systole   **d.** during neither phase

_____ **47.** When ventricles begin to relax, the valves in the aorta and pulmonary arteries:

    a. open in both

    b. close in both

    c. open in one, close in the other

_____ **48.** In atherosclerosis, blood pressure tends to:

    a. fall   **b.** rise   **c.** remain the same

_____ **49.** A person with red, irritated eyes uses eye drops to relieve the condition. Which statement best describes the effect(s) of the drops?

    a. The heart beats faster to improve overall circulation.

    b. The kidneys excrete more fluid.

    c. The blood vessels in the eye dilate.

    d. All of these take place.

    e. None of these is correct.

Key for questions 50–53

a. True   **b.** False

During the dive reflex:

_____ **50.** The heart rate quickens.

_____ **51.** Blood is shunted to the brain and heart.

_____ **52.** Blood is shunted to the intestines.

_____ **53.** The rate of respiration increases.

_____ **54.** Serotonin is released from:

    a. platelets   **c.** neutrophils   **e.** eosinophils

    b. erythrocytes   **d.** basophils

Key for questions 55–60

a. True   **b.** False

The lymphatic system:

_____ **55.** collects fluid released or expressed from the general circulation

_____ **56.** has capillaries, veins, and arteries just like the general circulatory system

_____ **57.** contains macrophages and lymphocytes

_____ **58.** includes the thymus and spleen

_____ **59.** is important in providing food and oxygen to body tissues

_____ **60.** includes nodes

_____ **61.** Which statement regarding cholesterol is correct?

    a. Cholesterol is a normal component of the body.
    b. High cholesterol is not dangerous.
    c. Cholesterol is inactivated by small amounts of low-density lipids.
    d. High-density lipids carry more cholesterol than low-density lipids.
    e. None of these is correct.

_____ **62.** Which listed blood pressure reading is the most abnormal?

    a. 105/65   **b.** 160/70   **c.** 145/105   **d.** 90/55   **e.** 150/75

Key Terms from the Text Chapter

aorta   *text page 469*
arteriole   *467*
artery   *466*
atrioventricular (AV) node   *470*
atrium   *465*
capillary bed   *467*
circulatory system   *461*
diastole   *470*
erythrocyte   *462*

inferior vena cava   *468*
leukocyte   *463*
lymph   *474*
lymphatic system   *474*
lymph node   *474*
platelet   *462*
precapillary sphincter   *472*
pulmonary artery   *469*
pulmonary circulation   *466*
sinoatrial (SA) node   *470*

superior vena cava   *468*
systemic circulation   *466*
systole   *470*
valve   *468*
vasoconstriction   *472*
vasodilation   *472*
vein   *467*
ventricle   *466*
venule   *467*

Concept Figure: The Vertebrate Heart and Circulation

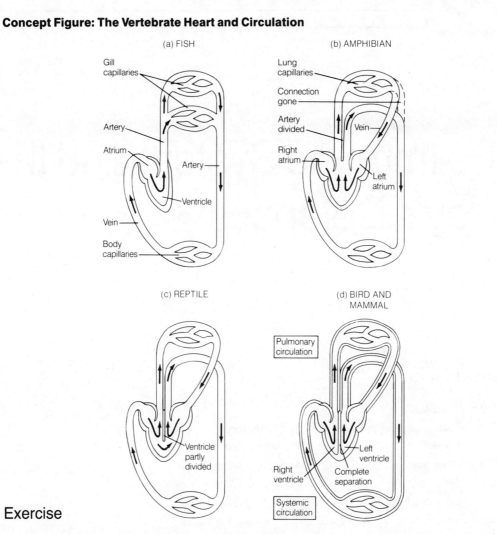

(a) FISH — Gill capillaries, Artery, Atrium, Artery, Ventricle, Vein, Body capillaries

(b) AMPHIBIAN — Lung capillaries, Connection gone, Artery divided, Vein, Right atrium, Left atrium

(c) REPTILE — Ventricle partly divided

(d) BIRD AND MAMMAL — Pulmonary circulation, Left ventricle, Right ventricle, Complete separation, Systemic circulation

Exercise

1. Using the figure as your reference complete the following chart by filling in the letter of the system that fits each description and citing a representative animal for each.

Description	System	Animal
Complete separation of oxygenated and deoxygenated blood; body-loop blood pumped at high pressure	_____	_____
Mixing of oxygenated and deoxygenated blood in a single ventricle, which receives the blood from two atria	_____	_____
The atrium pumps blood to the ventricle. Blood pressure is low in the tissues	_____	_____
A partially divided ventricle, which decreases the mixing of oxygenated and deoxygenated blood	_____	_____

2. What general biological process is responsible for the progression of circulatory system changes the drawings depict?

22

The Immune System and the Body's Defenses

Perspective and Review

Organisms are continually exposed to a wide variety of potentially harmful organisms and substances, including viruses, bacteria, and chemicals. To protect against such attacks, vertebrates have evolved a finely tuned defense mechanism, the **immune system**, which consists of a network of interacting molecules, cells, and organs. White blood cells, called **lymphocytes**, organize the defense. Differentiated lymphocytes are stored in and destroy invaders in the main organs of the immune system, the lymph nodes, spleen, and thymus. The immune system is closely allied with the circulatory and nervous systems, which help to regulate its activities.

The Body's Defenses: Major Players, Major Activities

There are two main types of immune responses: nonspecific, a fast-acting general mechanism; and specific, in which particular agents are aimed at specific targets. This is a slower-acting system that leads to immunity, or resistance to infection. Concept Table 22.1 summarizes both types of responses.

Concept Table 22.1   Nonspecific and specific immune responses

Nonspecific

1. Skin and mucous membranes, which act as barriers to invasion.
2. Inflammation, a physiological response to trauma, such as cuts or heat. Temperature and blood flow increase; white blood cells migrate to the wound to destroy invaders and engulf debris.

Specific

Antigens (foreign substances), stimulate **B cells (B lymphocytes)** to produce **antibodies**—proteins that recognize and bind to specific antigens. Antibody–antigen complexes are then destroyed by **macrophages**, or complement proteins. **T cells (T lymphocytes)** stimulate proliferation of B lymphocytes and also directly destroy foreign cells.

Antibodies: Defense Molecules Directed Against Specific Targets

Antibodies are immunoglobulins, Y-shaped globular proteins that consist of two identical heavy amino acid chains and two identical light chains. The tips of the Y recognize and bind to antigens, while the stem stimulates macrophage activity. Stem structure determines the role of an antibody, and, based on stem structure, biochemists recognize five main antibody classes. These include IgG (immunoglobulin G), which circulates in the blood, eliminating viruses and bacteria; IgA, found in body secretions; and IgE, which occurs in skin and in the lining of the intestine. IgA fights parasites and is involved in allergic responses.

B Cells: Mobilization and Memory

B cells are differentiated lymphocytes that produce and secrete antibodies. The type of immunity effected by B cells is known as the humoral immune response. Concept Table 22.2 outlines this system.

Concept Table 22.2   Significant features of B cells and humoral immunity

B cells	Small spherical cells that mature in bone marrow and whose surfaces are studded with antibodies. Each B cell carries and secretes antibodies with identical binding sites ("one cell, one antibody").
Humoral immunity	**Clonal selection mechanism:** A specific antigen "selects" the B cell with the best-fitting antibody. The resulting complex stimulates B cells carrying the same antibodies to proliferate and differentiate. Most develop into <u>plasma cells</u>, short-lived antibody-producing cells; others form <u>memory cells</u>, which act as an **immunological memory** that can produce a rapid response to any subsequent exposure. T cells and macrophages are also involved in stimulation of B cells by antigens.
Antibody synthesis	Gene reshuffling produces the vast array of antibodies present in the body. Three to four groups of genes encode antibody molecules, and during B-cell formation one gene from each group is randomly selected. This arrangement allows for many possible gene combinations; the human body can form antibodies with receptor sites of 64 million possible shapes.

T Cells: Direct Combat and Regulation

T-cell–based immunity, also called **cell-mediated immunity**, attacks large invaders such as cancers, tissue transplants, and viruses. Concept Table 22.3 outlines this type of immunity.

Concept Table 22.3   T cells and cell-mediated immunity

T cells	Lymphocytes that differentiate in the thymus; receptors on T-cell surfaces recognize antigens associated with **histocompatibility proteins**. An individual person has specific histocompatibility proteins recognized by T cells as self or nonself. These proteins stimulate T cells to destroy invaders and regulate the immune system.
Cell-mediated response	Under antigenic stimulation certain T cells proliferate and differentiate into <u>effector T cells</u>. Most of these are <u>cytotoxic</u> and poke holes in foreign cells, although a few promote inflammation. Effector T cells travel throughout the body, destroying any cell they encounter that has a foreign antigen on its surface. Half of all T cells serve as immune-system regulators; these include <u>helper T cells</u>, which stimulate the immune system, and <u>suppressor T cells</u>, which suppress the action of helpers and effectors.

Self-Tolerance

Immunologists believe that **self-tolerance**, the lack of an immune response to self, is controlled by macrophages. Macrophages do not allow intact substances from an individual's own body to enter T cells; thus "self" substances do not trigger an immune response in T cells.

Medical Manipulations: Short- and Long-Term Protection

Medical practitioners use two treatments involving the immune system to promote health and prevent disease. One of these is passive immunization, a short-term protective mechanism in which antibodies against a specific toxin are injected into the body. An example is the use of anti-venom to treat snakebites. In a second method, which results in active immunity, small amounts of antigen are injected into the body to stimulate the immune system. An example is vaccination against measles.

Thought Provoker

1. Explain why the immune system does not destroy "self" but can destroy foreign entities. In your answer be sure to name and indicate parts of the immune system.

Self-Test

For each statement or question choose the best response and mark your choice in the space provided. For some items you will select your response from a *Key*.

Key for questions 1–4
a. True   **b.** False

_____ **1.** AIDS can be transmitted via the placenta to the developing fetus.

_____ **2.** AIDS is caused by a bacterium.

_____ **3.** AIDS can be treated effectively with antibiotics.

_____ **4.** AIDS is predominantly a result of an attack on certain leukocytes.

_____ **5.** During an inflammation all but one of the following are true. Which is <u>not</u> true?

    a. There is an increased flow of blood to the affected area.
    b. Neutrophils are very active.
    c. There is pain and heat at the site of inflammation.
    d. The process protects against disease.
    e. An immune response cannot occur.

a. Macrophages   **c.** T lymphocytes   **e.** None of these
b. B lymphocytes   **d.** All of these

_____ **6.** cells that make antibody

_____ **7.** These arise from stem cells.

_____ **8.** cells that respond to foreign antigens or their products

_____ **9.** "helper" and "suppressor" cells

_____ **10.** cells that have antibody on their surface

_____ **11.** These are phagocytic.

_____ **12.** white blood cells

_____ **13.** so-called "plasma cells"

_____ **14.** cells involved in the cell-mediated immune response (choose two answers)

_____ **15.** "natural killer" cells

_____ **16.** cytotoxin-producing cells

_____ **17.** These respond during infectious disease processes.

_____ **18.** cells that contain pigment granules

_____ **19.** These circulate in the bloodstream and lymph.

_____ **20.** These ingest antigens.

_____ **21.** Antibodies are predominantly:

    a. protein   **c.** carbohydrate   **e.** none of these
    b. lipid   **d.** nucleic acid

_____ **22.** Antibodies react with substances that usually are termed:

    a. factors   **c.** couplers   **e.** ions
    b. antigens   **d.** coenzymes

_____ **23.** A substance that can facilitate human immune reactions and cause perforation of micro-bial cell membranes is:

    a. coupler   **c.** a coacervate   **e.** contactor
    b. coenzyme   **d.** complement

a. True   **b.** False

Antibodies:

_____ **24.** are glycolipids

_____ **25.** are shaped like the letter Y

_____ **26.** typically have three main reactive sites at each end of the molecule

_____ **27.** react only with specific kinds of molecules or structures

_____ 28. have two heavy chains and one light chain for each complete antibody molecule

_____ 29. researchers speculate that the possible number of different kinds of antibodies is:

       a. 1,000   **b.** 10,000   **c.** 100,000   **d.** 1 million   **e.** 100 million

Questions 30–34. Match each statement with the best choice from the _Key_, which lists the five different classes of antibodies.

a. IgA   **b.** IgG   **c.** IgM   **d.** IgD   **e.** IgE

_____ 30. This is known as secretory antibody.

_____ 31. Found in saliva, tears, milk, mucus.

_____ 32. most common immunoglobulin for virus/bacterial inactivation

_____ 33. an antibody that can cross the placenta

_____ 34. Levels of this antibody are elevated during allergic responses and helminthic infections.

_____ 35. A group of cells has been stimulated by a foreign substance. A memory cell begins to divide rapidly, giving rise to a distinct subpopulation of cells. These new cells are a:

       a. colony   **c.** coagulum   **e.** conglomeration
       b. clone   **d.** congress

_____ 36. Current evidence suggests that antibody molecules are encoded by approximately how many different genes?

       a. 3 or 4   **c.** 100–200   **e.** over 1 million
       b. about 10   **d.** about 1,000

_____ 37. An AIDS patient would have a large number of damaged or injured:

       a. erythrocytes   **c.** helper cells   **e.** ocular cells
       b. suppressor cells   **d.** platelets

_____ 38. Monoclonal antibodies are made by:

       a. T cells   **c.** monocytes   **e.** neutrophils
       b. B cells   **d.** eosinophils

_____ 39. In Rh factor disease the mother is Rh _____ and the baby is Rh _____, respectively:

       a. positive, negative   **c.** negative, negative   **e.** none of these
       b. positive, positive   **d.** negative, positive

_____ 40. Interleukin 2 and 3 are secreted by:

       a. macrophages   **c.** suppressor cells   **e.** eosinophils
       b. helper cells   **d.** neutrophils

Key Terms from the Text Chapter

antibody _text page 481_
antigen _481_
B cell (B lymphocyte) _481_
cell-meditated immune
  response _491_

histocompatibility protein
  _491_
immune system _478_
immunological memory _488_
lymphocyte _481_

macrophage _481_
self-tolerance _493_
specific immune response
  _481_

Exercise

Match each immune system organ, cell, and molecule in column A with its function or role from column B.

A

Cytotoxic T cells

Memory cells

Heavy-chain constant regions

B cells

Lymph nodes

B cells and antibodies

Antigen

Histocompatibility proteins

Macrophages

Vaccines

B

Responsible for humoral immune response

White blood cells involved in specific immunity

Divide to form clones

Resistance to infection

Effectors that eliminate "nonself" cells

Triggers an immune response

Trap antigen molecules

Determine where an antibody goes

Provide active immunity

Cellular "fingerprints" that mark "self" cells

Respiration: Gas Exchange in Animals

CHAPTER IN BRIEF

Perspective and Review

All animals must constantly take in oxygen in order to burn carbohydrates aerobically (Ch. 5), and they must also expel carbon dioxide. As you learned in Chapter 4 of your text, gas exchange in cells occurs by diffusion, the spontaneous movement of substances from areas of high concentration to areas of low concentration. Many cells in large multicellular organisms are too distant from the environment for simple diffusion to operate, so specialized structures for gas exchange have evolved. These and other adaptations have features that enable them to meet the demands of the particular milieu in which an animal lives. For example, to find food the Weddell seal must remain submerged for long periods at great depths. To meet its oxygen requirements during this time, the seal has proportionately twice as much blood as does a human, and a higher percentage of red blood cells, which contain oxygen-bearing hemoglobin. The animal also experiences a <u>dive reflex</u>, an adaptation that shunts blood to the brain, spinal cord, and other specific regions, thereby ensuring oxygen availability to critical tissues. Such adaptations underscore one of the main themes of this chapter: An animal's activities are limited by the quantity of oxygen available.

Gas Exchange in Animals: Life-Supporting Oxygen for Every Cell

Diffusion of gases across cell membranes must take place through a watery medium, but diffusion is far slower in water than in air. These two facts greatly influenced the evolution of respiratory structures, and, in some animals (such as sponges), constrained the entire shape and activity of the animal. Gas exchange in unicellular organisms takes place via diffusion across the cell membrane. However, more elaborate structures are necessary in multicellular organisms, which generally rely on blood or some internal fluid for gas transport. Concept Table 23.1 describes the respiratory structures found in the main animal groups.

Concept Table 23.1   Animal respiratory structures

Animal group	Significant features
Lower invertebrates	Sponges are porous, permitting water to flow past all cells. Flatworms are less than 2 mm thick, so gases can diffuse directly across the body wall.
Arthropods	Insects and other arthropods have **tracheae**, air tubes linked to the outside via **spiracles**. Tracheae branch into **air capillaries** deep in the tissues. Incoming oxygen dissolves in drops of fluid in the air capillaries and diffuses into the cells.
Fishes	Most fishes have internal **gills** protected by **opercular flaps**. Each gill is divided into **gill filaments**, composed of platelike **lamellae**. Lamellae increase the surface area for gas exchange and are supplied with a network of capillaries. A **countercurrent flow** between blood in the capillaries and surrounding water increases the efficiency of oxygen uptake.
Amphibians	Gas exchange generally takes place across the skin surface, though most amphibians have lungs with small surface areas. Some forms, such as axolotls, have external gills.
Birds	Birds (and mammals) have saclike **lungs** rich in capillaries, where gas exchange takes place. **Air sacs** interconnect with the lungs; the sacs' position and bellowslike operation pushes incoming air in a unidirectional flow over the respiratory surfaces, ensuring a higher level of oxygen for flight muscles. Air sacs also lighten a bird for flight.
Mammals	Blind-ended lungs are enclosed in a fluid-filled **pleural sac** and rest on the diaphragm. The lungs operate by **tidal ventilation**, which is less efficient than unidirectional flow; hence mammalian lungs have special adaptations to increase the rate of gas exchange.

Respiration in Humans and Other Mammals

Concept Table 23.2 outlines the components and functions of the respiratory structures found in humans and other mammals.

Concept Table 23.2 Respiration in humans and other mammals

Components and airflow	Air flowing in through the mouth or **nasal cavity** is directed via the **larynx** (voice box) into the **trachea**. This tube divides into two large **bronchi**, which in turn are subdivided into hundreds of **bronchioles**. These terminate in small sacs, known as **alveoli**, which are surrounded by capillaries and lined with moist epithelial cells to enhance gas exchange.
Ventilation (breathing in and out— **tidal ventilation**)	Contracting intercostal muscles at the start of inhalation lift the ribs and flatten the **diaphragm**. The resulting decrease in pressure in the lungs draws air from the atmosphere into the alveoli—a natural migration from an area of high pressure to one of low pressure. Exhalation results when these steps are reversed.
Ventilation control	The medulla region of the brain controls ventilation by responding to changes in CO_2 concentration in the blood.

Gas Pressure and the Mechanisms of Gas Exchange

The rate of diffusion in the lungs is increased by **partial pressure**—the pressure exerted by a gas, in a mixture of gases—which is proportional to its volume. The partial pressure of oxygen in the lungs is greater than that in the blood capillaries surrounding the alveoli. Because gases move from areas of high concentration to those of low concentration, oxygen diffuses from the lungs into the blood. The reverse is true for CO_2, which diffuses from the capillaries into the lungs and is exhaled.

Hemoglobin is an iron-containing pigment in red blood cells that binds oxygen. Each hemoglobin molecule contains four iron atoms that bind with oxygen in lung capillaries to form oxyhemoglobin. In the tissues, oxyhemoglobin encounters low oxygen concentrations and liberates its oxygen load into the blood plasma. From there oxygen diffuses into individual cells in the tissues. Although some waste CO_2 in the blood dissolves in plasma, or combines with hemoglobin depleted of oxygen (deoxyhemoglobin), most reacts with water. This reaction forms carbonic acid, which dissociates into bicarbonate ions (HCO_3^-) and hydrogen ions (H^+). The enzyme carbonic anhydrase speeds up the reaction. Bicarbonate ions travel in the blood to the lungs, where it is reconverted to CO_2 and water and CO_2 is exhaled. Hydrogen ions bind to amino acid side chains in hemoglobin and help neutralize blood pH.

Under certain conditions, such as increased muscle activity, the cellular environment can become acidic. This decrease in pH causes hemoglobin molecules to release oxygen more easily to oxygen-starved cells—a phenomenon known as the **Bohr effect**.

Thought Provokers

1. In no more than 500 words, comment on this statement: A totally anaerobic world would manifest a totally different respiratory system in the animal kingdom.

2. Compare and contrast the different types of respiratory systems seen in the animal kingdom. You might consider organizing your answer in a table.

Self-Test

For each statement or question choose the best response and mark your choice in the space provided. For some items you will select your response from a *Key*.

Key for questions 1–9
a. True   **b.** False

Weddell seals:

———— **1.** are mammals

———— **2.** use gills while deep diving

———— **3.** per kilogram of body weight have more hemoglobin than a normal human

In the "dive reflex," during an actual deep, prolonged dive:

———— **4.** The seal's heart rate speeds up.

———— **5.** The seal's muscles function anaerobically.

———— **6.** The seal's muscles require energy.

———— **7.** The seal's muscles use lots of oxygen toward the end of the dive.

———— **8.** Blood supply to the brain and spinal cord is maintained.

———— **9.** The seal's liver can release large amounts of additional red blood cells into the bloodstream to accommodate oxygen needs.

———— **10.** The amount of hemoglobin or the number of red blood cells would be greatest in which population? People living:

    a. on a high mountain plain   **d.** in cities
    b. in the jungle   **e.** in the desert
    c. in Antarctica

Questions 11–21. Select responses from the *Key* to indicate the mode of respiration of each of the listed organisms.

    a. simple diffusion only   **d.** tracheae and spiracles
    b. lungs   **e.** none of these
    c. gills

———— **11.** amoeba

———— **12.** seal

———— **13.** axolotl

———— **14.** beetle

———— **15.** human

———— **16.** housefly

———— **17.** sponge

_____ **18.** robins, bluejays, sparrows, and crows

_____ **19.** salmon and tuna

_____ **20.** platyhelminthes

_____ **21.** animals with opercular flaps

_____ **22.** The amount of oxygen per gram would be greatest in:

    a. air   **b.** water

_____ **23.** Gas and heat exchanges occur most efficiently under which condition?

    a. countercurrent flow   **b.** normal, noncountercurrent flow

_____ **24.** The fluid-filled sacs of the lungs are called the:

    a. peritoneums   **c.** pleura   **e.** alveoli
    b. periostia   **d.** pneumoniae

Questions 25–28. Using the _Key_, supply the appropriate answer for the type of ventilation present in the animals listed.

  a. tidal ventilation   **b.** unidirectional flow ventilation

_____ **25.** bird

_____ **26.** mammal

_____ **27.** fish

_____ **28.** amphibian

_____ **29.** Indicate the correct order of structures through which air flows into the respiratory tract.

    a. trachea, pharynx, bronchioles, bronchi, alveoli
    b. trachea, pharynx, bronchi, bronchioles, alveoli
    c. pharynx, trachea, bronchioles, bronchi, alveoli
    d. trachea, pharynx, alveoli, brochioles, bronchi
    e. pharynx, trachea, bronchi, bronchioles, alveoli

_____ **30.** Which one of the following statements about cystic fibrosis is <u>not</u> correct?

    a. Cystic fibrosis is caused by a recessive gene.
    b. It results in large amounts of watery fluid in the lungs.
    c. It is frequently fatal; average life span of a CF person is 30 years.
    d. The gene in question is localized to chromosome #7.
    e. The regulation of chloride-ion exchange is disturbed in this disease.

_____ **31.** Which one of the following statements about cigarette smoking is probably <u>not</u> correct?

    a. Smoking decreases the chances of a nervous breakdown due to the calming effects of nicotine.
    b. Smoke immobilizes cilia.
    c. Smoke destroys alveolar cells.
    d. Smoking increases the chances of acquiring heart disease and emphysema.
    e. Smoking increases the chances of getting lung cancer.

Key for questions 32–35, relating to events or conditions that affect air pressure in the lungs (I) and/or pleural spaces (II).

a. Both I and II increase.
b. Both I and II decrease.
c. I increases, II decreases.

d. I decreases, II increases.
e. There is neither an increase nor a decrease in I or II.

_____ **32.** The intercostal muscles contract.

_____ **33.** The diaphragm moves up.

_____ **34.** A firing response is transmitted from the medulla.

_____ **35.** The intercostal muscles relax.

_____ **36.** The medulla is a _____ reflex center of the brain.

        a. voluntary   **b.** involuntary

Questions 37–42. If A is greater than B, mark A; if B is greater than A, mark B; if both are almost or exactly equal, mark C.

		a	b
_____	**37.** sensing ability of the brain	carbon dioxide levels	oxygen levels
_____	**38.** breaths per stride	4-legged animals	2-legged animals
_____	**39.** tissue damage during oxygen deprivation	muscle	brain
_____	**40.** percentage of blood as red blood cells	humans	seals
_____	**41.** percentage of blood as red blood cells	humans	yaks
_____	**42.** oxygen release from erythrocytes	acidic pH	basic pH

Key Terms from the Text Chapter

alveolus *text page 503*
Bohr effect *508*
bronchiole *503*
bronchus *503*
countercurrent flow *501*
diaphragm *505*

esophagus *503*
gill *500*
larynx *503*
nasal cavity *503*
partial pressure *506*
respiration *499*

thoracic cavity *505*
tidal ventilation *502*
trachea *502, 503*
ventilation *505*

Concept Figure: Diffusion of Gases in the Body

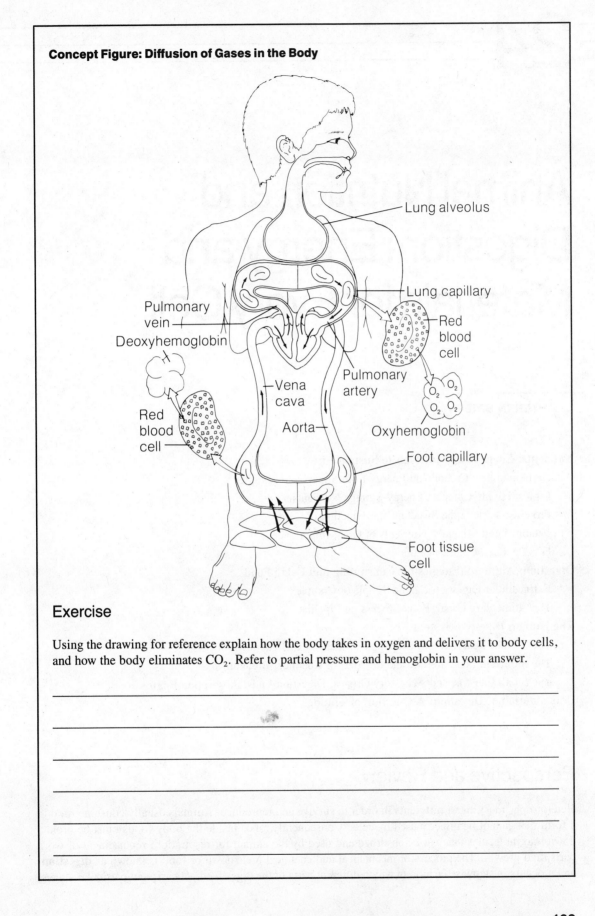

Exercise

Using the drawing for reference explain how the body takes in oxygen and delivers it to body cells, and how the body eliminates CO_2. Refer to partial pressure and hemoglobin in your answer.

_____

_____

_____

_____

_____

_____

24

Animal Nutrition and Digestion: Energy and Materials for Every Cell

CHAPTER IN BRIEF

Perspective and Review

Heterotrophs must ingest **nutrients** in order to survive and reproduce. Animals usually consume food in a form that cannot be directly used by cells. Consequently, once inside the body foods must be broken down into molecules that can be absorbed and used by the animal for respiration, replacement of worn parts, and growth. The process of mechanical and chemical breakdown of food is known as **digestion**, and it occurs in stepwise fashion in which different parts of the digestive tract carry out particular stages.

Animals receive their nutrients from a variety of sources, but an animal's anatomy and physiology are closely allied to its diet and nutritional needs. Omnivores, such as humans and wild boars, have teeth adapted for grinding plant and animal matter. The koala bear, a eucalyptus specialist, has enzymes that detoxify terpenes and other poisons in eucalyptus leaves.

Nutrients: Energy and Materials To Sustain Life

Animals need a constant supply of carbon and nitrogen and a source of energy. Concept Table 24.1 outlines the main groups of compounds that provide these essential requirements, namely, carbohydrates, lipids, proteins, vitamins, and minerals. See text Chapter 2 to review the chemical structures of these compounds.

Concept Table 24.1 Essential nutrients

Carbohydrates	Carbohydrates are broken down into sugars and starch and ultimately glucose, the main source of energy for glycolysis and respiration. Many hervibores have bacteria in their guts that break down complex carbohydrates such as cellulose that other animals, such as humans, cannot process.
Lipids	Animals and plants store energy as lipids. Lipids in the form of fat deposits also cushion internal organs, provide insulation, and are necessary for the absorption of certain vitamins. Linoleic acid is an **essential fatty acid**; that is, it cannot be manufactured by the human body and therefore must be ingested.
Proteins	Life processes and body structure depend on proteins. Body proteins include: collagen in skin, bone, and cartilage; muscle; hormones; and enzymes. Protein cannot be stored and so must be ingested daily. The body can manufacture 12 of the 20 amino acids it needs to build proteins; the remaining eight so-called **essential amino acids** must be ingested.
Vitamins	Function as coenzymes and enzyme activators. Fourteen are needed by the body and are described in Table 24.1 of your text. Fat-soluble vitamins, such as A, D, E, and K, are stored in fat tissues; water-soluble forms—vitamin C and B vitamins—move into the bloodstream and any excess amounts are excreted.
Minerals	Essential inorganic elements, such as sodium and potassium, divided into two classes based on the amounts required by the body. Major minerals are required in amounts greater than 0.1 g per day, while less than 0.1 g per day of minor minerals are needed. Important minor minerals include iron, zinc, copper, and iodine.

Calories

Energy content of food is measured in kilocalories (kcal), also called Calories (Cal). A Calorie is the amount of energy needed to raise the temperature of 1 gram of water by 1°C; an apple contains about 100

Cal of energy-yielding compounds. Individuals have a minimum daily energy requirement that varies with numerous factors, including age and sex.

Digestion: Animal Strategies for Consuming and Using Food

In simple invertebrates cells engulf food particles, which are digested inside the cell in a process termed **intracellular digestion**. While this mechanism does away with the need for a mouth and gut, it also puts a constraint on body size. Larger animals have evolved structures and mechanisms for **extracellular digestion**, the breakdown of food in a cavity and subsequent absorption of nutrients across the lining of the cavity. In lower animals such as cnidarians this cavity is a simple, internal sac. Vertebrates evolved a more organized **alimentary canal**.

The vertebrate alimentary canal is a tube with two openings that is divided into five specialized regions: mouth, esophagus, stomach, small intestine, and large intestine (see Concept Table 24.2). Within this tube a four-step digestion process takes place: (1) mechanical grinding of food; (2) breakdown of macromolecules into monomers; (3) absorption of monomers into the lymphatic system or bloodstream; (4) and resorption of water and elimination of digestive wastes. The alimentary canal is four layers thick. The inner lining, or <u>mucosa</u>, produces enzymes and mucus; the <u>submucosa</u> is rich in blood vessels, lymph vessels, and nerves; the <u>muscle layer</u> propels food through the gut by **peristalsis**; and the outer <u>serosa</u> anchors the gut within the body cavity. Each layer is differentially developed in different parts of the system, depending on the function of that region. <u>Accessory organs</u>—the salivary glands, liver, gallbladder, and pancreas—secrete enzymes and other substances into the alimentary canal that aid digestion.

The Human Digestive System

The human alimentary tract is roughly 8 meters long. Concept Table 24.2 summarizes its specialized organs and their roles in digestion.

Concept Table 24.2 The human digestive system

Mouth	Teeth and the tongue in the mouth grind food and mix it with **saliva** (secretions of the **salivary gland**) into a moist **bolus**. Except for some carbohydrate digestion via <u>amylase</u> present in saliva, only mechanical digestion occurs in the mouth.
Esophagus	A muscular tube that transfers food to the stomach via the <u>cardiac sphincter</u>.
Stomach	Mixes food with gastric juices to form **chyme**. The stomach mucosa is lined with **gastric pits** that secrete **HCl** (an enzyme activator) and **pepsinogen**, which, converted to **pepsin**, digests proteins. Mucus protects the stomach lining. Chyme is pushed through the <u>pyloric sphincter</u> to the small intestine.
Small intestine	A 6-meter-long tube where chemical digestion is completed and absorption takes place. Accessory organs secrete necessary enzymes and other substances; the **pancreas** secretes proteases, lipases, and amylase and neutralizing bicarbonate ions; **bile salts** synthesized by the **liver** and stored

Continues

Concept Table 24.2   The human digestive system (continued)

| | as **bile** by the **gallbladder** aid in lipid digestion. The folded lining is covered in **villi** and **microvilli**, projections that increase the absorptive surface area. |
| **Large intestine** | The **colon** and **rectum**. In the colon, water, vitamins, and ions are reabsorbed from chyme, and wastes are stored; wastes are egested as **feces** through the rectum and out through the anus. |

Coordination of Digestion: A Question of Timing

Digestion is controlled by the nervous and hormonal systems. The taste and smell of food causes the brain to stimulate secretion of digestive enzymes, as does the presence of food in the stomach. In addition, food in the stomach lowers stomach pH; this triggers the secretion of <u>gastrin</u>, which in turn stimulates the production of more HCL, thus aiding digestion. Two other hormones, <u>secretin</u> and <u>cholecystokinin</u>, coordinate the timing and amounts of digestive enzymes secreted.

Thought Provokers

1. Plants need take in only a few simple nutrients to support life processes. By contrast, a human must take in complex nutrients to stay alive. Explain the biochemical reasons for this difference; and discuss the role of enzymes and genes in your answer.

2. Both an amoeba and a human consume food, and there are both similarities and major differences in each organism's nutritive and digestive processes. Describe as many of these similarities and differences as you can. Be as specific as possible, based on what you have learned in this and previous chapters.

Self-Test

For each statement or question choose the best response and mark your choice in the space provided. For some items you will select your response from a *Key*.

Key for questions 1–5

a. omnivore   **c.** carnivore   **e.** none of these
b. herbivore   **d.** all of these

_____ **1.** moth

_____ **2.** koala bear

_____ **3.** lion

_____ **4.** human

_____ **5.** goats, sheep, horses, and cows

Key for questions 6–11

a. monosaccharide   **c.** polysaccharide   **e.** all of these
b. disaccharide   **d.** none of these

_____ **6.** sucrose

_____ **7.** lactose

_____ **8.** starch

_____ **9.** fructose

_____ **10.** cellulose

_____ **11.** glucose

Questions 12–28. Choose the <u>best</u> answer from the *Key*.

a. lipid(s)   **c.** protein(s)   **e.** none of these
b. carbohydrate(s)   **d.** all of these

_____ **12.** are considered essential nutrients

_____ **13.** when metabolized yield the most energy per gram

_____ **14.** may be used as a source of energy

_____ **15.** the best term to describe collagen

_____ **16.** what hormones are

_____ **17.** contain the elements C, H, O, N

_____ **18.** hydrolysis of this compound yields glycerol

_____ **19.** hair

_____ **20.** needed for absorption of vitamins A, D, E, and K

_____ **21.** source of leucine, tryptophane, and lysine

_____ 22. A person mixing beans and rice in a diet is trying to complete and complement the needs for balanced _____ synthesis.

_____ 23. compounds involved in structural and cellular functions

_____ 24. Most severe cases of starvation are related to a lack of this one compound.

_____ 25. The cornea of the eye is largely _____ in character.

_____ 26. The one compound with the least amount of oxygen

_____ 27. Fatty acids are a part of this.

_____ 28. the main food storage molecule of animals

_____ 29. Essential amino acids are amino acids that:
   a. cause death
   b. cannot be made by the organism
   c. are made by the organism and are important for growth and reproduction
   d. are needed by all life
   e. are burned up in metabolism

_____ 30. The major role of vitamins is as:
   a. coenzymes
   b. ions
   c. chelators
   d. pH regulators
   e. inhibitors of metabolic processes

Questions 31–40. Choose from the _Key_ the essential element in human nutrition that best matches each numbered statement.

| a. Fe | c. Cl | e. S | ac. Cu | ae. Se |
| b. Ca | d. I | ab. Na | ad. Mg | bc. P |

_____ 31. part of the stomach acid

_____ 32. deficiency related to goiter

_____ 33. required for the synthesis of hemoglobin

_____ 34. the essential element in hemoglobin/myoglobin

_____ 35. metallic component of normal teeth

_____ 36. corresponding nonmetal found in normal teeth

_____ 37. needed for the synthesis of thyroid hormone

_____ 38. found in two amino acids and many proteins

_____ 39. one of the most abundant monovalent cations

_____ 40. deficiency causes headache, exhaustion, weakness, and anemia

_____ 41. A Calorie is the amount of heat needed to raise the temperature of _____ of water _____ degrees C.
   a. 1 liter, 10   c. 1 gram, 10   e. 1 liter, 1
   b. 1 gram, 100   d. 1 gram, 1

_____ **42.** A calorie (compare with question 41) is the amount of heat needed to raise the temperature of _____ of water _____ degrees C. (Use the choices for question 41 to answer this question.)

Key for questions 43–45

a. Involves a hydrolytic biochemical reaction
b. Does not involve a hydrolytic reaction

_____ **43.** protein digestion

_____ **44.** fat digestion

_____ **45.** starch digestion

_____ **46.** The relative length of the intestinal tract of which animal would be the longer?

       a. carnivore   **b.** herbivore

Key for questions 47–48

a. serosa   **c.** muscular   **e.** none of these
b. mucosa   **d.** submucosa

_____ **47.** the tissue layer responsible for peristalsis

_____ **48.** the region between the mucosa and the muscle layer

Key for questions 49–53

a. cheeks   **c.** soft palate   **e.** salivary glands
b. tongue   **d.** teeth

_____ **49.** location of the principal taste-sensing area

_____ **50.** You have three pairs of these.

_____ **51.** principal function is to break food into smaller pieces

_____ **52.** produces amylase

_____ **53.** prevents food from entering the nasal cavity

Key for questions 54–68

a. the stomach   **c.** the large intestine   **e.** all of these
b. the small intestine   **d.** two of these   **ab.** none of these

_____ **54.** peristalsis occurs in

_____ **55.** involved in digestion

_____ **56.** where chyme is formed

_____ **57.** cholecystokinin produced and released here

_____ **58.** functions in an alkaline environment

_____ **59.** most enzymatic digestion occurs here

_____ **60.** pepsin is produced here

_____ **61.** The pyloric sphincter controls the opening to this structure.

_____ **62.** contains an acid environment

_____ **63.** site of the gastric pits

_____ **64.** site for the removal of large amounts of water

_____ **65.** where the villi and microvilli are located

_____ **66.** Ulcers are the direct result of the chemical activity here.

_____ **67.** Secretin is produced here.

_____ **68.** Secretin travels to and affects this area.

Key for questions 69–77.

a. liver   **c.** gallbladder   **e.** thyroid
b. pancreas   **d.** spleen

_____ **69.** insulin producer

_____ **70.** Bile salts are made here.

_____ **71.** glucagon producer

_____ **72.** secretes bicarbonate

_____ **73.** storage place for manufactured bile

_____ **74.** glycogen storage site

_____ **75.** Cirrhosis is a disease of this organ.

_____ **76.** organ affected in a person with cholecystitis

_____ **77.** organ that can detoxify certain chemicals and poisons

_____ **78.** Gastrin is a(n):

     a. hormone   **c.** vitamin   **e.** metal
     b. enzyme   **d.** toxin

_____ **79.** Bile is involved in the breakdown of:

     a. protein   **c.** polysaccharides   **e.** none of these
     b. sugars   **d.** nucleic acids

Key for questions 80–85, related to vitamins

a. folic acid   **d.** pyridoxine   **ab.** vitamin C
b. niacin   **e.** riboflavin   **ac.** choline
c. thiamin   **ad.** pantothenic acid

_____ **80.** deficiency related to scurvy, with gum bleeding, skin hemorrhages, delayed wound healing

_____ **81.** component of phospholipids

_____ **82.** part of coenzyme A

_____ **83.** constituent of amino acids and nucleic acids

_____ **84.** B_1 vitamin; deficiency causes Beri-Beri; coenzyme for CO_2 removal

_____ **85.** B_6 vitamin; deficiency causes cracks at corners of the mouth and sensitivity to light

Key Terms from the Text Chapter

alimentary canal   *text page* 521

bile   *528*

chyme   *526*

colon   *530*

digestion   *511*

esophagus   *525*

essential amino acid   *515*

extracellular digestion   *521*

feces   *530*

gallbladder   *528*

intracellular digestion   *521*

liver   *528*

microvillus   *529*

mineral   *517*

nutrient   *511*

nutrition   *512*

pancreas   *526*

pepsin   *526*

peristalsis   *523*

rectum   *530*

saliva   *525*

stomach   *525*

villus   *529*

vitamin   *515*

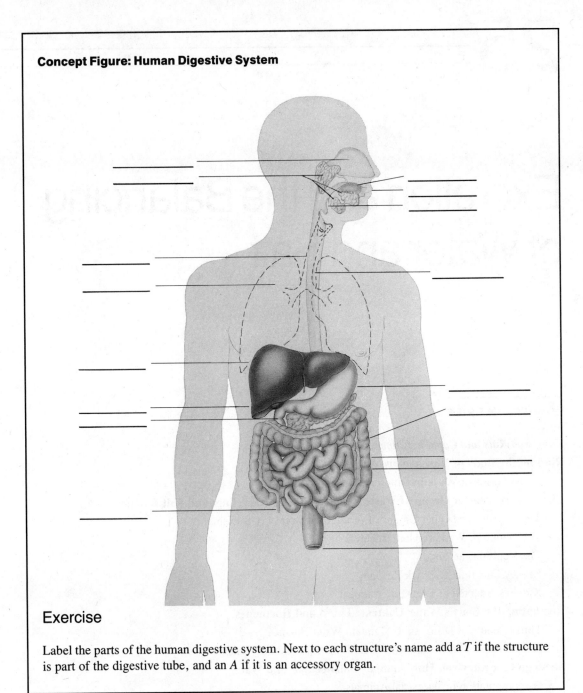

Exercise

Label the parts of the human digestive system. Next to each structure's name add a *T* if the structure is part of the digestive tube, and an *A* if it is an accessory organ.

25

Excretion and the Balancing of Water and Salt

CHAPTER IN BRIEF

Perspective and Review

To maintain homeostasis, the concentration of internal substances must remain constant. Metabolism tends to upset this internal balance because it produces waste products; as a result the body must keep making adjustments. Various systems of the body work to maintain homeostasis: The lungs remove carbon dioxide, and sweat glands in the skin excrete salt and small quantities of ammonia and urea. However, the **kidneys** are the critical excretory organs that function to maintain homeostasis, as they filter a variety of metabolic wastes from the blood and act to excrete or conserve water. Because they are selective in what they excrete, the kidneys play a major role in regulating the composition and pH of internal fluids. This selectivity in turn is regulated by the nervous and hormonal systems.

Animals living in different habitats show differing adaptations of the excretory system. Desert mammals need to conserve water, and so have kidneys with extremely long water-absorption tubules. Conversely, aquatic mammals that need to get rid of excess water have short water-absorption tubules. Behavioral modifications also help to maintain water and salt balance; for instance, animals in hot climates avoid excess water loss by being active only at night.

Ridding the Body of Nitrogenous Wastes

Organisms must **excrete** metabolic waste products in addition to excess water and salts. Carbon dioxide and water resulting from lipid and carbohydrate breakdown are expelled through the lungs or skin. Ammonia, a toxic nitrogenous waste from protein metabolism, is excreted in one of three forms: ammonia, uric acid, or urea. Concept Table 25.1 describes how different organisms excrete these substances.

Concept Table 25.1 Nitrogenous excretory compounds	
Ammonia	Excreted by protists, fish, and aquatic invertebrates directly into the surrounding water; via the contractile vacuole in protists and via gills in fish.
Uric acid	Birds, reptiles, and terrestrial invertebrates detoxify ammonia by converting it into insoluble uric acid in the blood. The uric acid is then removed from the blood by the kidneys and expelled through the cloaca as guano. This strategy conserves water.
Urea	Mammals and some fish excrete urea, which is converted from ammonia by the liver. Urea is then removed from the blood via filtration in the kidneys, concentrated into urine, and excreted via the urinary tubes.

The Kidney: Master Organ of Waste Removal, Water Recycling, and Salt Balance

Human kidneys are paired, bean-shaped abdominal organs that filter blood. Each kidney receives blood from a renal artery, while a renal vein returns filtered blood to the circulation. A **ureter** transports urine from each kidney to the **bladder**, where it is stored until it exits the body via the urethra. Concept Table 25.2 describes the structure and functioning of the human kidney. Figures 25.7–25.10 in your text illustrate the kidney filtration system in detail.

Concept Table 25.2   The human kidney: Structure and function

Structure	The kidney is divided into an outer **cortex**, the site of blood filtration; a **medulla**, composed of fan-shaped regions where solutes and water are conserved; and a **pelvis**, an expanded region of the ureter where urine is concentrated. **Nephrons**, the filtration units of the kidneys, span the cortex and medulla regions.
Nephron structure	A system of blood capillaries and tubules. A **Bowman's capsule**, which is lined with **podocytes** that form a meshlike filter, surrounds a bundle of **capillaries** called a **glomerulus**. An incoming arteriole branches into glomerular capillaries. After blood is filtered in the glomerulus it enters an exit arteriole that leads to a system of **peritubular capillaries** that merge with venous vessels leading away from the kidney. Filtered material passes from Bowman's capsule into a convoluted tubule (text Figure 25.9A) that is divided into five main regions: the **proximal tubule**, nearest the capsule; the **descending limb** that dips into the medulla; a **loop of Henle**; an **ascending limb** that leads back to the cortex; and a **distal tubule**. Groups of distal tubules converge into **collecting ducts** through which urine passes toward the renal pelvis.
Overall function	Blood is filtered in the Bowman's capsule, and after processing in the nephron tubule the resulting **filtrate** flows to a collecting duct.
Processes	Three main processes occur in the nephron:

1. **Filtration.** The meshlike filter of the capsule removes small molecules such as water, amino acids, and urea from blood.

2. **Tubular reabsorption.** Occurs mainly in the loop of Henle. Useful substances such as amino acids and ions are returned to the blood plasma of the peritubular capillaries by active transport. Other chemicals are removed by passive transport. Water returns to the capillaries by osmosis.

3. **Tubular secretion.** In the proximal and distal tubules, remaining wastes are removed from the blood into the tubules. The **filtrate**, now <u>urine</u>, flows into the renal **pelvis** and eventually to the bladder.

Regulating the Body's Water Content: Thirst and Hormones

Two mechanisms control water balance in animals: <u>thirst</u> and <u>hormone activity</u>. As water loss increases blood solute concentrations, nerve cells in the hypothalamus signal thirst. Subsequent fluid intake distends the stomach, which triggers inhibition of the thirst response. Two hormones control water loss by influencing water reabsorption in the kidneys. **Antidiuretic hormone (ADH)** regulates the permeability of the distal tubules to water, and **aldosterone** regulates salt reabsorption, which in turn affects osmosis. The kidneys also play a part in adjusting blood pressure. When blood salt content is high they excrete less water, increasing blood volume. They can also raise blood pressure indirectly by releasing the enzyme **renin**, which interacts with a blood protein to generate **angiotensin**, a hormone that causes blood vessels to constrict.

Strategies for Survival: How Animals Balance Salt and Water

Osmoregulation is the process by which animals maintain a steady internal concentration of water and solutes. Concept Table 25.3 describes how different groups of animals osmoregulate.

Concept Table 25.3   The maintenance of salt and water balance

Terrestrial animals	Counteract water loss by drinking and via mechanisms for dumping salt. Insect cuticles, mammalian fur and behavioral modifications also inhibit water loss. Malpighian tubules of insects, nephridia in earthworms, vertebrate kidneys, and the nasal tubes of birds are the main osmoregulatory organs.
Aquatic animals	Many invertebrates are osmoconformers and have body fluids isotonic to the surrounding water. Others are osmoregulators and maintain a steady solute concentration regardless of the external environment. Aquatic vertebrates are in this latter category. The blood of freshwater fish and amphibians is hypertonic relative to their environment, so such animals excrete large amounts of dilute urine to get rid of excess water. Conversely, most marine fishes, reptiles, and mammals have body fluids hypotonic to seawater and need to conserve water.

Thought Provokers

1. Write a one-page essay that defends or contradicts the statement "A human cannot survive without kidneys." Use relevant facts and examples in your argument.

2. Explain how the structure of the human kidney relates to its functions.

3. Compare the osmotic and excretory problems encountered by freshwater fish, saltwater fish, and humans in their typical environments, and describe how each organism copes with and solves these problems.

Self-Test

For each statement or question choose the best response and mark your choice in the space provided. For some items you will select your response from a *Key*.

_____ 1. Which of the following is <u>not</u> a means by which the kangaroo rat obtains or preserves water?

    a. eating cactus spines
    b. oxidative metabolism
    c. concentrated urine
    d. eating seeds
    e. absorption of water from feces in the intestinal tract

_____ 2. Which of the following is <u>not</u> a waste product of nitrogen metabolism?

    a. uracil   **c.** urea   **e.** protein
    b. uric acid   **d.** ammonia

_____ 3. Which of the following is the cause of gout?

    a. uracil   **c.** urea   **e.** protein
    b. uric acid   **d.** ammonia

_____ 4. The compound that causes gout is the direct result of the metabolism of:

    a. proteins   **c.** lipids   **e.** steroids
    b. nucleic acids   **d.** phospholipids

Questions 5–10. Using the *Key*, indicate which, if any, are the typical, predominant wastes excreted by the listed organisms.

a. nitrogen gas   **c.** urea   **e.** uracil
b. ammonia   **d.** uric acid

_____ 5. protists and bony fish

_____ 6. birds

_____ 7. humans

_____ 8. aquatic invertebrates

_____ 9. reptiles

_____ 10. mammals

Key for questions 11–15

a. ureter   **c.** kidney   **e.** renal artery
b. bladder   **d.** urethra   **ab.** renal vein

_____ 11. Connects the kidney to the bladder.

_____ 12. exit passageway to outside environment for voiding urine

_____ 13. storage sac for urine

_____ 14. the blood-filtering device that produces urine

_____ 15. Supplies blood to the kidney.

Key for questions 16–20

a. medulla   **c.** cortex   **e.** epidermis
b. pelvis   **d.** dermis

_____ **16.** outer portion of the kidney

_____ **17.** where the collecting tubules are located

_____ **18.** two regions where nephrons are located

_____ **19.** the inner or central area of the kidney

_____ **20.** Distinct drops of urine are formed and move to the ureters from this region.

Key for questions 21–31

a. ascending limb   **d.** distal tubules   **ac.** collecting ducts
b. Bowman's capsules   **e.** descending limb   **ad.** proximal tubule
c. collecting tubules   **ab.** loop of Henle   **ae.** glomerulus

_____ **21.** where the first urine is produced and captured

_____ **22.** the duct through which urine first begins to travel

_____ **23.** Distal tubules empty into this structure.

_____ **24.** Podocytes are a part of this.

_____ **25.** The ascending limb empties here.

_____ **26.** The glomerulus is pressed against this structure.

_____ **27.** jumbled, yarnlike structures

_____ **28.** U-shaped structure of the nephron

_____ **29.** the drain into the renal pelvis

_____ **30.** the major site of initial reabsorption of initial kidney filtrate

_____ **31.** the vessel closest to a Bowman's capsule

_____ **32.** Initial kidney filtrate most closely resembles the liquid portion of:

    a. water   **c.** milk   **e.** fibrin
    b. syrup   **d.** plasma

_____ **33.** Nutrient reabsorption in the kidney occurs predominantly via:

    a. active transport   **c.** osmosis   **e.** none of these
    b. passive transport   **d.** diffusion

Questions 34–35. If A is greater than B, mark A; if B is greater than A, mark B; if both are approximately the same, mark C.

		a	**b**
_____	**34.** relative length of loop of Henle	humans	kangaroo rats
_____	**35.** relative length of loop of Henle	humans	beavers

a. True   **b.** False

_____ **36.** ADH (antidiuretic hormone) is manufactured by the pituitary gland.

_____ **37.** Alcohol consumption decreases diuresis.

Questions 38–41. If A is greater than B, mark A; if B is greater than A, mark B. If both are approximately equal, mark C.

		a	b
_____	**38.** levels of ADH in person eating	sardines	lettuce
_____	**39.** diuresis in person eating	sardines	lettuce
_____	**40.** ADH levels in	32-oz-beer drinker	sardine eater
_____	**41.** amount of diuresis in	beer drinker	water drinker

_____ **42.** Which one of the following does aldosterone <u>not</u> do when active?

     a. Behaves like a hormone.
     b. Increases water uptake into the blood.
     c. Causes sodium ions to be pumped into the blood.
     d. Increases the concentration of potassium in urine.
     e. Increases urine production.

Key for questions 43–47

a. True   **b.** False

The hormone angiotensin:

_____ **43.** is made under the influence of renin produced by the kidney

_____ **44.** is made from protein in the blood

_____ **45.** causes blood vessels to dilate

_____ **46.** elevates blood pressure

_____ **47.** stimulates the adrenals to secrete aldosterone

Questions 48–50. Using the *Key*, indicate the nature of the body fluid of each of the listed animals relative to its typical or usual habitat.

a. hypertonic   **b.** hypotonic   **c.** isotonic

_____ **48.** freshwater fish

_____ **49.** shark

_____ **50.** saltwater fish

Questions 51–52. Using the *Key*, indicate, for freshwater and marine fishes, the active mechanism of salt exchange in gills.

a. Na^+ pumped out is greater than Na^+ taken in.
b. Na^+ pumped in is greater than Na^+ excreted.
c. Rate of Na^+ uptake is equal to the rate of Na^+ excreted.

_____ **51.** gills of freshwater fish

_____ **52.** gills of saltwater fish

_____ **53.** The solute concentrate of the blood of sharks is significantly influenced by which compound?

        a. urea   **b.** salt   **c.** protein   **d.** sugar   **e.** lipids

Key Terms from the Text Chapter

aldosterone *text page 545*
angiotensin *546*
antidiuretic hormone *545*
bladder *538*
Bowman's capsule *540*
capillaries *540*
collecting duct *541*
distal tubule *541*

excretion *536*
filtrate *542*
filtration *540*
glomerulus *540*
kidney *538*
loop of Henle *540*
nephron *540*
osmoregulation *547*

proximal tubule *540*
renin *546*
tubular reabsorption *540*
tubular secretion *540*
urea *536*
ureter *538*
uric acid *536*

Concept Figure: Kidney Function

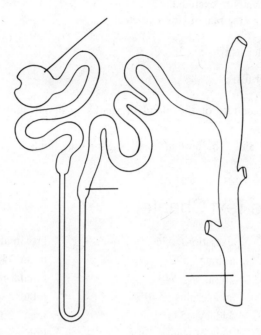

Exercise

1. Add the following labels to the drawing:

Glomerulus   Proximal tubule
Collecting duct   Distal tubule
Loop of Henle   Nephron

2. Using arrows show where blood enters the nephron and where urine exits to the bladder.

3. Name the three basic processes that a nephron carries out, and use brackets to show (approximately) where each occurs.

26

Hormones and Other Molecular Messengers

CHAPTER IN BRIEF

Perspective and Review

Your mood, weight, stage of development and most other aspects of life are controlled by **molecular messengers**, chemicals essential to survival and normal functioning. Such substances control body performance by regulating physiology and behavior in ways that prevent or provoke change. Some molecular messengers maintain homeostasis by preventing fluctuations, while others trigger developmental changes such as the onset of puberty. Hormones are one class of molecular messengers; they are compounds produced by one set of cells and transported to another set where they bind with proteins to alter the cells' activities. For example, the hormone **ecdysone** is secreted by cells in the thorax of silkworms and diffuses throughout the animal's tissues. Cells sensitive to the hormone differentiate, and this is how the worm metamorphoses into an adult moth.

Molecular messengers interact with the nervous system to maintain homeostasis. The nervous system senses the environment and stimulates the appropriate messenger response to effect necessary changes.

Molecular Messengers: An Overview

Concept Table 26.1 summarizes the sources, activity, and types of molecular messengers.

Concept Table 26.1 Molecular messengers	
General mechanism	**Regulator cells** detect perturbations within and/or outside the body and release molecular messengers in response. The messengers diffuse through a fluid to act on **target cells**, cells that perform the required activity.
Sources	Most messengers are secreted by either **endocrine glands** (ductless glands) or **exocrine glands** (glands with ducts that usually lead the messengers out of the body). Chemically, messengers may be either hydrophobic or hydrophilic.
Mode of action	Hydrophobic messengers enter the cell and bind with **receptors**. Messenger-receptor complexes bind to regions of DNA, activating genes that code new proteins. Hydrophilic messengers bind to receptors outside the cell, triggering a series of events that act on a **second messenger** inside the cell, which acts to alter the cell's activity.
Types of messengers	Five main classes: **Paracrine hormones** act on cells adjacent to the ones that secreted them; **neurotransmitters** transmit nerve signals; **neurohormones** are secreted by nerve cells; **true hormones** are nonneural hormones secreted by cells or glands; **pheromones** act on other individuals at a distance.

Hormones and the Mammalian Endocrine System

Mammalian hormones fall into four molecular groups: **polypeptide hormones**, **steroid hormones**, **amine hormones**, and **fatty acid hormones**. Humans have about ten endocrine glands (illustrated in Figure 26.8 of your text). Two of these, the **hypothalamus** and the **pituitary gland**, control the activities of other endocrine glands. Concept Table 26.2 describes the main functions of these glands.

Concept Table 26.2   Major endocrine glands and their hormones

Gland	Hormone	Effects
Hypothalamus	Releasing and inhibiting hormones	Stimulate/inhibit release of specific pituitary hormones
Pituitary		
Posterior lobe (stores hormones)	**ADH**	Regulates water reabsorption in the kidneys
	Oxytocin	Stimulates milk release in mammary glands
Anterior Lobe	**FSH** and **LH**	Stimulate sex hormone and gamete production in gonads
	Thyrotropin	Stimulates thyroid gland
	ACTH	Stimulates adrenal cortex
	Growth hormone	Affects growth
	Prolactin	Stimulates milk synthesis
Thyroid	**Thyroxine (T_4 and T_3)**	Govern metabolic and growth rates
Parathyroid	**Calcitonin**	Decreases blood calcium levels
	Parathyroid hormone	Raises blood calcium levels
Adrenal gland (**cortex** and **medulla** interact to maintain homeostasis and overcome stress)		
Medulla	**Ephinephrine (adrenaline)**	Increases blood glucose levels and dilates respiratory tubes
	Norepinephrine	Increases heart rate
Cortex	**Glucocorticoids**	Increase sugar, protein, and fat metabolism. ACTH stimulates the cortex to produce **cortisol**, which increases glucose metabolism and provides a quick energy source
	Mineralocorticoids	Include **aldosterone**, which regulates sodium and potassium uptake and release in the kidneys
Pancreas	**Insulin** and **glucagon**	Affect carbohydrate metabolism in reciprocal directions
Gonads		
Ovaries	**Estrogen**	Stimulates female development
	Progesterone	Stimulates growth in the uterus
Testes	**Androgens**	Stimulate male development and behavior

Hormones and Physiological Change

Hormones and Homeostasis

Hormones continually adjust the internal components of the body to maintain homeostasis. **Diabetes mellitus** is one disorder that can result when this mechanism fails to operate correctly. **Beta cells** in the pancreas secrete insulin in response to nutrients in the blood. Insulin causes the liver and other organs to remove and store glucose until it is needed by the body. When blood glucose levels fall, alpha cells in the pancreas detect this drop and release glucagon, resulting in the release of glucose into the blood. Beta cells of diabetics fail to produce insulin; instead, diabetics metabolize lipids, making the blood so acidic that coma and death can follow.

Cyclic Physiological Changes

Hormones govern daily (**circadian**), monthly, and yearly cycles. Melatonin, a hormone secreted by the **pineal gland** in response to darkness, promotes sleep and inhibits gonad activity. Melatonin may also influence human reproduction, puberty, and mood.

Hormones are also responsible for permanent developmental changes, such as puberty in humans and **metamorphosis** in insects. In arthropods, **ecdysone** controls the timing of molting and **juvenile hormone** governs the type of molt.

Hormones and Evolution: Invariant Agents of Change

Molecular messengers are similar throughout all living forms. Insect metamorphosis and human puberty are both controlled by steroids. This indicates the ancient origin of these messengers, which must have been conserved through millions of years of evolution.

Thought Provokers

1. Name at least three specific diseases that result from hormone deficiencies. Explain the nature of each disease and how each may be cured or treated.

2. Compare and contrast human hormones with those found in lower animals. Use plenty of examples.

3. Trace the events through which epinephrine is released, reaches target cells, and ultimately exerts a specific effect in the organism.

Self-Test

For each statement or question choose the best response and mark your choice in the space provided. For some items you will select your reponse from a *Key*.

Key for questions 1–10
a. True   **b.** False

_____ **1.** Ecdysone is an insect hormone.

_____ **2.** Ecdysone is responsible for changes associated with metamorphosis.

_____ **3.** A hormone may typically bind to many different types of cells in many different tissues.

_____ **4.** Hormones work by initiating or inhibiting changes inside cells.

_____ **5.** Hormones are usually best considered as secondary messengers rather than primary messengers.

_____ **6.** DNA can be considered a hormone molecule.

_____ **7.** RNA is a hormone.

_____ **8.** The pituitary, thyroid, and adrenal glands are endocrine glands.

_____ **9.** Female hyenas produce more male hormone than do male hyenas.

_____ **10.** Erythropoietin is a hormone.

Questions 11–16. Match each of the numbered statements listing different types of molecular messengers with the best corresponding description in the *Key*.

a. true hormones   **c.** paracrine hormones   **e.** neurohormones
b. pheromones   **d.** neurotransmitters

_____ **11.** primitive hormones that act on cells immediately adjacent to the ones that secreted them

_____ **12.** organic molecules that act on individuals at a distance

_____ **13.** nonneural hormones released directly into blood or tissue spaces

_____ **14.** nerve-signal relay compounds

_____ **15.** ecdysone

_____ **16.** secretions of the adrenals and thyroid

Questions 17–23. Match each of the following hormones or hormone classes with the appropriate biochemical group from the *Key*.

a. amine   **b.** fatty acid   **c.** polypeptide   **d.** steroid

_____ **17.** luteinizing hormone

_____ **18.** thyroxin

_____ **19.** prostaglandins

_____ **20.** testosterone

_____ **21.** oxytocin

_____ **22.** estrogens

_____ **23.** ecdysone

Questions 24–35. For each hormone or condition listed, use the *Key* to indicate the associated organ or site of manufacture.

a. adrenals   **c.** pituitary   **e.** parathyroids
b. thyroid   **d.** hypothalamus   **ab.** none of these

_____ **24.** ACTH

_____ **25.** oxytocin

_____ **26.** hypothalamic releasing factors

_____ **27.** prolactin

_____ **28.** hypothalamic release-inhibiting factors

_____ **29.** ADH

_____ **30.** cretinism

_____ **31.** epinephrine

_____ **32.** testosterone

_____ **33.** goiter

_____ **34.** cortisol

_____ **35.** norepinephrine

Key for questions 36–45.

a. ACTH   **d.** parathyroid hormone   **ac.** cortisol
b. thyroxine   **e.** epinephrine   **ad.** prolactin
c. calcitonin   **ab.** oxytocin   **ae.** glucagon/insulin

_____ **36.** also known as adrenaline

_____ **37.** causes bone to release Ca^{++}

_____ **38.** assists glucose entry into the cell

_____ **39.** secreted by anterior pituitary, affects the adrenals

_____ **40.** speeds up metabolism of sugars and fats

_____ **41.** fight-or-flight hormone

_____ **42.** causes the liver to release glucose into the blood

_____ **43.** Stress causes release of this hormone, as well as increased heartbeat and rapid breathing.

_____ **44.** excess calcium deposited into bones

_____ **45.** Prednisone is a compound most closely related to this hormone.

Questions 46–52. Using the _Key_, indicate the organ or location where you would find each structure listed.

a. atop the kidneys   **c.** neck area   **e.** none of these;
b. brain area   **d.** reproductive tract   some other site

_____ **46.** pituitary

_____ **47.** adrenals

_____ **48.** hypothalamus

_____ **49.** testes

_____ **50.** thyroid

_____ **51.** pancreas

_____ **52.** ovary

_____ **53.** Glucagon is produced by which gland?

a. pituitary   **c.** parathyroids   **e.** pancreas
b. hypothalamus   **d.** pineal

_____ **54.** Which substance is related to the sleep response?

a. melanin   **c.** ACTH   **e.** oxytocin
b. melatonin   **d.** adrenaline

_____ **55.** The pineal gland is located near the spleen and liver.

a. True   **b.** False

Key Terms from the Text Chapter

adrenal gland   *text page 565*

amine hormone   *560*

beta cell   *568*

circadian rhythm   *568*

cortisol   *566*

diabetes mellitus   *568*

ecdysone   *570*

endocrine gland   *556*

epinephrine   *565*

exocrine gland   *556*

fatty acid hormone   *560*

glucagon   *568*

goiter   *565*

hypothalamic releasing factor   *564*

hypothalamic release-inhibiting factor   *564*

hypothalamus   *561*

insulin   *568*

juvenile hormone   *570*

metamorphosis   *555*

molecular messenger   *555*

neurohormone   *557*

neurotransmitter   *557*

pancreas   *568*

paracrine hormone   *557*

parathyroid gland   *565*

pheromone   *557*

pineal gland   *568*

pituitary gland   *561*

polypeptide hormone   *559*

receptor   *556*

second messenger   *556*

steroid hormone   *559*

target cell   *556*

thyroid gland   *565*

thyroxine   *565*

true hormone   *557*

Concept Figure: Molecular Messengers

Regulator cell

Molecular messenger

DNA

New activity

Target cells

Second messenger

Altered protein

New activity

Exercise

1. Complete the drawing to show the two pathways of molecular messenger activity. Below, describe each pathway in a sentence, noting the basic features of each.

   Pathway no. 1: _____

   _____

   Pathway no. 2: _____

   _____

2. Name and define the five types of molecular messenger.

Messenger	**Defined as:**
1. _____	_____
2. _____	_____
3. _____	_____
4. _____	_____
5. _____	_____

27

How Nerve Cells Work to Control Behavior

CHAPTER IN BRIEF

Perspective and Review

The nervous system, together with the endocrine system, allows an animal to function as an integrated unit. The nervous system gathers information on the external and internal environments and integrates this information to produce useful and coordinated responses to a wide variety of conditions. For example, the nervous system permits an animal to detect a predator and to react by fleeing. Such responses are possible because **nerve** cells communicate with each other and are often organized into highly elaborate networks.

Nerve Cells Are Structured for Long-Range Communication

Neurons are the nerve cells that gather and transmit information to other cells in the body. Specialized **glial cells**, or support cells, surround, protect, and nourish neurons, and may also affect their function. **Dendrites**, fine processes extending from the main body of the neuron, collect signals from other neurons or from the environment and pass them to the **soma**, or main cell body. These signals are integrated in the soma and sent via an **axon** to another neuron. The axon, a tubular process, terminates in a knob-like **bouton** in a specialized region called a **synapse** close to another neuron. The signal-sending neuron is called a **presynaptic cell**, while the cell receiving the signal is a **postsynaptic cell**.

Electrifying Action: The Nerve Impulse

A <u>nerve impulse</u> is an electrochemical chain reaction. As your text describes in detail (pp. 575–576) it results from a series of localized changes in a neuron's membranes that allows certain ions to move into and out of the cell.

Neurons are electrically **polarized**; that is, the inside of the cell has lower positive charge relative to the outside of the cell. This difference in charge creates an <u>electric potential</u>—a measurable amount of potential energy. For a resting neuron this electrical imbalance, or <u>resting potential</u>, is -70 mV. The imbalance results from a higher concentration of potassium ions relative to sodium ions inside the cell, compared to the relative concentrations of these substances outside the cell. Three proteins act to maintain this state. The **potassium channel** allows potassium ions to leak from the cell, leaving behind negatively charged proteins that in turn give the cell's interior its slight negative charge. At the same time, the **sodium channel** closes, to prevent most sodium ions from entering the cell. A third protein, the **sodium-potassium pump**, works in opposition to both channels, also helping maintain the status quo. Concept Table 27.1 describes how resting potential is overcome to generate a nerve impulse, and how the impulse is transmitted. These events are illustrated in Figures 27.5 and 27.6 in your text.

Concept Table 27.1 Generation and propagation of a nerve impulse (action potential)

Generation	A region of a neuron is stimulated, causing some sodium channels to open and sodium ions to enter the cell. The cell begins to **depolarize**. At -50 mV most sodium channels in the stimulated region open and sodium ions rush into the cell. As a result, the electrical charges inside and outside the cell reverse. This charge reversal is the nerve impulse, or **action potential**.
Refractory period	The time after an action potential when no additional stimulus can evoke another action potential in that neuron.
Propagation	An action potential is transmitted to the entire neuron. This propagation occurs as sodium ions diffuse from a nonstimulated region of a neuron to the stimulated region, resulting in depolarization of the nonstimulated region and the action potential. This sequence is repeated until the impulse has been transmitted the length of the neuron.
Impulse direction	Nerve impulses travel in one direction only; the refractory period prevents reverse propagation.
Conduction speed	In general, the larger the axon diameter, the faster the axon conducts a nerve impulse. In vertebrates a **myelin sheath**, a

Continues

Concept Table 27.1   Generation and propagation of a nerve impulse (action potential)

	lipid-rich layer, insulates the axon and increases the speed of impulse transmission.
All-or-none response	Every nerve impulse has the same magnitude regardless of how powerful the stimulus. A more intense sensation results from the stimulation of a greater number of neurons.

How Neurons Communicate Across Synapses

Neurons communicate with each other across synapses. Some neurons relay messages directly via an electrical connection; others rely on chemicals. Concept Table 27.2 describes how each of these synapses works.

Concept Table 27.2   Electrical and chemical synapses

Electrical synapses	Presynaptic and postsynaptic cells are joined by *gap junctions*. Pores perforate both cell membranes at these junctions and allow the ions that generate an action potential to move directly from a presynaptic to a postsynaptic cell. Communication between neurons is rapid across electrical synapses, but messages cannot be modified for special conditions.
Chemical synapses	The most common type of synapse in higher animals. These function more slowly and require more steps, but the messages can be refined for special conditions. A *cleft* separates presynaptic and postsynaptic cells. An action potential arriving at the bouton of a presynaptic cell causes calcium ions to enter the cell. These stimulate the release of **neurotransmitters**, which cross the cleft and bind to receptors on the receiving cell, thereby triggering an action potential in that cell.
Neurotransmitters	Molecular messengers such as *acetylcholine* and *norepinephrine*. **Neuromodulators** are compounds that remain in the vicinity of a synapse and influence the response of the receiving cell.
Types of synapses	In *excitatory synapses* the binding of neurotransmitters to receptor cells stimulates the firing of an impulse by decreasing polarization. In contrast, *inhibitory synapses* discourage an impulse by increasing polarization.
Summation	Process in which a neuron "sums up" all the information reaching it over a short time interval. If excitatory synapses are greater than inhibitory ones, an action potential is triggered in that neuron.

How Networks of Neurons Control Behavior

Neurons are arranged into circuits, spatial organizations allowing an animal to receive, integrate, and act on information from its environment. The **reflex arc** is one such circuit, generally mediating rapid and involuntary behavior (such as dropping a hot plate) and requiring no input from the brain.

Vertebrate bodies contain over 1,000 types of neurons, which fall into three main categories. **Sensory neurons** receive information and transmit it towards the spinal cord or brain, which are the integrating centers. **Interneurons** in the integrating centers relay messages between neurons. They also integrate and coordinate incoming and outgoing messages. **Motor neurons** often connect with interneurons to relay messages from the brain or spinal cord to muscles or secretory glands. Motor neurons effect responses to the information collected by a sensory neuron.

Learning

Learning can involve habituation or sensitization and is due to changes in the effectiveness with which signals cross a synapse. **Habituation** is a progressive decrease in a response to a weak stimulus, when the stimulus is constantly repeated with no adverse consequences. After habituation, sensory neurons release less neurotransmitter, reducing the likelihood that motor neurons will fire. In **sensitization**, extra neurotransmitters are released, triggering more action potential in a motor neuron. It occurs when a strong stimulus results in undesirable consequences so that the sensitized animal responds to the slightest stimulus.

Thought Provokers

1. Write a short, storylike dialogue in which you comment clearly and concisely on each of the following concepts from this chapter on the nervous system. Be sure to relate the concepts to one another.

   a. "all or none"
   b. sodium/potassium channels
   c. resting potential

   d. action potential
   e. nodes of Ranvier
   f. tetrodotoxin

2. Make a chart that compares the advantages and disadvantages of rapid-relay nerve transmissions and slow-relay nerve transmissions, and the basic transmission mechanism(s) that operates in each case.

Self-Test

For each statement or question choose the best response and mark your choice in the space provided. For some items you will select your response from a *Key*.

_____ 1. An input signal arrives at a nerve cell and the nerve cell responds. From among the following, choose the correct pathway of signal transmission.

   a. axon, dendrites, soma
   b. dendrites, axon, soma
   c. soma, axon, dendrites
   d. axon, soma, dendrites
   e. dendrites, soma, axon

_____ 2. Select the correct sequence of activities of a functioning nerve cell.
   a. ion diffusion, depolarization, action potential
   b. depolarization, ion diffusion, action potential
   c. depolarization, action potential, ion diffusion
   d. action potential, depolarization, ion diffusion
   e. action potential, ion diffusion, depolarization

Questions 3–10. A and B are compared with regard to a property, character, or feature. If A is greater than B, mark A; if B is greater than A, mark B; if A and B are essentially equivalent, mark C.

		a	b
_____ 3.	comparative length	axons	dendrites
_____ 4.	number per neuron	axons	dendrites
_____ 5.	resting neuron's intracellular:	K^+	Na^+
_____ 6.	resting neuron's negative charge	inside cell	outside cell
_____ 7.	ease of ion passage across channel in resting neuron	Na^+	K^+
_____ 8.	rate of signal transmission	wide axon	narrow axon
_____ 9.	efficiency of impulse transmission	demyelinated nerve	myelinated nerve
_____ 10.	ratio of chemical to electrical synapses	lower animals	higher animals

Key for questions 11–16
a. True   b. False

_____ 11. Schwann cells are part of the myelin sheath.

_____ 12. Ions can flow across the nodes of Ranvier.

_____ 13. A neurotransmitter binding to an adjoining nerve cell causes the potassium channels, but not the sodium channels, to open up in that adjoining cell.

_____ 14. The insecticide parathion prevents the release of acetylcholine from vesicles, inhibiting nerve impulses.

_____ 15. Persons with myasthenia gravis have too many receptors for acetylcholine on their nerve cells.

_____ 16. Curare blocks neurotransmitter activity.

Key for questions 17–21
a. acetylcholine   c. norepinephrine
b. epinephrine   d. dopamine

_____ 17. also known as adrenaline

_____ 18. transmits messages in the brain and also from neurons of certain skeletal muscles

_____ 19. Clinical depression, appetite loss, and low energy levels may well be related to low levels of this.

_____ **20.** elevated in stress and fight reactions

_____ **21.** Deficiency of this is related to Parkinson's disease, with symptoms that include tremors, rigidity, and weakness.

Key for questions 22–26.

a. excitatory synapse   **b.** inhibitory synapse

_____ **22.** opens channels to potassium

_____ **23.** opens some channels to chloride

_____ **24.** causes the interior of the cell to become more negative

_____ **25.** some channels for sodium begin to open up

_____ **26.** a nerve fires or discharges

Key for questions 27–30

a. True   **b.** False

_____ **27.** Some reflex arcs do not have interneurons.

_____ **28.** An impulse that activates a muscle arrives there via a sensory neuron.

_____ **29.** In a habituation response, the amount of neurotransmitter at the site is increased in comparison to the normal situation.

_____ **30.** Calcium channels are important in certain types of nerve transmissions.

Key Terms from the Text Chapter

action potential *text page* 576
axon 574
bouton 574
dendrite 574
depolarized 576
glial cell 574
habituation 585
interneuron 584

motor neuron 584
myelin sheath 579
nerve 574
neuron 574
neurotransmitter 582
polarized 576
postsynaptic cell 574
potassium channel 575
presynaptic cell 574

reflex arc 583
sensitization 588
sensory neuron 584
sodium channel 575
soma 574
summation 582
synapse 574
synaptic vesicle 581

Concept Figure: Ions, Channels, and Pump Proteins

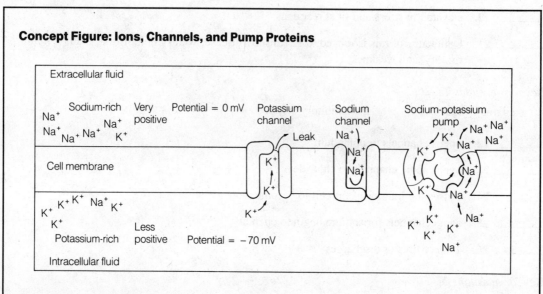

Exercise

Using the drawing as a reference, list the three proteins that function to keep a resting neuron at −70 mv. Give the specific role of each.

Protein   **Role**

a. _____   _____

b. _____   _____

c. _____   _____

The Senses and the Brain

Perspective and Review

In order to survive, an animal must be able to sense its environment, interpret the stimuli it receives, and act accordingly. The nervous system makes possible all these functions. In vertebrates the brain acts as the controller; it interprets messages from sense organs and stimulates responses. Radial animals, such as the cnidarian *Hydra*, have the most basic nervous systems—a network of nerve cells and fibers that conducts impulses from one area to another. Such animals are capable of only the simplest responses. In contrast, the highly complex nervous organization of vertebrates allows for more elaborate behaviors and activities.

Window on the World: Sense Organs

Sense organs are groups of specialized cells that detect stimuli and relay them to the brain. Although different sense organs are specialized for detecting particular stimuli, all sense organs function in the same way—highly sensitive sensory processes not covered by a myelin sheath detect stimuli and convert them into nerve impulses. Senses fall into three main categories. The first includes so-called "special" senses: sight, hearing, smell, touch, and taste. The second involves senses that detect the body's position and motion. Finally, most animals have senses that detect harmful stimuli.

Humans rely heavily on their senses of hearing and vision. Concept Table 28.1 describes the structure and functioning of the ear and eye, the two sense organs responsible for detecting sound and vision, respectively. The ear is also responsible for detecting motion and maintaining balance. Figures 28.5 and 28.9 in your text illustrate the structure of both organs.

Concept Table 28.1   Structure and function of the human ear and eye

The Ear

Structure	The external ear consists of a pinna, and an ear canal leading to the middle ear. The middle ear contains the *ear drum*, or *tympanum*, and three middle ear bones. These connect to the inner ear, a series of fluid-filled canals, including the coiled **cochlea**. The *basilar membrane*, a tissue partition in the cochlea, attaches to rows of hair cells crowned by bundles of threadlike **stereocilia**.
Hearing mechanism	Sound waves travel as pressure waves through the air and enter the ear canal, causing the tympanum to vibrate. These vibrations are transmitted by the middle ear bones to the cochlea. Vibrations reaching the cochlea compress the cochlear fluid, which in turn causes the hair cells to move relative to the tectorial membrane. This motion bends the stereocilia. Nerve impulses triggered by this mechanical event are transmitted to the brain via the auditory nerve. The brain interprets the pitch and intensity of the sound.
Balance and Motion	Balance and motion are detected by three fluid-filled semicircular canals in the inner ear. Acceleration and deceleration generate nerve impulses by causing the fluid to bend hair cells associated with these canals. *As with hearing, a mechanical force is transduced into an electrical signal.*

The Eye

Structure	The outer region of the eye, the **cornea**, is clear. A muscular diaphragm, the **iris**, surrounds an opening, or **pupil**. Light passing through the pupil strikes the **lens** and is focused onto a multilayered **retina**, which contains **photoreceptor cells** of two types: **Rods** are sensitive to low light but cannot distinguish color; **cones** need more light but can detect color.

Continues

Vision	Light striking a photoreceptor cell alters the shape of *retinal*, a molecule in the light-sensitive pigment **rhodopsin**. This shape change sets off a series of events that causes the rod cell to stop inhibiting a sensory neuron. Consequently, the neuron fires and sends a signal to the brain, via the *optic nerve*.

Nervous System: From Nerve Nets to the Human Brain

Humans have a highly sophisticated nervous system, and are capable of many complex behaviors not seen in lower animals. By comparing simple and complex animals, five general trends in the evolution of the nervous system become evident. These are: (1) The more complex an animal the more complex its nervous system; (2) cephalization—a concentration of nerve cells in the anterior region of the body; (3) bilateral symmetry in the organization of the nervous system, facilitating coordinated movements; (4) the more complex an animal the greater number of interneurons it has; and (5) concentration of neurons into an anterior brain and bilateral organization of ganglia.

Organization of the Vertebrate Nervous System

The vertebrate nervous system is organized into the central nervous system (CNS) and peripheral nervous system. The CNS, which coordinates information, consists of the brain and spinal cord. The peripheral nervous system performs actions and connects the various parts of the body to the CNS. The interplay between these two systems allows an animal to sense and respond to stimuli.

The Peripheral Nervous System: The Neural Actors

Concept Table 28.2 outlines the main features of the peripheral nervous system. Figure 28.13 in your text illustrates how this system interacts with the CNS.

Concept Table 28.2   The peripheral nervous system

Structure and Function	Consists of sensory and motor neurons. Senses changes and generates responses but does not process information.
Components	
Sensory neurons	Thirty-one pairs of sensory neurons that arise from the spinal cord. These relay messages from various regions of the body to the CNS.
Motor neurons	Neurons that radiate from the ventral root of the spinal cord; organized into two systems. The *somatic nervous system* generates voluntary muscle contractions. The *autonomic nervous system* regulates the internal environment via two sub-

Continues

systems that act in opposition: *Sympathetic nerves* tend to speed up activity, whereas *parasympathetic nerves* slow it down.

The Central Nervous System: The Information Processor

The central nervous system interprets and coordinates information collected by the peripheral nervous system. Concept Table 28.3 summarizes the main components of the human CNS.

Concept Table 28.3 Main components of the human central nervous system

Spinal cord	Responsible for preliminary integration of signals from sensory neurons and interneurons. It consists of an inner core of neurons and unmyelinated nerve fibers. Surrounding the core is an outer white layer of axons that relays messages to and from the brain.
Brain	Plays the main role in neural integration; is divided into three main interconnecting regions: brainstem, cerebellum, and cerebrum.
Brain stem	The lower region of the brain, organized into four main areas. The **medulla oblongata** regulates homeostasis. The **pons** and **midbrain** relay sensory information from the eyes and ears to other parts of the body. The *hypothalamus* regulates the pituitary and is involved in homeostasis. The **thalamus** serves as a relay area to the cerebrum.
Cerebellum	Coordinates muscle movements.
Cerebrum	The largest region of the brain; consists of two adjacent hemispheres. In humans the outer cerebral layer, the **cerebral cortex**, encompasses 90% of the brain's cells. Sensations, motor ability, cognitive functions, emotions, and character traits can all be traced to specific regions in the cerebrum. Figure 28.18 in your text maps the specific functions of these regions.

Thought Provokers

1. In a few paragraphs, discuss the spinal cord and its nerves and their activities in the human body.

2. Describe at least three significant discoveries about the human brain that have come to light in recent years. Your answer can include unusual side effects of brain injuries.

Self-Test

For each statement or question choose the best response and mark your choice in the space provided. For some items you will select your response from a *Key*.

_____ 1. Sensory organs have bare dendrites that are not covered with a myelin sheath.

      a. True   **b.** False

_____ 2. Which of the following <u>cannot</u> be detected by the senses of animals?

      a. pressure   **d.** pain

      b. heat   **e.** All of these can be detected.

      c. molecules

_____ 3. Which stimulus enables the pit organs of snakes to sense prey?

      a. heat   **b.** light   **c.** electrical impulse   **d.** weight   **e.** touch

_____ 4. The cochlea is filled with:

      a. air   **b.** fluid   **c.** bones   **d.** microorganisms   **e.** nothing

_____ 5. Which animal is best able to discriminate the directions of sounds above and below it?

      a. amoeba   **b.** insect   **c.** snake   **d.** human   **e.** owl

_____ 6. High-pitched sounds are detected where in the cochlea?

      a. tip   **d.** all areas

      b. base   **e.** none of these; the cochlea can-

      c. middle   not detect pitch.

Key for questions 7–10

a. True   **b.** False

_____ 7. Permanent deafness can result when stereocilia are destroyed.

_____ 8. Semicircular canals function in balance and in motion detection.

_____ 9. An owl locates prey via ultrasound waves that travel towards the prey and bounce back.

_____ 10. One ear of an owl is higher than the other.

Key for questions 11–16

a. retina   **b.** lens   **c.** cornea   **d.** pupil   **e.** iris

_____ 11. colored portion of the eye

_____ 12. This regulates the amount of light entering the eye; it works like a camera shutter.

_____ 13. This contains cones and rods.

_____ 14. This is the protective outer layer of the eye.

_____ 15. This is necessary for the focusing of light.

_____ 16. This contains photoreceptor cells.

_____ 17. Light striking a rhodopsin molecule has what effect on rhodopsin?

      a. straightens the molecular chain   **d.** destroys the chain

      b. bends the chain   **e.** none of these

      c. has no effect on the chain

Key for questions 18–21

a. True   **b.** False

_____ **18.** Rod cells function in a manner opposite that of typical neurons.

_____ **19.** Rod cells have sodium channels that are open in the dark.

_____ **20.** In the dark, neurotransmitters inhibit sensory neurons.

_____ **21.** The very same photoreceptors in the brain can tell not only the intensity of a light source but also its position.

_____ **22.** Which group first evolved cephalization?

      a. snails   **c.** amoebae   **e.** worms

      b. insects   **d.** hydra

Key for questions 23–31.

a. medulla oblongata   **d.** thalamus   **ab.** cerebrum

b. pons and midbrain   **e.** reticular formation   **ac.** cerebellum

c. hypothalamus

_____ **23.** serves as a link between the nervous and endocrine systems

_____ **24.** is a relay area to the highly convoluted cerebrum that surrounds it

_____ **25.** sends signals from eyes, ears, and tongue to other parts of the brain

_____ **26.** coordinates and integrates the activities of muscles, joints, and tendons, providing smoothness and equilibrium to motor functions

_____ **27.** is the lowest part of the brain stem, which regulates respiratory rate, heart rate, and blood pressure

_____ **28.** the seat of perception and consciousness

_____ **29.** regions that make up the brain stem

_____ **30.** regulates appetite, body temperature, water balance, and the digestive system

_____ **31.** emotions and character traits reside here

Key for questions 32–40

a. True   **b.** False

_____ **32.** Brain tissue has no pain receptors.

_____ **33.** Dorsal root ganglia send out effector signals from the spinal cord.

_____ **34.** Neurons for sensation and movement of the trunk are fewer in number in humans than neurons for the face and hands.

_____ **35.** When animals such as birds and rabbits are compared to humans, the number and kinds of specific neurons devoted to similar functions is proportionately similar.

_____ **36.** It is known that in some injuries or diseases a person may recognize a face but not a voice, or vice versa, depending on the type of injury or disease.

_____ **37.** Injury to the hippocampus region of the brain primarily affects short-term memory.

_____ **38.** In terms of activities distribution the brain is remarkably symmetrical.

_____ **39.** Left-handed people tend to show language activity on both sides of the cerebral cortex.

_____ **40.** Surgically cutting the corpus callosum destroys the functioning of both parts of the brain.

Key Terms from the Text Chapter

brain stem   *text page 604*
cerebellum   *604*
cerebral cortex   *605*
cerebrum   *604*
cochlea   *593*
cone   *596*
ganglion   *599*
hippocampus   *607*

medulla oblongata   *604*
midbrain   *604*
motor cortex   *607*
nerve net   *599*
photoreceptor cell   *596*
pons   *604*
reticular formation   *604*
retina   *596*

rhodopsin   *596*
rod   *596*
semicircular canal   *595*
sense organ   *592*
sensory cortex   *607*
split brain   *609*
stereocilium   *593*
thalamus   *604*

29

The Dynamic Animal: The Body in Motion

Perspective and Review

Movement helps animals solve a variety of life's problems, such as capturing food, escaping a would-be predator, driving off a rival, and reproducing. To generate movement specialized muscle cells contract, thereby transmitting force to the skeleton. The muscular, skeletal, and physiological systems interact during physical activity so that an animal can perform necessary tasks and still maintain homeostasis. Muscles and skeletons also adapt to stress over an individual's lifetime. For example, regular exercise causes body cells to use more oxygen; as a result the body develops a larger and stronger heart, greater muscle mass, and stronger bones. These systems also change over evolutionary time as species become specialized for particular life-styles. For example, birds have highly developed pectoral muscles used in flight.

The Skeleton: A Scaffold for Support and Movement

The skeleton supports the body and also facilitates movement. There are two basic skeletal types. **Hydroskeletons**, found in sea anemones and snails, consist of a liquid core within a tension-resistant sheath. **Antagonistic muscle pairs**—groups of muscles that move the same object in opposite directions—push against this incompressible fluid, displacing it to another region of the body and generating movement. Rapidly moving land animals require more support, provided by a brace-framework solid skeleton made of minerals and proteins. In many invertebrates, such as insects, an outer **exoskeleton** serves this purpose, while vertebrates have an internal bony skeleton, or **endoskeleton**. **Bones** support the vertebrate body, anchor muscles, encase vital organs, form blood cells, and store calcium and phosphate ions. Concept Table 29.1 outlines the main features of the mammalian skeleton.

Concept Table 29.1 Significant features of the mammalian skeleton

Axial skeleton	Supports the main body axis. It consists of the **skull**, ribs, **vertebral column** (composed of interlocking **vertebrae**), and the tailbone.
Appendicular skeleton	Bones that support the appendages, including the **pectoral** and **pelvic girdles**.
Bone structure	The long shaft of a bone is the **diaphysis**; it expands into the **epiphysis**, a region that articulates with other bones. Cartilaginous **ligaments** (linking bone to bone), and **tendons** (linking bone to muscle) attach to projections called **processes**. **Joints** allow bones to move with respect to each other.
Fine structure	An outer solid layer of *compact bone* provides support. A *spongy bone* region at each end of a bone provides strength near joints. **Marrow**, the site of blood cell synthesis, occupies spaces down the center of the bone shaft. Bone cells called **osteoblasts** secrete proteins and minerals; **osteoclasts** reabsorb calcium and phosphates from bone for use in other areas of the body.
Action	Bones can pivot at joints and perform work because of the way in which antagonistic muscle groups attach to them.

Muscles: Motors of the Body

Skeletal muscle attaches to and propels the bones of the skeleton. Its contractions are responsible for voluntary movements.

Skeletal muscle is composed of giant, multinucleated cells called muscle fibers. **Myofibrils** in each cell do the actual contracting. A myofibril consists of repeating units of **sarcomeres**, arrays of actin and myosin filaments that overlap along part of their length. Muscle contraction occurs when actin filaments slide past myosin, shortening the sarcomere. When each sarcomere in a muscle fiber becomes shorter, the whole fiber does also. This *sliding filament mechanism* of muscle contraction relies on specific features of actin and myosin: Projecting myosin **heads** bind actin molecules and rotate, sliding the actin forward. The sequence of binding and rotating happens repeatedly for each myosin molecule as a muscle contracts. The process is powered by ATP, as Concept Table 29.2 describes.

Three sets of membranes help stimulate muscle fibers to contract. When an action potential reaches a muscle cell, it is transmitted to the *plasma membrane*. From there, *transverse tubules* channel the signal to the final set of membranes, the *sarcoplasmic reticulum*, inside the cell. The sarcoplasmic reticulum then releases stored calcium ions into the cytoplasm, and these generate muscle contraction.

Concept Table 29.2   How ATP powers the sliding filament mechanism

Energy event	Mechanism step
1. Myosin head "grasps" ADP and phosphate group	Myosin head binds actin.
2. ADP and phosphate are released.	Myosin head rotates in "power stroke"; actin filament slides.
3. ATP molecule joins myosin.	Myosin disengages from actin.
4. ATP yields ADP and phosphate, releasing energy.	Myosin head cleaves ATP.
5. Step 1 repeats.	Step 1 repeats.

Along with skeletal muscle, vertebrates have two additional muscle types. **Cardiac muscle**, found only in the heart, propels blood through the circulatory system. **Smooth muscle** moves food through the alimentary canal and provides tension in the arteries, bladder, and uterus. Both of these muscle types are not under voluntary control. They differ from skeletal muscle in organization but operate in much the same manner.

Three systems provide energy for muscle contraction, depending on the intensity and duration of muscle activity. Concept Table 29.3 summarizes these three energy systems.

Concept Table 29.3   Energy sources (ATP) for muscle cell contraction

Source	Significant features
Intermediate system	Provides energy for short, explosive muscle activity. There are two components to this system: small amounts of ATP stored in muscle cells, and a high-energy compound, *creatine phosphate*, stored in muscle cells, which regenerates ATP.
Glycolytic energy system	Fuels activities lasting one to three minutes. Glycolysis in the cytoplasm of muscle fibers cleaves glucose in the absence of oxygen to generate a few ATP molecules. Fast-twitch fibers derive most of their ATP from this source.
Oxidative energy system	Sustains activities lasting more than three minutes. This system, based on cellular respiration, uses oxygen and generates many ATP molecules per molecule of glucose burned. Energy comes from metabolism of carbohydrates, fatty acids, and amino acids stored in other areas of the body. Slow-twitch fibers, rich in myoglobin, obtain most of their ATP in this way.

Exercise Physiology and Survival

During a fight-or-flight response, the hypothalamus secretes a releasing factor that triggers a sequence of hormone-mediated events that prepare the body for physical activity. Heart rate and blood pressure rise and glycerol and fatty acid blood levels increase, as does oxygen intake. Secretion of epinephrine intensifies and prolongs the various effects. Athletic training mimics this response.

Thought Provokers

1. Construct a table that names the three different types of muscle cells and describes the structural features, function, and location of each.

2. Suppose you decide to bend your little finger. Briefly explain the molecular mechanism of muscle contraction from the time a neuron is stimulated to actual contraction.

3. Suppose that a muscle becomes active and then continues to function (aerobically) for the next hour. Describe the sequence of biochemical events that provides energy to keep the muscle working.

4. Explain the difference between slow-twitch and fast-twitch muscle fibers.

5. Explain some of the ways that athletic training alters body physiology and muscle tissues.

Self-Test

For each statement or question choose the best response and mark your choice in the space provided. For some items you will select your response from a *Key*.

Key for questions 1–12

a. True   **b.** False

_____ 1. Flagella, cilia, and muscle contain large amounts of protein.

_____ 2. The bone structure of a horse is better adapted for running than is the bone structure of a human.

_____ 3. Collagen is a protein.

_____ 4. Earthworms, snails, and sea anemones have hydroskeletons.

_____ 5. The hyoid bone in humans is an unjointed tail bone.

_____ 6. In growing individuals the processes of bones become larger as the muscles become stronger.

_____ 7. Osteoporosis is a condition of the bone related to the overactivity of the osteoclasts.

_____ 8. Overactivity in young people may damage bones and result in failure of normal growth.

_____ 9. In joints, bursitis is a more serious condition than is arthritis.

_____ 10. Muscle fibers typically contain one or more nuclei.

_____ 11. Muscle cells contain myofibrils.

_____ 12. Lower back pain may be caused by a pinched nerve in the spinal cord.

_____ 13. The main inorganic component of bone is:

    a. calcium phosphate   **d.** calcium hydroxide
    b. calcium chloride   **e.** calcium oxide
    c. calcium carbonate

Questions 14–16

_____ 14. Total number of bones in the human body:

    a. 106   **b.** 156   **c.** 186   **d.** 206   **e.** 286

_____ 15. The number of human vertebrae:

    a. 23   **b.** 33   **c.** 43   **d.** 53   **e.** 63

_____ 16. The number of pairs of ribs in humans:

    a. 6   **b.** 12   **c.** 24   **d.** 36   **e.** 48

Key for questions 17–20

a. ligaments   **c.** processes   **e.** epiphysis
b. tendons   **d.** diaphysis

_____ 17. This is the longest part of the femur.

_____ 18. These attach bones to muscle.

_____ **19.** This is the expanded end of the femur.

_____ **20.** These attach bones to bones.

_____ **21.** Red blood cells are manufactured in:

    a. marrow   **c.** compact bone   **e.** none of these
    b. spongy bone   **d.** the periosteum

Questions 22–24. Comparing actin and myosin, if the numbered characteristic is greater for actin, mark A; if greater for myosin, mark B; if the same for both actin and myosin, mark C.

_____ **22.** thickness of fibril   _____ **23.** lighter color of fibril   _____ **24.** cleavage of ATP

Key for questions 25–30

a. cranium   **c.** pectoral   **e.** none of these
b. sternum   **d.** pelvic

_____ **25.** The fontanels are most closely associated with this.

_____ **26.** bone structure that protects the heart

_____ **27.** bone of the spinal cord

_____ **28.** related to the hip area

_____ **29.** bone related to the foot

_____ **30.** bones related to the shoulder

Key Terms from the Text Chapter

antagonistic muscle pair *text page 614*
appendicular skeleton *615*
axial skeleton *615*
bone *615*
cardiac muscle *624*

endoskeleton *615*
exoskeleton *615*
hydroskeleton *614*
joint *618*
ligament *617*
myofibril *620*

sarcomere *620*
skeletal muscle *619*
smooth muscle *624*
tendon *617*
vertebral column *615*

Concept Figure: Muscle Contraction

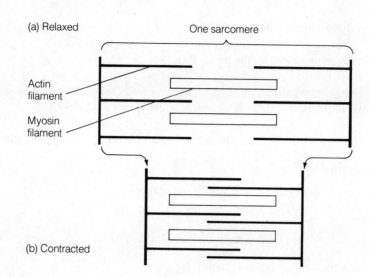

(a) Relaxed

One sarcomere

Actin filament

Myosin filament

(b) Contracted

Exercise

The diagram represents the sliding filament mechanism of muscle contraction. To review this mechanism, fill in the following blanks.

Thin filaments are called: _____

Thick filaments are called: _____

Unit that shortens during a muscle contraction: _____

Filament with an oarlike head: _____

Structure that binds actin: _____

Two-part process that slides actin past myosin: _____

Energy source for this process: _____

30

Plant Architecture and Function

CHAPTER IN BRIEF

Perspective and Review

Plants, unlike animals, are immobile, and their form and function reflect this fact. Plants usually rely on wind or animals to carry male gametes (pollen) to female gametes. Consequently, the shape, color, or fragrance of a flower is often adapted to attract specific pollinators, with a reward of nectar. Seeds must also be dispersed, and here again animals, wind, or water play vital roles. Some plants produce attractive, fleshy fruits, while others have hooked seeds that attach to passing animals.

Stems support the plant and also carry leaves and flowers. While large, flat leaves can increase the plant's capacity for photosynthesis, this feature must be balanced against the need to protect against water loss across leaf surfaces. Structural modifications help to maintain the equilibrium; for instance, desert plants may have small leaves covered with a thick cuticle.

The Plant Body: Plant Tissues and Growth Patterns

Vascular plants are characterized by an internal transport system, sexual reproduction, and the presence of a waterproof seed coat. Gymnosperms and angiosperms produce seeds; only angiosperms have flowers. All vascular plants have subsurface roots and above-ground shoots. Three types of root systems provide support and nourishment: **taproots**, **fibrous roots**, and <u>adventitious roots</u>. Complex plants have tissue systems that perform important physiological functions. Concept Table 30.1 summarizes the three main systems; a detailed description of cell types in each system appears in Table 30.2 of your text.

Concept Table 30.1   Plant tissue systems

Tissue system	Tissues and functions
Dermal	Protects the plant from water loss and injury. In a young seedling the dermal layer consists of an *epidermis*. This is replaced by the *periderm* in trees and woody shrubs.
Ground	Stores starch and provides support. There are three main tissue types; **parenchyma**, used for storage, photosynthesis, and repairs; **collenchyma** and **schlerenchyma** both provide support.
Vascular	Transports fluids and provides structural support. **Xylem**, composed of **tracheids** and **vessel members**, transports water and minerals. **Phloem**, consisting of **sieve tube members** and their associated **companion cells**, conducts dissolved sugars and protein.

Plants show a pattern of continuous **open growth**, with **meristems** constantly giving rise to new cells. **Apical meristems** are growth regions at the tips of roots and shoots that produce **primary growth**. **Lateral meristems** increase the thickness of stems and roots by a process known as **secondary growth**. **Annual plants** complete their life cycle and die within a year. **Biennials** have a two-year life cycle. And **perennials** live for many years and generally bloom and set seed many times before dying.

Flowers, Fruits, Seeds, and Plant Embryos: The Architecture of Continuity

Concept Table 30.2 describes the main components of flowers, and plant development after fertilization. Plant reproductive structures and fertilization are covered in detail in Chapter 17.

Concept Table 30.2 Flowers and plant development

Flower	Modified leaves composed of sepals, petals, stamens—the male parts, where pollen develops—and carpels—the female region, housing the ovary.
Fertilization	*Double fertilization* results in a diploid embryo and a triploid endosperm that nourishes the embryo.
Seed formation	Fruit, generally derived from the ovaries, protects the seed and aids dispersal. A hard seed coat develops from the ovule wall, while inside the seed the **radicle** (embryonic root) and **plumule** (embryonic shoot) arise. A short stem, the **hypocotyl**, bears the embryo's first leaves, known as **cotyledons**. **Monocots** have one cotyledon; **dicots** have two.
Germination	Germination occurs when the seed absorbs water and swells and the embryo bursts from the seed coat.
Development	**Primordia**, undifferentiated meristematic tissue, gives rise to leaves, shoots, and flowers. Leaves are first to develop, so the plant can begin to photosynthesize. The position at which a leaf arises is called a **node**. Flower and stem **buds** develop in the angle between leaf and stem.

Structure and Development of Roots

Concept Table 30.3 outlines the structure and development of **roots**, the plant's anchoring, absorptive, and storage structures.

Concept Table 30.3 Structure and development of roots

Vertical structure	Roots are divided into three major zones: the *zone of cell division*—the apical meristem and protective **root cap**; the *zone of elongation*—the region where individual cells elongate; and the *zone of maturation*—the site of cell differentiation.
Tissue systems	
Dermal	An outer epidermal layer; absorbs water and minerals. **Root hairs** greatly increase the absorptive area.
Ground system	Located inside the epidermis; a thick **cortex** where starch is stored. The inner **endodermis** of the cortex is a waterproof layer surrounding the vascular system.
Vascular system	A cylindrical core of xylem, phloem, and **pericycle**.

Continues

Concept Table 30.3   Structure and development of roots (continued)

Secondary growth	The pericycle gives rise to two lateral meristems: **vascular cambium**, which gives rise to phloem and xylem (mature xylem cells are nonliving and form **wood**); and **cork cambium**, which generates a new waterproof layer, the **cork**.

Structure and Development of the Shoot

Concept Table 30.4 describes the structure and development of the plant **shoot**.

Concept Table 30.4   Structure and development of the plant shoot

Tissue systems

Dermal	Distinguished by stem epidermis with a **cuticle** to prevent desiccation. In addition, hairlike **trichomes** help to retard water loss.
Ground	A cortex containing both parenchyma and collenchyma cells; the latter provide extra support.
Vascular	Xylem and phloem, arranged into *vascular bundles*. Monocots and some dicots have bundles scattered throughout the stem. However, most dicots have bundles arranged around a central **pith**, with a layer of cambium between xylem and phloem. This cambium layer allows for secondary growth in dicots.
Secondary growth	As in the root, lateral meristems give rise to vascular and cork cambium. In woody plants the stems are composed largely of dead xylem. Because secondary growth ruptures the original cortex and epidermis, a new protective layer, **bark**, is made up of cork, periderm, and phloem. Bark prevents against water loss, parasites, and diseases.

The Structure and Development of Leaves

Leaves carry out photosynthesis and, via transpiration, help draw water and minerals up through the plant. Concept Table 30.5 outlines the structure and development of leaves.

Concept Table 30.5   Structure and development of leaves

Structure	Components include a flat **blade** and a **petiole**, which attaches the leaf to the stem. *Simple* leaves are characterized by single blades, whereas *compound* leaves have many small leaflets.

Continues

Concept Table 30.5	Structure and development of leaves (continued)
Tissue systems	
Dermal	Epidermis covered by a cuticle. Openings in the epidermis, known as **stomata**, allow passage of gases and water.
Ground	A central **mesophyll** layer, made up of two types of parenchyma: *palisade parenchyma*—the main photosynthetic tissue; and *spongy palisade*, which provides large areas for carbon dioxide absorption.
Vascular	**Veins**, bundles of xylem and phloem cells, transport substances within leaves.

Thought Provokers

1. Briefly explain how a plant's leaves, stem, and roots are integrated systems that contribute to the life and survival of the plant. Cite functions of each part and use appropriate terminology.

2. Define each of the following and give a specific example that illustrates or supports the definition.

   a. Casparian strip

   b. stomata

   c. meristem

   d. cambium

   e. perfect flower

Self-Test

For each statement or question choose the best response and mark your choice in the space provided. For some items you will select your answer from a *Key*.

Key for questions 1–2

a. True   b. False

_____ 1. Gymnosperms and angiosperms produce seeds.

_____ 2. In higher plants, external fertilization is more common than internal fertilization.

_____ **3.** Which of the following is <u>not</u> part of the shoot?

    a. stem   **c.** leaves   **e.** root

    b. branches   **d.** flowers

_____ **4.** Which of the following lacks a taproot?

    a. grass   **c.** dandelion

    b. carrot   **d.** pear tree

Key for questions 5–14, relating to the three basic kinds of plant tissue.

a. epidermal tissue   **b.** ground tissue   **c.** vascular tissue

_____ **5.** vessel members

_____ **6.** sclerenchyma

_____ **7.** parenchyma

_____ **8.** tracheids

_____ **9.** cuticle-secreting cells

_____ **10.** xylem

_____ **11.** collenchyma

_____ **12.** sieve tubes

_____ **13.** periderm

_____ **14.** phloem

Questions 15–22. For each numbered question select the response (A or B) that correctly identifies various characteristics of phloem and xylem.

Phloem   Xylem

_____ **15.** _____ **16.** Cell type   **a.** alive   **b.** dead

_____ **17.** _____ **18.** Transport materials   **a.** water/minerals   **b.** sugar/amino acids/ water

_____ **19.** _____ **20.** Route of transmission   **a.** roots to leaves   **b.** movement from regions of high to low concentration

_____ **21.** _____ **22.** Cell types   **a.** sieve tube/ companion cell   **b.** tracheids/ vessel members

Questions 23–26. Indicate which item from the *Key* gives rise to each of the numbered items.

a. apical meristem   **b.** lateral meristem

_____ **23.** wood

_____ **24.** cork

_____ **25.** root tips

_____ **26.** ends of stems

Key for questions 27–29

a. annual   **b.** biennial   **c.** perennial

_____ **27.** celery, carrots

_____ **28.** marigolds, zinnias

_____ **29.** tulips, dahlias, roses

Questions 30–33. For each numbered concept, indicate whether A or B is greater or plays a larger role.

		a	**b**
_____	**30.** degree of secondary growth	perennial	annual
_____	**31.** attraction of insects	sepals	petals
_____	**32.** open growth	plants	animals
_____	**33.** ploidy of a seed's:	embryo	endosperm

Key for questions 34–38

a. female flower part   **b.** male flower part

_____ **34.** style

_____ **35.** stamens

_____ **36.** carpel base

_____ **37.** stigma

_____ **38.** filaments

Key for questions 39–40

a. monoecious   **c.** imperfect
b. perfect   **d.** dioecious

_____ **39.** a plant that produces both male and female flowers on the same individual

_____ **40.** a plant that produces only female flowers

Key for questions 41–45

a. monocot   **c.** both monocots and dicots
b. dicot   **d.** neither monocots nor dicots

_____ **41.** grasses and corn

_____ **42.** pear trees

_____ **43.** lilies and palms

_____ **44.** plants with parallel venation on leaves

_____ **45.** plants whose seedlings have paired seed leaves

Key for questions 46–50, seed parts which relate to

a. radicle   **c.** cotyledon   **e.** epicotyl/hypocotyl
b. integument   **d.** plumule

_____ **46.** the tiny shoot of the embryo

_____ **47.** covering of the seed

_____ **48.** the root region of the embryo

_____ **49.** region just above and below leaves

_____ **50.** in a peanut, the two oval pairs of the nut

Questions 51–60. Using the *Key* indicate where each of the numbered items might be found in a plant.

a. roots   **c.** leaves   **e.** roots, stems, and leaves
b. stems   **d.** two of A, B, and C   **ab.** none of these

_____ **51.** phloem/xylem

_____ **52.** Casparian strip

_____ **53.** cap cells

_____ **54.** bark

_____ **55.** stomata

_____ **56.** cambium

_____ **57.** palisade and spongy cell layer

_____ **58.** endodermis

_____ **59.** pericycle

_____ **60.** parenchyma

Key Terms from the Text Chapter

annual plant *text page 639*

apical meristem *638*

bark *649*

biennial *639*

blade *650*

bud *641*

Casparian strip *644*

collenchyma *636*

companion cell *638*

cork *646*

cork cambium *638*

cortex *644*

cotyledon *640*

cross-pollination *640*

dermal tissue system *635*

endodermis *644*

epicotyl *641*

fibrous root *634*

ground tissue system *635*

hypocotyl *641*

lateral meristem *638*

meristem *638*

mesophyll *651*

node *641*

open growth *638*

parenchyma *636*

perennial *639*

pericycle *646*

petiole *650*

phloem *637*

pith *646*

plumule *640*

primary growth *638*

primordium *641*

radicle *640*

root *634*

root cap *642*

root hair *642*

sclerenchyma *636*

secondary growth *638*

shoot *634*

sieve tube member *638*

taproot *634*

tracheids *637*

trichome *647*

vascular cambium *638*

vascular tissue system *635*

vein *651*

vessel member *637*

wood *648*

xylem *637*

Exercise

Fill in the chart: Identify the three main tissue systems in a vascular plant, give the role of each system, and list at least two tissue types included in each system.

Tissue system	Role	Representative tissue types
1.		1. 2.
2.		1. 2.
3.		1. 2.

Regulators of Plant Growth and Development

CHAPTER IN BRIEF

Perspective and Review

Plants must germinate, flower, and set seed at the correct time if they are to persist. For most plants, these events occur when conditions are optimal for growth (such as warm, sunny days), pollinators are available to ensure fertilization, and other flowers are also in bloom. Consequently, plants respond to a series of environmental stimuli, known as *external regulators*. In addition, *internal regulators* control plant growth and development. These are molecular messengers, which act in a similar manner to animal hormones, although they are chemically quite different.

Plant Hormones: Five Major Kinds

Plants respond to environmental conditions primarily by modifying their growth. Growth is either stimulated or inhibited by plant hormones, small molecules that trigger responses within a plant. There are five main hormone classes: Three promote and regulate growth, while the remaining two inhibit growth or promote maturation. Concept Table 31.1 summarizes the role of each class.

Concept Table 31.1   Plant hormones, regulators of growth and development

Class	Main effects
Gibberellins	Regulate plant growth, in particular stem lengthening, and development of new leaves and branches. Also affect germination, flowering, and fertilization. Gibberellins are produced by a variety of plant organs.
Auxins	Promote growth through cell elongation. Manufactured in the shoot apical meristem and developing leaves, auxins travel downward to roots. They prevent lateral growth and are involved in plant orientation in space, growth of the ovary wall, and the prevention of leaf and fruit drop.
Cytokinins	Promote the growth of lateral buds and help to prevent leaf senescence. Cytokinins are transported in the vascular system from the root upwards through the plant.
Abscisic acid	Inhibits growth by counteracting the influence of growth hormones. Plays an important role in plant dormancy, stomata behavior, and abscission (leaf and fruit drop).
Ethylene	A gas at room temperature, ethylene is produced by ripening fruits and transported by air. It stimulates the ripening of nearby fruits, plays a part in promoting senescence and abscission, and may be involved in plant defense.

Internal and External Regulators of Germination

Environmental cues interact with plant hormones to trigger seed germination. Plants are adapted to respond to environmental stimuli that indicate the most advantageous times for germination. In spring, increasing temperatures and daylength usually trigger germination in the seeds of temperate zone plants. In dry areas, moisture stimulates germination by leaching out growth-inhibiting hormone, present in the seed. When grass seeds take up water they produce a gibberellin that causes secretion of an enzyme that converts starch, stored in the seed, to sugar, a necessary source of energy for the growing embryo.

Growth and Development After Germination: The Influence of Environment and Hormones

Plants orient in space with regard to light, gravity, and water via **tropisms**—movement with respect to a stimulus. Shoots are positively phototropic; that is, plants grow towards light, thereby maximizing their exposure to the sun. Roots are positively geotropic; that is, they grow downward into the soil, in the same direction as the pull of gravity. By contrast, shoots are negatively geotropic. Plants also show movements other than tropisms. Known as nastic responses, these movements are in response to a stimulus rather than with respect to a stimulus. A nastic response explains why the leaves of a Venus's-flytrap shut when an insect triggers sensitive hairs inside the trap.

External and internal stimuli also influence plant shape. Light, in particular, can have a major impact on a plant's growth pattern. **Phytochrome**, a light-sensitive pigment, exerts a strong influence on growth; it has two forms, P_{fr}, which absorbs far red light, and P_r, which absorbs red light. A plant growing in the dark converts its P_{fr} to P_r, which causes the plant to become etiolated—long, spindly, and pale. When phytochrome inside plant cells is in the P_{fr} form, the plant grows normally.

Auxins produced in the apical bud of a plant inhibit lateral growth by a process known as **apical dominance**. The interaction between apical dominance and root-produced cytokinins is responsible for the conical shape of many trees.

Controlling Influences on Flowering and Fruit Formation

Flowering and fruit set must be correctly timed to ensure successful reproduction. Concept Table 31.2 outlines the main factors that trigger flowering and fruit development.

Concept Table 31.2 Factors influencing flowering and fruit development

Flowering

Temperature	Many plants flower only after exposure to cold, a process known as *vernalization*.
Daylength	Rather than relying on temperature, some plants flower in response to **photoperiod**—relative lengths of day and night. *Short-day plants* require nights longer than a critical duration in order to flower. For *long-day plants*, nights must be shorter than a specific duration.
Hormones	Many plant physiologists believe that a hormone they call **florigen** stimulates flowering. However, some botanists argue that "florigen" is actually the combined effects of many plant hormones.
Fruit development	Some seeds, such as those of strawberries, secrete auxins that stimulate fruit to ripen. Ethylene also promotes fruit development.

Senescence, Leaf Dropping, and Plant Dormancy

Several events control **senescence** (the process of aging and dying) and **abscission** (the dropping of mature fruit or dying leaves). In annual plants, which die after seed dispersal, flowering and environmental cues often trigger senescence. Many perennials conserve resources over winter by being **deciduous** (dropping their leaves). In autumn deciduous trees withdraw nutrients from their leaves to store them in the trunk and roots. Environmental cues cause chlorophyll in the leaves to degrade, and consequently leaves lose their color. Leaf abscission is controlled by a combination of environmental factors and hormones. Auxins, produced in large quantities in summer, inhibit abscission. With decreasing auxin production in autumn and accompanying weather changes, leaves drop.

Plant Protection: Defensive Responses to External Threats

Many plants produce <u>secondary compounds</u> that combat diseases and predators. These compounds act by one of four general mechanisms. Concept Table 31.3 summarizes these four mechanisms.

Concept Table 31.3 Plant Defenses	
Defense	**Mode of action**
Repellents	Volatile compounds, such as mustard oils, that discourage pests from eating a plant or laying eggs on it.
Poisons	Toxins, such as cyanide compounds, that poison attackers.
Digestion inhibitors	Compounds that block the action of an attacker's digestive enzymes.
Life cycle disrupters	Compounds that disrupt the normal development of insect larvae feeding on particular plants.

Over evolutionary time, many plant predators have evolved countermeasures to deal with these toxins. Some, such as *Chrysomela* beetles, sequester the toxins and use them in their own defenses against predators. Recent evidence suggests that attacks on one plant can stimulate nearby plants to produce secondary compounds, perhaps in response to an airborne cue given off by the attacked plant. In addition, plants can wall off a damaged area to protect healthy tissues.

Thought Provokers

1. Compare and contrast the biochemistry and functions of plant and animal hormones.

2. Define/explain each of the following in 100 words or less: (a) phototropism; (b) flowering; (c) bud maturation; and (d) regulation of germination.

Self-Test

For each statement or question choose the best response and mark your answer in the space provided. For some items you will select your response from a *Key*.

Key for questions 1–11, which relate to characteristics of plant hormones.

a. auxins   **c.** cytokinin   **e.** ethylene
b. abscisic acid   **d.** gibberellins

_____ **1.** is chemically related to adenine

_____ **2.** growth inhibitor

_____ **3.** growth hormone produced in leaves

_____ **4.** functions in the closing of stomata

_____ **5.** gaseous hormone

_____ **6.** 2, 4-D and 2, 4, 5-T are related to this hormone.

_____ **7.** is less mobile than auxins; moves from root to shoot

_____ **8.** Distribution of this hormone is responsible for phototropism.

_____ **9.** is responsible for dormancy

_____ **10.** "One rotten apple spoils the barrel" relates to the effects of this hormone.

_____ **11.** cause of foolish-seedling disease

_____ **12.** When auxin is administered to one side of a cut stem, the effect is:

     a. The stem elongates on the side with the auxin.
     b. The cells on that side die.
     c. Nothing happens.
     d. Cells on the opposite side die.
     e. Cells on the opposite side grow and divide faster.

_____ **13.** Which statement is most correct?

     a. Seeds are generally impervious to water.
     b. Light is necessary for seed germination.
     c. Dark is necessary for seed germination.
     d. Germination occurs more rapidly in tropical plants and climates.
     e. Moisture is not a cue for germination.

Key for questions 14–17

a. True   **b.** False

_____ **14.** Some seeds can survive in a dormant state for hundreds of years.

_____ **15.** Nastic responses may be rapid and irreversible.

_____ **16.** Nastic responses may be slow and reversible.

_____ **17.** Nastic responses may be rapid and reversible.

_____ **18.** An etiolated plant would most likely:

    a. be short   **c.** be poisonous   **e.** not photosynthesize well

    b. have flowers   **d.** be dead

_____ **19.** The idea of vernalization implies that:

    a. Plants require water for growth.

    b. A cold period is needed.

    c. Seeds are produced in the autumn and winter.

    d. Auxins are produced throughout a plant's life.

    e. Auxins are produced only at certain times.

_____ **20.** Senescence is most closely related to the concept of:

    a. germination   **c.** conduction   **e.** abscission and death

    b. growth   **d.** tropism

_____ **21.** The purple-colored pigments in plants are:

    a. anthocyanins   **c.** carotenes   **e.** polysaccharides

    b. chlorophylls   **d.** xanthophylls

Questions 22–25. Match each statement with the best description from the _Key_.

a. repellant   **c.** digestive inhibitor

b. poison   **d.** life cycle disrupter

_____ **22.** nicotine

_____ **23.** tannin

_____ **24.** cyanide

_____ **25.** camphor

Key Terms from the Text Chapter

abscisic acid   _text page 657_   deciduous   _667_   photoperiod   _664_

abscission   _657_   dormancy   _657_   phytochrome   _662_

apical dominance   _663_   ethylene   _657_   senescence   _667_

auxins   _657_   florigen   _666_   tropism   _659_

cytokinins   _657_   gibberellin   _654_

32

The Dynamic Plant: Transporting Water and Nutrients

Perspective and Review

The absorption of water and inorganic nutrients, as well as the manufacture of sugars, is essential to plant survival. Being rooted to one spot, plants depend heavily on the surrounding soil to provide these inorganic nutrients and water. During their evolution many plants have become adapted to particular soil types. For example, nitrogen-fixing bacteria cannot survive in highly acidic soils, and consequently plants such as the Venus's-flytrap that grow in acid soils are insectivorous, obtaining their nitrogen by trapping and digesting insects.

The inner-tube-like transport system of vascular plants carries water and other nutrients to all parts of a plant. Plants minimize the energy expended in drawing in and transporting water and minerals by using the physical properties of water itself. The result is efficient distribution of water, minerals, and photosynthetic products throughout a plant, whatever its height or degree of specialization.

How Plants Take in Water and Restrict Its Loss

Water, essential for plant survival, diffuses into root hairs from the surrounding soil. Once inside the plant it flows either through cell cytoplasm or between cells of the root cortex until reaching the endodermis. Because of the waterproof Casparian strip, water is forced through the cytoplasm and membrane of endodermal cells and into xylem. Parenchyma cells are continually pumping solutes into the xylem cells, and the resulting higher concentration of solutes in xylem allows water to diffuse into it by osmosis. There are a number of possible mechanisms by which water can move upward in a plant, and Concept Table 32.1 describes them.

Concept Table 32.1   Water movement in plants

Root pressure	Water pressure builds up in roots, and as a result water pushes upwards in the xylem. *Guttation*, the accumulation of water droplets on leaves, is caused by root pressure.
Capillary action	The tendency of water to creep upwards in a thin tube; occurs in narrow xylem and phloem vessels.

Neither of the above two mechanisms can fully account for the upward movement of water in tall plants.

Transpiration pull theory (cohesion-adhesion-tension theory)	Explains how most water moves from roots to the upper parts of a plant. According to this model, as water evaporates from leaves and stems by **transpiration**, water in xylem is pulled upward. This movement occurs because water molecules cohere in a chain and also adhere to cell walls. The water-molecule chain is under constant tension, and as long as evaporation and tension are maintained, the movement continues. On hot days, the tension can become strained, and the chain may break. Water flow then stops, and the plant wilts.

Plants lose most of their water through small pores called stomata. Stomata also allow carbon dioxide, necessary for photosynthesis, to enter the plant. Consequently the plant must balance its need for carbon dioxide (open stomata) against the need to prevent water loss (closed stomata). Each stoma is flanked by two **guard cells**. When these cells are full of water, turgor pressure forces them apart and the stoma opens. When guard cells lose water, they become flaccid, slumping together to close the stoma. Other factors that regulate stomatal opening and closing include the levels of potassium ions, carbon dioxide, light, and temperature and daily rhythms.

How Plants Absorb Needed Mineral Nutrients

Plants require 16 different essential elements. Of these elements, the seven needed in large quantities are known as **macronutrients**. The remaining **micronutrients** are required in very small amounts. Concept Table 32.2 summarizes the main functions of macronutrients and lists the micronutrients.

Concept Table 32.2   Plant nutrients

Macronutrients

Carbon, Hydrogen, and Oxygen	Present in organic compounds, the biological roles of these nutrients are discussed in text chapters 2–6.
Nitrogen	Nitrogen is an essential component of proteins. Plants cannot absorb gaseous nitrogen and must obtain it instead **fixed** into *ammonia* or *nitrate ions*. **Legumes** have root **nodules** containing **nitrogen-fixing** bacteria that supply the plant with nitrogen. Nonlegumes derive their nitrogen from any of three sources: (1) bacteria in soil that convert nitrogen to ammonia; (2) excess soil nitrates produced by legumes; and (3) ammonifying bacteria associated with decaying matter.
Calcium	Acts as an intracellular messenger and plays a structural role as an important component of *pectin*.
Potassium	Regulates osmosis and activates enzymes.
Phosphorous	An important component of nucleic acids and high-energy molecules such as ATP.
Sulphur	Required for building proteins and for manufacture of some fats and coenzymes.
Magnesium	Occurs in chlorophyll and cofactors.

Micronutrients

Essential to all plants	Iron, chlorine, manganese, boron, zinc, copper, molybdenum.
Essential to some plants	Silicon, sodium, cobalt.

Soil, the main source of minerals for plants, has an organic component, known as underlined humus, and an inorganic part. Pores and air spaces in soils serve as reservoirs of water, minerals, and oxygen. Minerals are actively absorbed by the plant, a process that requires energy. Most land plants form symbiotic associations with mycorrhizal fungi, which greatly increase surface area for absorption and may also supply growth hormones to plants.

Moving Sugar and Other Nutrients Throughout the Plant

While plants synthesize sugar in leaves, they store it mostly in roots. Botanists believe that sugar is **translocated** in phloem cells from leaves to storage cells by a process known as **mass flow**. According to the **mass flow theory**, companion cells in the leaves load sugar into sieve tube members. The accompanying increase in solute concentration causes water to be pulled into phloem by osmosis. Meanwhile, in the roots, the reverse process takes place and sugar moves out of phloem and into root cells, where the sugar concentration is lower. Pressure gradients thus push sugar from leaves to roots.

Depending on their solubility and molecular weight, inorganic nutrients are carried to a final destination by xylem, or move passively through cell membranes and are transported by phloem.

Improving the Breed: Engineering Useful Plants

Plant breeders currently use three techniques in efforts to improve crops. Traditional plant-breeding methods, while time-consuming, are well understood, predictable, and controllable. A more recent development, **tissue culture**, involves growing identical plants from somatic tissue fragments. Mutations, called somaclonal variations, arising from this technology give rise to new varieties. Tissue culture skirts the problems of genetic recombination, which occurs naturally during sexual reproduction, but it can result in undesired traits accompanying desirable characteristics. A third alternative is genetic engineering, through which researchers manipulate the genome of a target species with great precision, adding or deleting one or several genes. Using this laboratory technique geneticists hope to improve the nutritional value of plants and reduce their susceptibility to disease.

Thought Provokers

1. Compare and contrast the circulatory systems of higher plants and a higher animal such as a human. A table or chart might be a convenient format for your answer.

2. In a paragraph, support or contradict the statement that classical methods of plant breeding may soon be completely replaced by recently developed techniques of genetic recombination.

3. Name and describe the mechanism by which water entering a tree's roots is transported upward in a tree.

Self-Test

For each statement or question choose the best response and mark your choice in the space provided. For some items you will select your response from a *Key*.

Questions 1–15. Compare items A and B for each numbered statement. If greater for A than B, mark A; if greater for B than A, mark B; if approximately or exactly the same for both items, mark C.

		a	**b**
_____	1. daily water loss per gram	typical animal	typical land plant
_____	2. puncture wound of xylem in living plant	outward pressure	inward pressure
_____	3. K$^+$ in guard cells	plus abscisic acid	minus abscisic acid
_____	4. stomata opening	daytime	night
_____	5. stomata opening	drought conditions	normal conditions
_____	6. parenchyma pumping ions	into xylem	out of xylem
_____	7. guttation	dry days	moist days
_____	8. hypertonicity	xylem	tissue around the xylem
_____	9. utilization directly by plants	N$_2$	NH$_3$
_____	10. need for fertilizer	peas, beans	corn, wheat
_____	11. symbiotic bacteria	*Azotobacter*	*Rhizobium*
_____	12. flow of water and ions	upward	downward
_____	13. number of	guard cells	stoma
_____	14. amount in a plant	macronutrients	micronutrients
_____	15. nitrogen fixation	nonlegumes	legumes

Questions 16–25. Match each numbered role with the appropriate element from the *Key*.

a. carbon   **e.** silicon   **ad.** boron
b. nitrogen   **ab.** sulfur   **ae.** cobalt
c. calcium   **ac.** iron   **bc.** molybdenum
d. magnesium

_____ 16. part of the chlorophyll molecule and involved as a cofactor in many enzymes

_____ 17. essential to nitrogen assimilation and fixation

_____ 18. another metal essential for nitrogen fixation

_____ 19. found in all organic compounds

_____ 20. found in the cell wall of grasses and horsetails

_____ 21. present in some amino acids and proteins and coenzyme A

_____ 22. involved in the synthesis of chlorophyll; present in cytochromes

_____ **23.** may be involved in nucleic acid synthesis, sugar transport, auxin metabolism

_____ **24.** metal found in cell walls and associated with pectin

_____ **25.** associated with starch-digesting enzymes and cell membrane permeability

Key Terms from the Text Chapter

cohesion-adhesion-tension
 text page 676
guard cell _674_
legume _678_
macronutrient _678_

mass flow theory _683_
micronutrient _678_
nitrogen fixation _678_
nodule _679_
soil _681_

tissue culture _685_
translocation _683_
transpiration _676_
transpiration pull theory _676_

Exercise

Match each structure or process in the left column with the best description in the right column.

Stomata	Transpiration-pull theory
Guttation	Regulate water loss
Root nodules	Water and nutrient absorption
Translocation	Model for phloem transport
Cohesion, adhesion of water molecules	Nitrogen-fixing bacteria
Mass flow	Diffusion and osmotic pressure
Soil	Provides all inorganic nutrients
Water entry into plant roots	Nutrient movement in phloem
Root hairs and mycorrhizae	Root pressure

33

The Genetic Basis for Evolution

CHAPTER IN BRIEF

265

Perspective and Review

An individual may change and develop during its lifetime, but it cannot evolve. Rather, evolution occurs when the allele frequencies of a population change. And in order for allele frequencies to change, different alleles for a given trait—genetic variation—must be present in the population. Genetic variation is a central theme in population genetics. Many evolutionists study the amount of variation in populations, how such variation arises, and what factors act on variation to cause species to evolve.

Genetic Variation: The Raw Material of Evolution

In the 1930s, biologists started to merge Darwin's evolutionary theories with the findings of modern genetics. The result was the synthetic theory of evolution, or modern synthesis—an explanation of **evolution** in genetic terms. This theory is continually modified as new knowledge comes to light.

Population geneticists study changes in allele frequencies in a **gene pool**—the total number of alleles present in a population. The development of protein electrophoresis enabled population geneticists to look at variation on a fine scale, and to distinguish between alleles differing by as little as a single base pair. Genetic variation is usually measured as percent heterozygosity. Concept Table 33.1 summarizes important aspects of genetic variation.

Concept Table 33.1   Genetic variation

Extent of variation	Biologists have discovered a surprisingly large degree of genetic variation in many species. For example, humans are heterozygous at about 10% of loci. Cheetahs have one of the lower rates of heterozygosity among mammals, 0.067%.
Sources of variation	*Mutations*, *gene duplication and divergence*, and *exon shuffling* can generate new alleles and genes. Once a sufficient number of alleles exists, *random assortment* and *recombination* in sexually reproducing organisms can rearrange those alleles.
Maintenance	Genetic variation is maintained in populations. *In the absence of external forces, the frequency of an allele in a population will not change.* This statement is known as the **Hardy-Weinberg principle**.
Causes of change	Five factors can result in **evolution**—changes in allele frequencies in a population over time. These are **natural selection**, **mutation**, **gene flow**, **nonrandom mating**, and **genetic drift**.

Agents of Evolution: What Causes Allele Frequencies to Change?

Concept Table 33.2 describes the five agents that can alter allele frequencies in populations.

Concept Table 33.2 Mechanisms of changes in allele frequencies

Natural selection	Natural selection acts on alleles already present in a population, changing their frequencies as a result of differential survival and reproduction. Simply stated, only the **fittest** individuals survive to reproduce. **Adaptation**, the accumulation of traits that increase fitness, is the result of natural selection. Natural selection can affect a population in one of three ways. **Directional selection** favors one extreme form of a trait over all others. **Stabilizing selection** favors the mean, or average, expression of a trait. **Disruptive selection** favors the two extremes of a trait while acting against the average.
Mutation	A mutation will slightly alter allele frequencies, but mutations are most important in providing new alleles on which natural selection or drift can act.
Gene flow	The process involved when individuals migrating from one population to another remove alleles from one group and introduce them to a second, with a corresponding change in allele frequency in both populations.
Genetic drift	Unpredictable changes in allele frequency due to random events. This effect is most pronounced when population size is small. When a disaster wipes out most of the individuals in a population, it also reduces the amount of genetic variation within that group. Biologists call this kind of sudden shrinkage in variation a **population bottleneck**. Genetic drift may also be important when a few individuals break off from a larger group to establish a new population, a phenomenon known as the **founder effect**.
Nonrandom mating	The tendency of individuals of one particular genotype to mate with individuals of another specific genotype can lead to changes in allele frequencies. **Sexual selection**, the choosing of a mate based on particular physical or behavioral traits, is one form of nonrandom mating.

Selectionists believe that natural selection is the main evolutionary force. At the other extreme, neutralists argue that most genetic variation results from neutral mutations, unpredictable genetic drift, and gene flow. Many biologists hold an intermediate point of view, that there are sufficient nonneutral mutations for selection to act upon, even if most mutations are neutral.

How New Species Arise

A species is defined as groups of populations that can interbreed to produce healthy and fertile offspring. This definition implies that species are *reproductively isolated* from one another. There are a number of **reproductive isolating mechanisms (RIM)** that prevent species from interbreeding. In habitat isolation species use different portions of a habitat, or live in different habitats; in seasonal isolation different species mate at different seasons; in mechanical isolation species have differing reproductive structures that effectively prevent interbreeding; and in behavioral isolation individuals of two species do not recognize each other as appropriate mates.

Most biologists believe that the majority of new species arise by allopatric speciation, when two populations become geographically isolated and diverge genetically until barriers to reproduction eventually emerge. The founder effect can also cause allopatric speciation. Other forms of speciation include parapatric speciation, which occurs in populations with overlapping territories, usually because each population is adapting to different ecological roles. Sympatric speciation occurs when reproductive isolating mechanisms arise within a population living in the same area. These mechanisms can be behavioral, ecological, or genetic, such as polyploidy, a common cause of sympatric speciation in plants.

The Modern Synthesis and Major Trends in Evolution

Biologists distinguish two types of evolution. **Microevolution** refers to allele changes occurring within populations, whereas **macroevolution** describes evolution above the species level.

By examining the history of morphological changes in evolving taxa, evolutionists have noted several phylogenetic trends. These are summarized in Concept Table 33.3.

Concept Table 33.3 Patterns of evolutionary descent	
Gradual change	Small changes in allele frequencies in a population can lead to major morphological differences over geological time. An example is the diminishing size of the cheetah.
Divergent evolution	Reproductive isolating mechanisms split one population into two. Each subsequently evolves different traits, changing away from the ancestral type and from each other. **Adaptive radiation** occurs when divergence happens simultaneously among a number of related populations.
Convergent evolution	Occurs when similar phenotypic characters arise in unrelated lineages. For example, sharks and dolphins have both evolved a streamlined shape related to their aquatic life-style. When two or more physically similar and related lineages evolve in the same direction *away* from the ancestral type, **parallel evolution** is said to have taken place.
Coevolution	Two species evolve together because they interact so closely that each species' fitness depends on the other.

Currently there are two models of microevolution. Phyletic gradualism holds that morphological change occurs slowly during evolution and that such shifts are sometimes, though not always, associated with speciation. The opposite view is put forward in the punctuated equilibrium model, which holds that species remain the same for long periods and then undergo periods of rapid change in small populations. This results in new species that are very different from their ancestors.

A key question in macroevolution is whether microevolutionary mechanisms (such as genetic drift and mutations) can lead to the evolution of taxa above the species level. Some microevolutionary phenomena, including preadaptation and developmental mutations, can account for changes over evolutionary time. However, microevolution cannot explain extinctions. Extinction is the complete loss of a species or group of species, and is the ultimate fate of all species. At least five mass extinctions have occurred during Earth's history, and many biologists attribute these to rapid climatic and environmental changes following a period of glaciation.

Thought Provokers

1. Briefly explain the influence of an organism's genotype on its "survivability" and potential for evolutionary change.

2. Cite five different mechanisms that can increase or decrease the frequency of genes or alleles in a population. Use pertinent examples in your answer.

Self-Test

For each statement or question choose the best response and mark your choice in the space provided. For some items you will select your answer from a *Key*.

_B_ 1. Darwin and Mendel were contemporaries and codevelopers of the theory of evolution.
   a. True   **b.** False

_A_ 2. The sum of all the alleles in a population is termed:
   a. the gene pool   **c.** genetic variation   **e.** genotype
   b. hybrid vigor   **d.** gene resources

_A_ 3. Much genetic variation is "hidden" in the genome of an individual.
   a. True   **b.** False

_E_ 4. The actual number of human genes is approximately:
   a. 1,000–2,000   **c.** 5,000–10,000   **e.** 50,000–100,000
   b. 3,000–5,000   **d.** 10,000–30,000

_B_ 5. In humans the degree of heterozygosity among all genes averages approximately:
   a. 1–2%   **c.** 25–35%   **e.** 65–75%
   b. 8–12%   **d.** 45–55%

Key for questions 6–9
a. all of these choices   **c.** recombination   **e.** exon shuffling
b. base pair mutation   **d.** gene duplication

_A_ 6. mechanisms of genetic variation

_D_ 7. a mechanism that accounts for different forms of embryonic and adult hemoglobin

_B_ 8. AT → GC transition

_E_ 9. mechanism that operates with respect to genes for the immune system, LDL receptor protein, blood-clotting protein, and skin cell growth factor

_A_ **10.** The genetic condition known as brachydactyly—short, stubby fingers—is:

    a. dominant   **d.** caused by a lethal gene

    b. recessive   **e.** associated with hemophilia

    c. sex-linked

Questions 11–18. Indicate whether, as a criterion for evaluating a population by the Hardy-Weinberg law, each of the numbered situations is **A.** applicable or **B.** not applicable.

_A_ **11.** There are regular deaths in the population.

_B_ **12.** Mutations occur frequently in the population.

_A_ **13.** The population's birth rate is very high.

_B_ **14.** New members immigrate into the population.

_A_ **15.** No members of the population emigrate.

_A_ **16.** Birthing stops when the temperature falls below 25°C.

_B_ **17.** The population is composed of 250 individuals.

_B_ **18.** Solar radiation inhibits the metabolism and growth of about 25% of the exposed organisms.

Key for questions 19–25

a. directional selection   **d.** all of these

b. stabilizing selection   **e.** none of these

c. disruptive selection

_C_ **19.** mechanism responsible for the existence of two different phenotypes in swallowtail butterflies

_A_ **20.** phenomenon associated with the peppered moth in industrialized England

_B_ **21.** selection type reflected in horseshoe crabs and coelacanths

_A_ **22.** The modern cheetah is a good example of this.

_B_ **23.** Gingko trees are a product of this kind of selection.

_A_ **24.** source of insecticide and pesticide resistances

_B_ **25.** reason why intermediate-sized human babies predominate

_A_ **26.** Retinoblastoma is <u>all but one</u> of the following:

    a. a rare eye tumor of children

    b. a dominant trait

    c. a disease known to occur as a result of mutation

    d. less common than the normal condition

    e. associated with a change in allele frequency

Key for questions 27–28

a. True   **b.** False

_B_ **27.** According to the text, prairie dogs are animals that permit a high degree of immigration of newcomers into their colonies.

_A_ **28.** Genetic drift can affect the gene frequencies in a population.

_D_ **29.** With regard to a population bottleneck, which statement is most correct?

    a. Heterozygosity increases.
    b. The bottleneck is the result of a rapidly growing population.
    c. Alleles tend to be more randomized through the population.
    d. The surviving population may or may not be more successful than its predecessor.
    e. It occurs in plants but not animals.

_D_ **30.** Regarding the Amish, which one statement is <u>not</u> correct?

    a. They are descendants of the Swiss.
    b. They demonstrate the "founder effect" in genetics.
    c. Members of the group show some physical anomalies.
    d. As a group they are more heterozygous than people in their ancestral homeland.
    e. They survive well in modern society.

_A_ **31.** A species:

    a. May yield nonviable or sterile offspring when a member mates with an organism of a different species.
    b. May not be as susceptible to mutations as other species.
    c. In general does compete well with other species.
    d. By definition cannot hybridize.
    e. Is not a part of a genus.

_A_ **32.** A race or variant of a species may look different from the regular members of the species.

    a. True; clear examples are known to science.
    b. Probably true, although not actually proven.
    c. False; if it looks different it must be another species.
    d. False; there are no races or variants of a species.
    e. Two of the above statements are correct.

_B_ **33.** Which of the following is an example of an event that, if it occurs regularly, suggests nonrandom mating in a species?

    a. The female is trapped by the male.
    b. The female is attracted to a particular male among many males.
    c. The sexes engage in numerous polygamous relationships.
    d. There is only one sexual type in the population.
    e. The population is composed of hermaphrodites.

Questions 34–37. Geographic isolation is one of several mechanisms that can promote reproductive isolation and the evolution of new species. Match each of the following situations with the appropriate speciation mechanism from the *Key*.

a. allopatric   **b.** parapatric   **c.** sympatric

_C_ **34.** polyploidy in plants

_A_ **35.** Kabert's and Abert's squirrels in Grand Canyon Park

_C_ **36.** the mechanism that produced coddling moths adapted to attack walnut trees

_A_ **37.** the most distinct and severe type of isolation that restricts gene flow between populations

_____E_____ **38.** Horned dinosaurs developed scissorlike teeth and huge jaw muscles that:

    a. caused them to die
    b. resulted in carnivorous life-styles
    c. caused many cases of self-inflicted injury
    d. remains a mystery
    e. enabled them to eat fibrous plants

Key for questions 39–43, which deal with evolutionary patterns.

a. adaptive radiation   **d.** divergent evolution
b. parallel evolution   **e.** coevolution
c. convergent evolution   **ab.** none of these

_____D_____ **39.** Two populations of a common species become isolated from each other, genetic differences accumulate, and the species become reproductively isolated.

_____E_____ **40.** A plant mutates and produces a substance that causes smaller rather than larger colonizing insects to be selected for.

_____B_____ **41.** Similar and genetically related species show independent, similar changes away from the phenotype of a common ancestor.

_____A_____ **42.** Several populations of the same species each are subjected to selective environmental forces or changes that cause each population to develop new characteristics that may well result in new species.

_____C_____ **43.** Sharks, icthyosaurs, and dolphins show this evolutionary pattern.

_____D_____ **44.** Which statement is most correct?

    a. Many species have never had ancestors.
    b. The evolutionary evidence strongly favors phyletic gradualism over punctuated equilibrium.
    c. Evolutionary evidence strongly favors punctuated equilibrium over phyletic gradualism.
    d. In Earth's history, many species have gone extinct.
    e. Evolution of species no longer can occur.

_____E_____ **45.** Which statement best suggests mosaic evolution?

    a. Giraffes and okapi are closely related.
    b. Dinosaurs could well appear again in the near future.
    c. Food and evolution are important, connected concepts.
    d. Evolution in larger animals is easier to study and document than evolution in smaller animals.
    e. Archaeopteryx resembled birds and reptiles.

Key Terms from the Text Chapter

adaptation *text page* 700

adaptive radiation *709*

coevolution *710*

convergent evolution *709*

divergent evolution *708*

evolution *700*

founder effect *704*

gene flow *703*

gene pool *694*

Hardy-Weinberg principle *698*

hybrid *706*

macroevolution *708*

microevolution *708*

parallel evolution *709*

population genetics *694*

reproductive isolating mechanism (RIM) *706*

sexual selection *705*

speciation *706*

Exercise

Fill in the blanks to make a quick-reference chart that summarizes the agents of evolution and mechanisms of speciation.

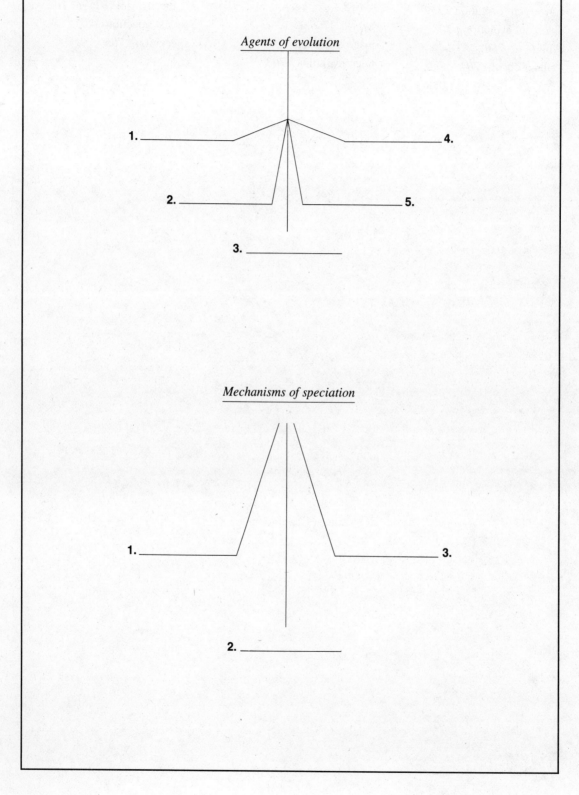

Agents of evolution

1. _____

2. _____

3. _____

4. _____

5. _____

Mechanisms of speciation

1. _____

2. _____

3. _____

Population Ecology: Patterns in Space and Time

Perspective and Review

Ecology is the study of living organisms and how they interact with one another as well as with their nonliving environments. By understanding the factors that influence the distribution and abundance of organisms, ecologists can predict the consequences of habitat destruction on the species that live there, and those that interact with them. Ecologists and evolutionists consider the concept of population to be central to the study of ecology, and a large area of these sciences is devoted to what is called population biology.

The Science of Ecology: Levels of Interaction

Ecology is concerned with biotic as well as abiotic interactions, and ecologists have organized their science into a four-tiered hierarchy. At the simplest level is the population, a collection of organisms of the same species occupying a defined geographical region. A community consists of two or more populations of different species living in the same geographical region. Ecosystem describes all the organisms in a particular area, together with the physical environment with which they interact. Finally, the biosphere is the entire planet, including all living and nonliving components.

Distribution Patterns: Where Do Populations Live?

Organisms are distributed in particular regions of the world and in particular habitats. A prime concern of population ecology involves distribution patterns and their causes. Concept Table 34.1 examines some of the concepts associated with population distributions.

Concept Table 34.1   Global and local patterns of distribution

Limits to Global Distribution

Physical factors	A species may be absent from a particular region because it is not adapted to the physical environment there. For example, cacti cannot survive in the arctic tundra. Genetic characters shaped by natural selection result in organisms that are adapted to their physical surroundings.
Biological factors	Certain species can dominate a particular area by monopolizing resources, or acting as predator or prey.
Geographical factors	Geographical barriers such as large oceans and mountain ranges can prevent a species from occupying an area, even if that area represents a suitable habitat for the species. Such barriers act as blocks to dispersal.

Local Distribution Patterns

Uniform	Individuals are evenly spaced within a species' range. This pattern is rare and usually occurs only where physical factors are also uniform and resource competition is strong.
Random	A pattern that occurs when resource conditions are uniform and individuals do not influence each other's spacing.
Clumped	The most common pattern of spatial distribution, in which groups of individuals separate from other groups. This pattern reflects the distribution of resources in habitats.

Constraints on Population Size

Certain factors constrain the size of a population and how population density changes over time. Ecologists use ecological density, the number of organisms in a population in a particular habitat, as a measure of population size. Clearly, the size of a population will increase if individuals are born or immigrate into the population, and decrease as a result of death and emigration. Ecologists express this concept by the following equation:

Change in no. of individuals (ΔN) = (births + immigration) – (deaths + emigration)

Death and birth are two major parameters influencing population size. Zero population growth occurs when the number of births and immigration equals the number of deaths and emigrations. The probability of survival varies with age, and is usually plotted on a survivorship curve. The shape of this curve varies between species. Late-loss (type I) curves have high late-life mortality. Constant-loss (type II) curves show an even death rate over all ages. Early-loss (type III) curves reflect high early-life mortality. Birth rates also vary with age, a relationship revealed by fertility curves. Ecologists have developed models of population growth based on birth and death rates. Concept Table 34.2 describes these models, and a number of factors that limit population growth.

Concept Table 34.2 Population growth models

Exponential (logarithmic) growth	Under ideal conditions populations will follow an explosive growth pattern known as *exponential, or logarithmic, growth*, represented graphically by a **J-shaped curve**. The rate of population growth is determined by the *maximum rate of reproduction* (r_m) and initial population size. It is described by the equation $$\frac{\Delta N}{\Delta t} = r^m \times N$$ where N = number of individuals and t = time.
Logistic growth	In nature, all populations are eventually resource-limited; that is, over time, a given level of resources can support only a certain population density. The density at which available resources become saturated is termed **carrying capacity** (K). Resource limitation gives rise to logistic growth, which generates an **S-shaped curve**. Logistic growth depends on the rate of population growth per individual (birthrate minus death rate) and the quantity of unused resources available at any given time. It is described by the equation $$\frac{\Delta N}{\Delta t} = r \times N \times \frac{K-N}{K}$$ where the final term describes unused resources.
Environmental limitations on growth	May be either *density-dependent*, such as disease, or *density-independent*, such as adverse weather.
Extrinsic regulating mechanisms	Originate outside the population and include biotic factors, such as predation, and abiotic factors, such as availability of shelter.
Intrinsic regulating mechanisms	Originate in an organism's anatomy, physiology, or behavior. These include migrations and competition.

Individuals have access to limited resources and apportion their resource use through either r or K **life history strategies**. **r-selected** species develop rapidly and reproduce early and are usually associated with unpredictable environments. K-selected species exhibit slow development and delayed reproduction and are often associated with fairly constant environments. Table 34.1 in your text outlines the traits associated with r and K species.

The Past, Present, and Future of the Human Population

Human population growth displays a J-shaped exponential curve. Phases of growth are associated with cultural advances that have enabled humans to increase the carrying capacity of their habitat. During the twentieth century, developed countries underwent **demographic transition**, the change from high birth and death rates to low birth and death rates. Developing nations have not yet made this change. Such countries show a pyramid-shaped **age structure**, representing a high birthrate and low death rate. Demographers predict that global population will double or triple in the next 50–150 years.

Thought Provokers

1. Describe the various limits on the global distribution of a species. Cite an example of your own choosing not given in the text.

2. The text uses the example of the Hohokam Indians to illustrate several kinds of population change over time. Briefly describe the Hohokam Indian population and the events that shaped their existence as a people.

Self-Test

For each statement or question choose the best response and mark your choice in the space provided. For some items you will select your answer from a *Key*.

_____ **1.** Which item includes all the others?

     a. population   **c.** community   **e.** ecosystem

     b. biosphere   **d.** individual

_____ **2.** Which term in question 1 best fits the definition "interacting living things plus physical factors of the environment"?

_C_ **3.** Using the code b = births, d = deaths, e = emigration, and i = immigration, which formula correctly expresses the change in density of a population?

    a. $b-e+d+i$ **d.** $b+i-d+e$

    b. $b+e-d-i$ **e.** $b-i-d-e$

    c. $b+i-d-e$

Key for questions 4–6, which relate to types of survivorship curves.

a. late loss   **b.** constant loss   **c.** early loss

_B_ **4.** many types of birds

_C_ **5.** many fish and invertebrates

_A_ **6.** humans

Key for questions 7–16, which relate to population growth curves.

a. J-curves   **c.** both J- and S-curves

b. S-curves   **d.** neither J- nor S-curves

_A_ **7.** represent logarithmic growth curves

_A_ **8.** represent exponential growth curves

_A_ **9.** occurs when birth rates exceed death rates

_A_ **10.** do (does) not occur under natural conditions in the real world

_C_ **11.** used to determine "carrying capacity"

_C_ **12.** used to plot population growth

_b_ **13.** measure(s) change in population numbers over time

_C_ **14.** used to measure the value K

_B_ **15.** graph that represents unlimited growth potential

_B_ **16.** how the history of the Hohokam Indians could be plotted

Questions 17–21. Indicate whether each of the numbered population control factors is predominantly:

a. intrinsic   **b.** extrinsic   **c.** neither intrinsic nor extrinsic

_B_ **17.** average annual rainfall

_A_ **18.** scramble competition

_A_ **19.** hormones

_A_ **20.** control competition

_B_ **21.** predators

Questions 22–26. Match each numbered item with the related lettered phrase.

_E_ **22.** prairie dogs   **a.** resorption of embryos

_B_ **23.** Pribilof Island reindeer   **b.** lichen availability

_D_ **24.** Hohokam Indians   **c.** donkey competition

_C_ **25.** bighorn sheep   **d.** alkali salt problems

_a_ **26.** kangaroos and koalas   **e.** plague epidemics

Key for questions 27–30

a. *r*-selection   **c.** *r* and *K*
b. *K*-selection   **d.** neither *r* nor *K*

_A_ **27.** characteristic of waterflea populations

_A_ **28.** characteristic of bacteria and dandelion populations

_B_ **29.** characteristic of elephant and giraffe populations

_B_ **30.** characteristic of human populations

_D_ **31.** Based on current evidence, which of the following is unlikely to be a problem in the twenty-first century?

     a. availability of fossil fuels
     b. disappearance of forests
     c. pollution
     d. declining populations
     e. food and fresh water supplies

Key Terms from the Text Chapter

age structure   *text page 733*
carrying capacity   *726*
demographic transition   *733*
ecology   *720*
exponential (logarithmic)
   growth   *725*

habitat   *722*
J-shaped curve   *725*
K-selection   *729*
life history strategy   *729*
logistic growth   *726*
population ecology   *719*

r-selection   *729*
S-shaped curve   *726*

The Ecology of Communities: Populations Interacting

Perspective and Review

The idea of an ecological **community** originated with early studies of plant ecology, at a time when much of the vegetation around the world had been classified and named. Initially some ecologists held the view that a community was a "superorganism," a highly specific interacting group of plants and animals. Other ecologists held the opposite view, that a community was a haphazard, unstructured mix of species that happened to be in the same area. Today most ecologists believe that the truth lies somewhere in between, and that a community consists partially of species that happened to migrate into the area and can survive under the prevailing conditions, and partially of species that depend on the presence of other species for their persistence there.

Habitat and Niche: Where Organisms Reside and How They Live

An organism's **habitat** is the place in which it usually lives. How it gets its energy, or its functional role within the community, is its **niche**. The potential range of all biotic and abiotic conditions under which an organism can obtain energy is its <u>fundamental niche</u>. However, few organisms occupy their fundamental niche, because interactions with other organisms often force species into a restricted, <u>realized niche</u>.

Competition Between Species for Limited Resources

Interspecific competition occurs when two different species use the same limited resource. Interspecific competition usually has a negative effect on population growth in both species. Concept Table 35.1 summarizes the range of possible outcomes resulting from such competitive interactions.

Concept Table 35.1 Interspecific competition

Competition models	Mathematical models reveal four possible results of interspecific competition. Two of these lead to **competitive exclusion**—the elimination of one species by another. The remaining two lead to coexistence of both species, either because each species restricts its own growth more than the other's, or because they reciprocally limit each other's growth.
Types of competition	*Exploitation competition* occurs when two species have equal access to a resource, while the use of aggressive behavior to keep other competitors from a resource is called *interference competition*.
Niche effects	By dividing up a resource, a process known as **resource partitioning**, two potentially competing species can coexist. Strong competition can result in **character displacement**, heritable changes in body structures or behaviors that enable competing species to exploit different resources.

The Hunter and the Hunted: Predation

Animals that kill and consume other animals are **predators**, and their food is known as **prey**. A predator has a negative effect on its prey, whereas the prey has a beneficial effect on the predator by providing it with energy. Concept Table 35.2 outlines short-term and long-term outcomes of predator–prey interactions.

Concept Table 35.2 Predator–prey interactions

Predation models	There are three possible outcomes of predator–prey interactions: (1) Increases in prey density lead to increases in predator density; predators eventually consume all available prey and both become extinct. (2) If prey have a total **refuge** from predation, then only predators become extinct. (3) If prey have a temporary refuge, both populations cycle and persist.
The coevolutionary race	Over time predators evolve more efficient ways to catch prey, and prey evolve more or different adaptations that enable them to escape being eaten.
Predator strategies	Predators with mobile prey often use *pursuit* or *ambush* tactics. Predators are generally larger, and have relatively larger brains, than their prey.
Prey responses	Prey exhibit various types of adaptations related to avoiding predation. These include **camouflage**—blending in with the surroundings; **aposematic**, or **warning**, **coloration**—development of brightly colored patterns that warn a predator that the prey is distasteful or toxic; and **mimicry**, in which nontoxic species mimic the warning patterns of poisonous ones.

There are other interactions where one species harms another and benefits by doing so: Parasites feed on a host organism and may or may not kill it over time; parasitoids develop inside the body of another organism. Pathogens are fungi, bacteria, or protists that obtain nourishment from organisms and usually kill their hosts.

Sharing and Teamwork: Commensalism and Mutualism

In **commensalism** one species benefits while the second is neither harmed nor helped. Commensal relationships occur, for example, among birds that nest in trees. Both interacting species benefit in a **mutualism**, such as that between the yucca plant and the yucca moth described in your text.

How Communities Are Organized in Space and Time

Following a disturbance, a regular progression of communities inhabits the previously disturbed area. This transition from one community type to another is known as **succession**. The first species to colonize an area after a disturbance make up a pioneer community. Pioneering species are usually fast-growing, *r*-selected species that are poor competitors. Gradually these species are replaced by a transition community and finally by an assemblage of organisms that forms a stable climax community. Climax species are usually slow-growing, competitively dominant, *K*-selected species. Species may affect succession in any of three ways. Facilitation occurs when pioneering species promote the growth of other species in the area; tolerance takes place when pioneering species neither help nor hinder the invasion of new species better adapted to prevailing conditions. Conversely, early species may prevent the colonization of certain species by the process of inhibition.

Species richness, a measure of the total number of species in a community, is dictated by many factors. Latitude has a big effect; many ecologists believe that the observed increase in species richness in areas progressively closer to the equator reflects the increased availability of resources, such as sunlight. Islands and peninsulas have fewer species than mainlands, because their <u>isolation</u> poses a barrier to dispersal.

Intermediate levels of disturbance and predation will lead to increased species richness. However, high levels of either will depress richness and lead to extinctions. High disturbance levels caused by the logging of tropical rainforests is endangering many tropical species and overall ecological stability.

Thought Provokers

1. Define resource partitioning and give at least two examples.

2. Choose an example of mimicry and briefly outline a model of natural selection/evolution that explains this phenomenon.

Self-Test

For each statement or question choose the best response and mark your choice in the space provided. For some items you will select your response from a *Key*.

Key for questions 1–10

a. True **b.** False

_A_ **1.** Predation can increase the species richness in a habitat.

_B_ **2.** When two species are competing in the same habitat one will become predominant.

_A_ **3.** <u>Commensalism</u> is a term that describes a relationship between two species where neither is harmed and one benefits.

_B_ **4.** In most cases of parasitism, the host is injured and dies.

_B_ **5.** An organism's habitat is the same as its niche.

_B_ **6.** Use of the same resources by two species always leads to the exclusion or elimination of the less efficient competitor.

_B_ **7.** Prey typically are able to destroy many predators in a short time.

_A_ **8.** The same resource can be used in different ways and at different times.

_A_ **9.** Aposematic coloring is important in mimicry.

_____A_____ **10.** Succession is a common, natural process in communities.

_____C_____ **11.** Which statement about yucca moths is <u>not</u> true?

  a. They are important to the life of the yucca.
  b. They intentionally pollinate the stigma.
  c. The caterpillars eat the seeds of the yucca.
  d. The moth is the yucca's sole agent of fertilization.
  e. The yucca is the sole source of food for larvae and adults.

_____E_____ **12.** Which term describes the niche of the mule deer or yucca moth?

  a. omnivore   **c.** carnivore   **e.** herbivore
  b. reproductive   **d.** camouflaged

_____C_____ **13.** In "competitive exclusion," one species:

  a. Causes another species' population to remain static.
  b. Does not thrive as well as another.
  c. Thrives better and eliminates the other species.
  d. Thrives and causes the other species to increase.
  e. Does not thrive and depresses the population of another species.

_____D_____ **14.** In the western United States what has happened with burros and bighorn sheep?

  a. Burros have become more dominant than bighorn sheep.
  b. Exploitation competition seems to be occurring.
  c. Interference competition may be occurring.
  d. all of these
  e. none of these

_____A_____ **15.** What happened to the larger lizard on St. Martin (discussed in your text) that altered this animal's realized niche?

  a. It survived.
  b. It did not thrive and died.
  c. It mated with smaller lizards and produced hybrids.
  d. It became more aggressive and displaced the smaller lizard.
  e. All but one of the above statements are correct.

Key for questions 16–20
a. True   **b.** False

In resource partitioning the same resource may be used:

_____A_____ **16.** at different times

_____A_____ **17.** in different areas

_____A_____ **18.** in different ways

_____A_____ **19.** by the same species

_____A_____ **20.** by different species

_____E_____ **21.** Regarding character displacement, what important feature in cats is affected?

  a. muscle development   **d.** claw position
  b. reproductive structures   **e.** tooth structure
  c. fur

___A___ **22.** Character displacement can bring about a partitioning of resources.

    a. True   **b.** False

___E___ **23.** Choose the predator–prey matchup that is <u>not</u> correct.

    a. *Didinium-Paramecium*
    b. lynx-hare
    c. wasp larvae–maggots of Mediterranean fruit fly
    d. large horsefly larvae–small frogs
    e. burros–bighorn sheep

Questions 24–29. Match each numbered question with a type of defense adaptation from the *Key*.

a. physical protection
b. chemical protection only
c. aposematic coloration and toxic properties
d. mimicry
e. camouflage

___A___ **24.** porcupines

___B___ **25.** eucalyptus and bombardier beetles

___C___ **26.** strawberry frogs of South America

___D___ **27.** Viceroy butterflies

___B___ **28.** creosote plants

___A___ **29.** cacti, locust trees, and wildebeest

Questions 30–35. Match each numbered description with a life-style from the *Key*.

a. commensalism   **c.** parasitism   **e.** saprophyte
b. mutualism   **d.** pathogen

___C___ **30.** tapeworms

___C___ **31.** ticks and mites

___B___ **32.** yucca plant and yucca moth

___A___ **33.** epiphytes

___A___ **34.** One species benefits, the other is not harmed.

___E___ **35.** organisms that feed off dead organisms or nonliving organic matter

___A___ **36.** Pick out the <u>incorrect</u> ending to the following statement.

An analysis of biotic communities like those in Glacier Bay, Alaska, indicates that:

    a. A single species generally predominates.
    b. "Survival of the fittest" is an applicable comment.
    c. Such communities show succession with pioneer, transition, and climax forms.
    d. Facilitation, tolerance, and inhibition occur.
    e. Mosses are early residents, and alder, hemlock, and spruce appear later.

Key for questions 37–40

a. True   **b.** False

_____A_____ **37.** Latitude and longitude can influence species richness.

_____A_____ **38.** A predator in a community may increase or decrease the number of other species.

_____A_____ **39.** Disturbances in communities can threaten the communities' existence.

_____A_____ **40.** Resources influence species richness.

Key Terms from the Text Chapter

aposematic (warning)
   coloration *text page 748*
character displacement *743*
coevolution *743*
commensalism *749*
community *738*

competitive exclusion *741*
habitat *740*
interspecific competition *741*
mimicry *748*
mutualism *749*
niche *740*

predator *744*
prey *744*
resource partitioning *743*
species richness *753*
succession *751*

36

Ecosystems: Webs of Life and the Physical World

Perspective and Review

An **ecosystem** consists of all the organisms in an area, together with their physical environment. The concept is important for two main reasons. First, many organisms modify the physical environment and affect other species through this modification. Second, global cycling of physical materials that support life is influenced by the rates of flow of nutrients and energy through local ecosystems.

Pathways for Energy and Materials: Who Eats Whom in Nature?

Ecologists place every organism in a community into a **trophic**, or feeding, **level** and construct a **food chain**, a diagram showing the flow of energy from one trophic level to the next. **Producers** represent the lowest trophic level; they are organisms that manufacture organic compounds from nonliving substances. Green plants are the main producers in terrestrial ecosystems. At the second trophic level are **consumers**, organisms that get their energy by eating producers or other consumers. Primary consumers are herbivores that consume producers; secondary consumers are carnivores that eat herbivores; and tertiary consumers are carnivores that prey on other carnivores. **Detritivores** decompose organic wastes and dead organic material and are important in recycling nutrients back into the community. Most organisms consume a variety of different species, and their food usually comes from more than one trophic level. The interconnected feeding relationships of species in a community is known as a food web.

How Energy Flows Through Ecosystems

Only 2% of the total solar energy reaching Earth is incorporated into the ecosystem (converted via photosynthesis to carbohydrate) by producers. This energy, called gross primary productivity, is the total amount of energy available to the ecosystem; it follows that an ecosystem is structured within the limits of its energy budget. Only half of the original 2% is available to consumers, and as the chain progresses only 10% of available energy is transferred from one level to the next. Ecologists show this relationship by means of an **energy pyramid** diagram. Some ecologists believe that most food webs are limited to four trophic levels, because energy is too hard to capture beyond that level. The energy pyramid also explains the phenomenon of **biological magnification**, the increasing concentration of toxins with increasing trophic level.

How Materials Cycle Through Ecosystems

Life-supporting physical materials cycle through living organisms and their environments in biogeochemical cycles. Concept Table 36.1 describes the most important of these cycles.

Concept Table 36.1 Biogeochemical cycles	
Water cycle	Atmospheric water falls to Earth as rain or snow and circles back to the atmosphere by evaporation and transpiration. Some systems lose over 90% of their water by transpiration. Removing vegetation breaks the link between transpiration and rain, resulting in ecological damage.
Carbon cycle	Producers trap carbon dioxide from air and water and use it to manufacture organic compounds. These in turn are transferred to consumers. Respiration returns carbon to the atmosphere. Carbon can leave the system for long periods in the form of geological deposits that, when eroded, return carbon to the cycle.
Nitrogen cycle	Bacteria in the soil make atmospheric nitrogen available to plants by converting it into nitrates and ammonia. Animals

Continues

	gain access to this nitrogen by eating plants. When organisms die or excrete nitrogenous compounds, <u>denitrifying bacteria</u> release nitrogen back into the soil.
Phosphorus cycle	The phosphorus cycle has both local and global circuits. On a local level, plants absorb phosphates from soils and rocks. Bacteria convert phosphorus in dead organic matter back into phosphates that re-enter the cycle. On a global scale, phosphorus can be transported by streams and rivers and accumulate in rocks for millions of years. Phosphorus added to aquatic systems can result in **eutrophication**.

How Human Intervention Alters Ecosystem Function

Three of the biggest threats against life on this planet that are the result of human intervention are the greenhouse effect, acid rain, and nuclear winter.

The Greenhouse Effect

Carbon dioxide allows sunlight to reach Earth but blocks the escape of heat. Levels of atmospheric carbon dioxide have dramatically increased in the twentieth century due to human activities such as burning fossil fuels and gasoline and the destruction of forests. Scientists believe that this scenario will lead to higher global temperatures, with accompanying climatic changes and melting of the polar ice caps.

Acid Rain

Sulphur and nitrogen oxides are released by the burning of coal and oil to operate factories and automobiles. In the atmosphere the oxides combine with water molecules to form sulphuric and nitric acids. When it rains, these acids return to the Earth as acid rain. Acid rain has been responsible for the destruction of fish populations in lakes, for killing trees, and for eroding ancient monuments. Scrubbers, which filter pollutants, can be installed at factories, but these would increase fuel bills and industry has so far resisted their use.

Nuclear Winter

The ultimate ecological threat is a nuclear winter, in which dust and smoke resulting from a nuclear war would block out sunlight. Using simulation models scientists predict that global temperatures would plunge below zero, photosynthesis would effectively stop, and most species would become extinct.

Thought Provokers

1. Define each of the following and explain how they relate to one another.

    a. autotroph

    b. heterotroph

    c. primary consumer

    d. secondary and tertiary consumers

    e. primary producers

2. Defend or contradict the statement: "Life would not be possible without plants."

3. Briefly discuss concentration and biological magnification in ecosystems. Cite some relevant examples.

Self-Test

For each statement or question choose the best response and mark your choice in the space provided. For some items you will select your answer from a *Key*.

Key for questions 1–10

a. primary producer   **c.** secondary consumers   **e.** detritivores
b. primary consumer   **d.** tertiary consumers

___A___ **1.** Heterotrophs are found in all categories <u>except</u> this one.

___B___ **2.** cows

___D___ **3.** fungi, bacteria, some insects, vultures

___A___ **4.** the hydrogen sulfide bacteria

___B___ **5.** caterpillars and grasshoppers

_A_ **6.** autotrophs

_C_ **7.** lions and tigers

_B_ **8.** the tubeworms of deep sea vents

_A_ **9.** green plants

_B_ **10.** herbivores

_A_ **11.** Which best describes the flow of energy through ecosystems?

  a. animate → inanimate → animate
  b. inanimate → animate → inanimate
  c. animate → animate → inanimate
  d. inanimate → inanimate → animate
  e. none of the above

_A_ **12.** Which is the most efficient energy conversion in humans?

  a. eating beans and rice
  b. eating steak
  c. eating fish
  d. drinking water
  e. All except one of the above are equally efficient.

_A_ **13.** Only the net primary productivity is available to consumers.

  a. True **b.** False

Questions 14–18 relate to the Hubbard Brook Forest experiment, which represents an important contribution to our understanding of energy flow. Think carefully and then supply the percentage energy loss from the *Key* that corresponds to the findings of these experiments.

a. 1% **b.** 2% **c.** 10% **d.** 15% **e.** 41–42%

_D_ **14.** reflected light

_E_ **15.** direct heating

_E_ **16.** evaporation

_B_ **17.** gross primary productivity

_A_ **18.** net primary productivity

_C_ **19.** Food chains rarely have more than how many links?

  a. 2 **b.** 3 **c.** 4 **d.** 5 **e.** 10

_E_ **20.** The word "trophic" is closest in meaning to:

  a. energy **b.** bonds **c.** movement **d.** ion **e.** feeding

_A_ **21.** The statement "plants create their own rain" would be most true for plants in a/an:

  a. forest **b.** lake **c.** pond **d.** river **e.** ocean

_A_ **22.** Biologists have discovered chemosynthetic autotrophs.

  a. True **b.** False

Key for questions 23–26, which refer to events associated with nitrogen fixation.

a. ammonification   **c.** nitrogen fixation
b. denitrification   **d.** nitrification

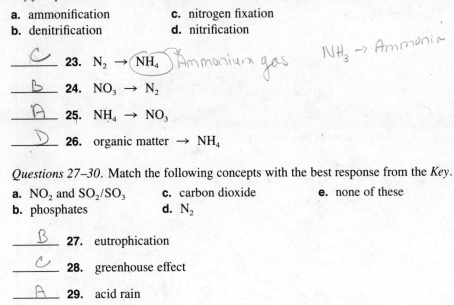

_C_ **23.** $N_2 \rightarrow$ (NH$_4$) Ammonium gas $NH_3 \rightarrow$ Ammonia

_B_ **24.** $NO_3 \rightarrow N_2$

_A_ **25.** $NH_4 \rightarrow NO_3$

_D_ **26.** organic matter $\rightarrow NH_4$

Questions 27–30. Match the following concepts with the best response from the *Key*.

a. NO_2 and SO_2/SO_3 **c.** carbon dioxide   **e.** none of these
b. phosphates   **d.** N_2

_B_ **27.** eutrophication

_C_ **28.** greenhouse effect

_A_ **29.** acid rain

_E_ **30.** nuclear winter

Key Terms from the Text Chapter

biological magnification *text page 766*

carbon cycle *768*

consumer *760*

detritivore *761*

ecosystem *758*

energy pyramid *764*

eutrophic *770*

food chain *761*

greenhouse effect *772*

nitrogen cycle *769*

nuclear winter *775*

oligotrophic *770*

phosphorus cycle *770*

producer *760*

pyramid of biomass *765*

trophic level *760*

water cycle *767*

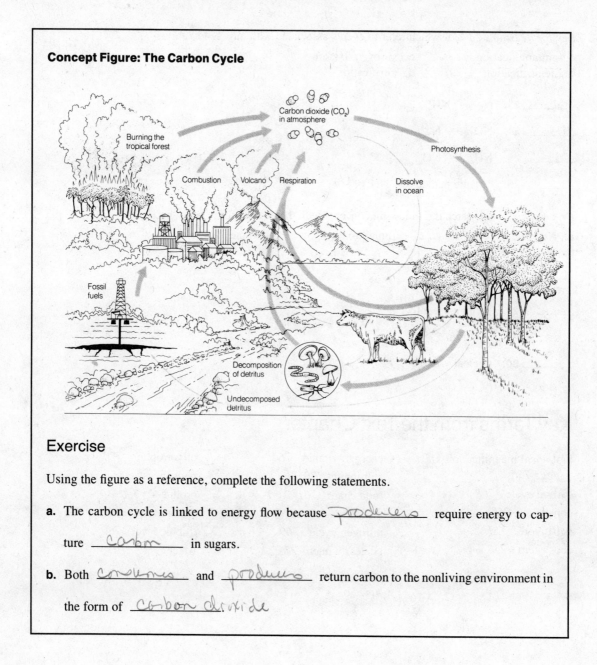

Concept Figure: The Carbon Cycle

Exercise

Using the figure as a reference, complete the following statements.

a. The carbon cycle is linked to energy flow because _producers_ require energy to capture _carbon_ in sugars.

b. Both _consumers_ and _producers_ return carbon to the nonliving environment in the form of _carbon dioxide_

The Biosphere:
Earth's Thin Film of Life

Perspective and Review

The surface regions of the Earth, its land, its waters, and the air above them, together with all living forms, make up the biosphere. The structure and functioning of the biosphere ultimately depend on sunlight, the source of energy.

The biosphere has many parts, from the tundra to tropical rainforests and the Earth's vast oceans. Even so, the biosphere is actually an incredibly complex and interconnected whole. Factors changing one biome can have devastating effects in other regions of the world. For example, the destruction of winter habitats of migratory birds can have serious consequences for other organisms in the birds' summer range. Logging tropical rainforests not only decimates that biome, but as most scientists believe, may contribute to the greenhouse effect, which could result in total destruction of the remaining biomes as we know them today.

What Generates the Earth's Climatic Regions?

Weather is the condition of the atmosphere at a specific place and time. **Climate** is the accumulation of seasonal weather patterns over long periods of time. Within the biosphere, climate is the main factor determining the abundance and distribution of organisms. Climatic patterns are a result of the Earth's rotation on a tilted axis, and the fact that the planet is heated most strongly by the sun at the equator. Warm air rises, cools, and condenses into droplets that subsequently fall to Earth as rain. Rainfall in the tropics is high because a strong sun pulls water into the atmosphere by evaporation and transpiration. Wind is the result of large air masses rising, cooling, and moving to new areas, where cool air falls and flows over the Earth's surface. Six major air currents spiral outward from the equator. Their directions and associated ascents and descents explain the Earth's climatic regions.

Winds blowing over ocean surfaces generate ocean currents, which can moderate climatic effects inland. Normally, air and ocean currents flow in a regular pattern. However, occasionally there occur temporary reversals in direction such as El Niño, with accompanying devastating effects for many organisms.

Biomes: Life on the Land

Ecologists use the term **biome** to describe major land communities. Biomes are defined by their dominant vegetation, which shows specific adaptations to climate. Communities with similar climates have organisms with similar adaptations, even when these species are unrelated. Figure 37.10 in the text illustrates the locations of the eight biomes defined in your text.

▪ **Tropical Rainforests**   Although representing only 3% of continental surface area, tropical **rainforests** contain over half of all living species. Rainfall amount is high (200–400 cm), temperatures average 77°F, and there is little or no wind. Light and minerals are usually the limiting resources. Adaptation to light restriction has resulted in three plant levels: the emergent layer—trees up to 50 m that capture direct sunlight; **canopy**—shorter trees with dense leaves and branches; and an understory—characterized by low light intensity. Many plants here have vines that extend up into the canopy. Trees have thick supporting trunks, known as buttresses, and shallow roots because soils are nutrient-poor. With little wind to carry pollen, animal pollinators are important to plant reproduction.

▪ **Tropical Savannas**   **Savannas** are tropical grasslands dotted with occasional, stunted trees. They occur in areas characterized by warm temperatures and an extended dry season. Most productivity is centered near the ground and so grazers are an important part of the community.

- **Deserts** Deserts receive little rainfall, either because they are in constant high pressure zones, lie far from oceans, or are in the rainshadow of mountain ranges. Desert organisms have adaptations for water conservation and keeping cool. Some deserts have seasonal rainfall, a time when desert flowers bloom in profusion.

- **Temperate Grasslands** Called <u>pampas</u>, <u>steppes</u>, and <u>veldt</u> in different regions of the world, these grasslands have rich soils and seasonal extremes of hot and cold temperatures. Recurrent fires prevent growth of trees.

- **Chapparal** As areas of temperate scrubland, **chapparal** experiences hot, dry summers and cool, wet winters. Frequent fires are also a feature of this biome. Chapparal plants, such as sage, are usually small, have hairy, leathery leaves, and stay green throughout the year.

- **Temperate Forests** Rainfall and temperatures are moderate, and seasons are pronounced in the **temperate forest** biome. Broad-leaved hardwoods tend to be the dominant vegetation. Leaf drop from these deciduous trees is an important source of nutrients, and produces a rich topsoil.

- **Coniferous Forest** Vast **coniferous forests** are abundant in northern regions with cold, snowy winters and short summers. Conifers do not shed their leaves and thus can begin to trap sunlight at the start of the short growing season. Leaves are needle-shaped and covered with a thick cuticle to combat water loss.

- **Tundra** The **tundra** zone is a cold, treeless plain. Even in summer the soil thaws only to about 1 m, leaving a permanently frozen soil underneath called **permafrost**. The presence of permanently frozen soil prevents tree growth. In summer, grasses, lichens, sedges, and mosses grow, mosquitos and flies are abundant, and many birds migrate to the tundra to feed on this seasonal food and to reproduce.

The polar ice caps of the North and South Poles lack major plants and as such are not true biomes. Mountains have elevation zones, known as <u>life zones</u>, that correspond to the biomes from equator to poles. These form because temperature and precipitation vary with altitude in the same way they vary with latitude.

Life in the Water

Most of the Earth's surface is covered with water, and most of that area is <u>marine</u> (salty ocean and sea). In general, aquatic systems differ from each other in important respects.

Ecologists divide freshwater systems into running and standing water bodies. Running water, like streams, carries more oxygen but fewer nutrients than standing water. As a stream becomes more slow-moving, nutrients and vegetation increase. Standing water is represented by lakes and is divided into three depth zones: the shallow **littoral zone**, rich in producers and consumers; a **limnetic zone**, the zone through which light can penetrate, supporting large populations of plankton; and the deep, dark **profundal zone**, with its associated scavengers and decomposers. A **thermocline** that forms in summer is broken as temperatures cool and winds churn the waters, bringing nutrients from the deeper regions of a lake up toward the surface.

Salt and fresh water mix in **estuaries**, where rivers flow into oceans. Estuaries are highly productive areas and often serve as nursery grounds for juvenile fish. Oceans are divided into three main regions. The **intertidal zone** extends along the coastline between high and low tides. Organisms living in this region are adapted to withstand the force of pounding waves and periodic exposure to air due to the flowing and ebbing of tides. The ocean's most productive area is the **neritic zone**, reaching from the intertidal zone to the continental shelf. Extensive kelp beds, coral reefs, and an abundance of consumers characterize this region. The offshore **oceanic zone** is unproductive due to the lack of essential nutrients.

Thought Provokers

1. Explain the significance of El Niño and its effects on the Galapagos Islands' climate and ecology.

2. Define each of the following in 25 words or less.

   a. biome

   b. Coriolis effect

   c. chaparral

   d. thermocline

Self-Test

For each statement or question choose the best response and mark your choice in the space provided. For some items you will select your response from a *Key*.

___E___ 1. The accumulation of seasonal weather events over a long period of time is called:
   a. temperature   c. evolution   e. climate
   b. humidity   d. systematics

Key for questions 2–4
a. True   b. False

___B___ 2. The sun heats the Earth most evenly at the poles.

___A___ 3. The equator receives more heat and light than any other region on our planet.

___A___ 4. The northern and southern hemispheres have opposite seasons at the same calendar time of the year.

Questions 5–13. For each numbered characteristic compare A and B. If greater for A than for B, mark A; if greater for B than for A, mark B; if exactly or almost the same for both, mark C.

		a	**b**
___B___	5. density of	warm air	cold air
___B___	6. moisture in air	at the poles	at the equator
___A___	7. radiation intensity	at the equator	at the poles

_B_ **8.** ocean temperature around Galapagos/Ecuador   El Niño event   normal events

_B_ **9.** animals in canopies   savanna   tropical rainforest

_B_ **10.** heat-holding capacity   air   water

_B_ **11.** amount of CO_2 in air   1910   1989

_A_ **12.** amount of atmospheric ozone   1974   1989

_A_ **13.** alkalinity of air, rivers, lakes   1910   1989

_A, E_ **14.** The Coriolis effects can be explained by which <u>two</u> main events listed below?

    a. spin of the earth
    b. diameter of the earth
    c. effects of the moon
    d. magnetic field of the earth
    e. heating and cooling of the atmosphere

_C_ **15.** Earth's atmosphere becomes divided into how many coils?

    a. 2   **b.** 4   **c.** 6   **d.** 8   **e.** 10

Key for questions 16–20

a. True   **b.** False

_A_ **16.** Wind blowing over the ocean surface sets the ocean's upper layers in motion.

_B_ **17.** The slow, circular motions of water in oceans are called gyrations.

_B_ **18.** During El Niño events trade winds push cold water along the equator toward Australia and Indonesia.

_B_ **19.** There is a rich upwelling of nutrients from deeper waters during El Niño.

_A_ **20.** Waters around the Galapagos warm during El Niño.

Questions 21–44. Using the *Key*, match each numbered statement or character with the appropriate type of biome.

a. tropical rainforest   **ab.** temperate forests
b. savanna   **ac.** coniferous forests
c. desert   **ad.** tundra
d. grasslands   **ae.** polar ice cap
e. chaparral

_AD_ **21.** cold, treeless plains

_A_ **22.** the most "life-productive" zone in relation to amount of life or area

_E_ **23.** known as temperate scrublands; contain hairy, leathery-leaved perennial plants

_AC_ **24.** White bears, seals, and penguins are found here.

_D_ **25.** treeless regions with frequent fires and rapid plant growth

_AD_ **26.** is home to sedges, lichens, mosses, heathers, lemmings, foxes, and owls

_A_ **27.** biome typical of the equator

_AD_ **28.** contains permafrost

_____A_____ **29.** In this biome light and mineral limitations are imposed on plants, and winds are blocked.

_____D_____ **30.** Bison, coyotes, armadillos, and snakes are found here.

_____A_____ **31.** Lianas and orchids are common to this biome.

_____C_____ **32.** Succulent plants are the most common plants here.

_____B_____ **33.** In Australia, kangaroos and dingos live here.

_____C_____ **34.** The greatest number of C_4 plants would be found here.

_____D_____ **35.** is the biome of pampas, steppes, and the veldt

_____C_____ **36.** Temperatures here regularly range up to 48°C.

_____B_____ **37.** are the major regions of the world with short trees and grasses; found in Africa, southwest Asia, and elsewhere

_____C_____ **38.** is the type of region where many plants grow quickly, flower, and form seeds that remain ungerminated for long periods of time

_____C_____ **39.** The Great Basin of Nevada and Utah represents this biome.

_____D_____ **40.** Prairies are typically this.

_____C_____ **41.** Contains plants with waxy leaves having few stomata or no leaves at all.

_____A_____ **42.** Epiphytes are common here, and there is a canopy and a forest floor with abundant moisture.

__AB__ **43.** Oak, maple, and hickory are common to this biome.

__AC__ **44.** Common trees here are pines, firs, spruces, and hemlock.

_____B_____ **45.** An important character of philodendrons is:

    a. Have no need for water.
    b. Photosynthesize well in low light.
    c. Grow well in the dark.
    d. Can grow in deserts.
    e. Do not need nutrients to grow.

_____B_____ **46.** What percentage of the Earth's surface is covered with water?

    a. 65   **b.** 75   **c.** 85   **d.** 90   **e.** 93.5

_____B_____ **47.** Most of the Earth's water can be classified as:

    a. fresh   **b.** saline   **c.** lifeless   **d.** frozen   **e.** radioactive

Key for questions 48–51, which relate to freshwater habitats.

a. profundal zone   **c.** limnetic zone
b. littoral zone   **d.** running water regions

_____D_____ **48.** Trout would be most common here.

_____A_____ **49.** Is a deeper area of water that contains predominantly insect larvae, scavengers, fishes, and some decomposers.

_____C_____ **50.** Is the region with the largest phyto- and zooplankton populations.

_____ **B** **51.** Water lilies, cattails, algae, amphibians, snails, fishes, and birds abound here.

_____ **E** **52.** Water is most dense at what temperature Centigrade?

      a. 0°   **b.** 1°   **c.** 2°   **d.** 3°   **e.** 4°

_____ **D** **53.** The major cycling of nutrients in a lake can best be explained by assuming:

      a. Fish and microorganisms stir up the lake.

      b. The evaporation of water by the sun is the major driving force.

      c. Winds create the necessary currents.

      d. There is movement of dense and less dense waters through the strata.

      e. There is activity of underground streams and rivers.

Questions 54–59. Match each numbered statement with a choice from the *Key.*

a. estuaries   **c.** intertidal zones   **e.** ocean

b. tide pools   **d.** neritic zones

_____ **E** **54.** regions beyond the continental shelf

_____ **D** **55.** the oceans' most productive regions

_____ **A** **56.** where fresh and salt waters meet and shrimp abound and reproduce

_____ **D** **57.** coral reefs

_____ **B** **58.** rocky locations that serve as habitat for various sea creatures

_____ **C** **59.** extensive coastal areas periodically exposed to air

_____ **D** **60.** Which set of conditions best describes today's Earth?

      a. elevated levels of oxygen, ozone, and carbon dioxide

      b. depressed levels of oxygen, ozone, and carbon dioxide

      c. nitrogen and oxygen content of air down, carbon dioxide content up

      d. ozone content down, carbon dioxide content up

      e. constant levels of oxygen, ozone, carbon dioxide

Key Terms from the Text Chapter

biome *text page 779*	intertidal zone *794*	taiga *790*
biosphere *779*	limnetic zone *793*	temperate forest *789*
canopy *784*	littoral zone *793*	temperate rain forest *790*
chaparral *789*	neritic zone *795*	thermocline *794*
climate *780*	oceanic zone *796*	tropical rain forest *784*
coniferous forest *790*	pelagic zone *796*	tundra *791*
desert *786*	permafrost *791*	weather *780*
desertification *788*	profundal zone *793*	
estuary *794*	savanna *786*	

Animal Behavior: Adaptations for Survival

Perspective and Review

An animal's behavior determines where it will live, what it will feed on, and other important aspects of its life. Like other characteristics, behavior evolves, and natural selection favors behaviors that lead to increased fitness. In social animals, fitness may be maximized by helping relatives, which share genes.

Genes Direct Development and Behavioral Capabilities

Behaviors have **proximate** and **ultimate causes**. For example, seagulls remove broken eggshells from the nest. The white color of a broken egg, which stimulates the bird to eject it, is the proximate cause. The ultimate cause of the behavior is the selective advantage it confers on the bird—nests without broken shells attract fewer predators. Experiments have proven that alleles (genes) control particular behaviors, and natural selection, acting on these alleles, shapes behaviors.

Experiences in the Environment Can Alter Behavior

Some behaviors have a strong genetic basis and change slowly over evolutionary time. Other behaviors can be modified by the environment during an individual's lifetime. A continuum of behaviors ranges from **instinct** (innate, unchangeable behaviors) to **learning**. Concept Table 38.1 summarizes the main types of behavior.

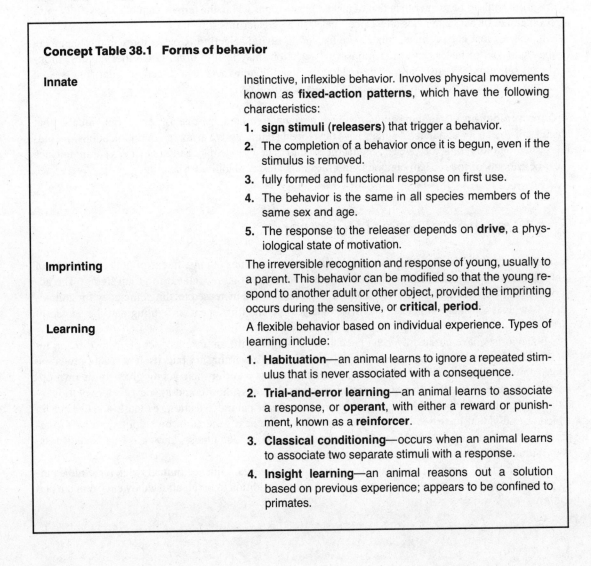

Concept Table 38.1 Forms of behavior

Innate	Instinctive, inflexible behavior. Involves physical movements known as **fixed-action patterns**, which have the following characteristics: 1. **sign stimuli (releasers)** that trigger a behavior. 2. The completion of a behavior once it is begun, even if the stimulus is removed. 3. fully formed and functional response on first use. 4. The behavior is the same in all species members of the same sex and age. 5. The response to the releaser depends on **drive**, a physiological state of motivation.
Imprinting	The irreversible recognition and response of young, usually to a parent. This behavior can be modified so that the young respond to another adult or other object, provided the imprinting occurs during the sensitive, or **critical, period**.
Learning	A flexible behavior based on individual experience. Types of learning include: 1. **Habituation**—an animal learns to ignore a repeated stimulus that is never associated with a consequence. 2. **Trial-and-error learning**—an animal learns to associate a response, or **operant**, with either a reward or punishment, known as a **reinforcer**. 3. **Classical conditioning**—occurs when an animal learns to associate two separate stimuli with a response. 4. **Insight learning**—an animal reasons out a solution based on previous experience; appears to be confined to primates.

How Natural Selection Shapes Behaviors

Animals have evolved particular behavior patterns associated with specific activities.

- **Locating and Defending a Home Territory** Many organisms locate suitable habitats by <u>taxis</u>—movement towards a particular stimulus. Ethologists believe that homing or migrating animals find their way via an **orientation** sense and the ability to **navigate**. **Navigation** that involves learning includes recognition of visual landmarks and the use of solar, stellar, or magnetic compasses.

- **Territory Defense** **Territoriality**, the defense of a space against invaders, is costly but usually confers an advantage in terms of finding mates or food, or hiding from predators.

- **Feeding Behavior** Ecologists have proposed and tested the **optimality hypothesis** to explain feeding behavior. This theory predicts that animals will act to maximize their energy intake while minimizing their risk of predation.

- **Reproductive behavior** Because females invest more energy in gametes, their <u>parental investment</u> in offspring tends to be greater than that of males. In situations where the female cannot successfully raise a brood alone, or where females are scarce, males show greater investment.

  In species that choose mates this choice has led to **sexual selection**. Competition among members of the same sex for mates, known as <u>intrasexual selection</u>, may lead to **dominance hierarchies**. In <u>intersexual selection</u>, one sex chooses desirable mates and thereby acts as a selective agent. Intersexual selection can give rise to elaborate courtship rituals and displays.

- **Communication** Communication involves a signal, emitted by one or more individuals, that changes the behavior of others. Animals have developed an impressive array of communications, including visual, auditory, olfactory, vocal, and tactile stimuli. The <u>waggle dance</u> of honey bees communicates the whereabouts of food. Light emitted by fireflies indicates availability for mating.

The Evolution of Social Behavior

A small number of animal species lives in groups, such as colonies of ants, flocks of gulls, and packs of wolves. **Sociobiology**, the study of social behavior, focuses on issues related to group living. The advantages of group living include early detection of predators and increased feeding efficiency for animals such as wolves that hunt in packs. The disadvantages include time spent in fighting and the spread of disease.

Behaviorists have puzzled over the phenomenon of **altruism**, an unselfish act performed by an individual for the benefit of others. For example, a bird issuing a warning cry puts itself at risk of predation while allowing others to escape. A scrub jay helping parents care for their young gives up its own opportunity to reproduce. If such acts reduce an individual's fitness, how could they evolve? Evolutionary biologists explain this behavior in terms of a special type of natural selection, called **kin selection**, in which an individual increases its genetic contribution to the next generation by helping relatives to reproduce. In the case of a "helper" jay that eventually breeds, its total fitness, known as **inclusive fitness**, is the sum of its relatives' fitness and its own personal fitness.

Sociobiologists continue to debate the extent to which genes influence human behavior. Studies indicate that many human traits have strong genetic bases, in addition to being affected by environment and culture.

Thought Provokers

1. Define the proximate cause and the ultimate cause of behavior and distinguish between them.

2. Briefly discuss the role of genes in animal behavior.

3. Define each of the following:

instinct:

imprinting:

trial-and-error learning:

insight learning:

Self-Test

For each statement or question choose the best response and mark your choice in the space provided. For some items you will select your answer from a *Key*.

_____ **1.** The study of behavior is called:
   a. ecology   **c.** pathology   **e.** physiology
   b. biology   **d.** ethology

_____ **2.** In Tinbergen's studies on gulls the rejection of bogus or phoney eggs was related to:
   a. size   **b.** shape   **c.** color   **d.** weight   **e.** chemical structure

_____ **3.** Studies with bees have determined that the ability to uncap a chamber and remove infected or diseased pupae is:
   a. a random behavior
   b. controlled by a single gene
   c. controlled by two genes
   d. related to the time of day
   e. Two or more of the foregoing are correct.

_____ **4.** Garter snakes show food preferences for either slugs or fish/frogs. If snakes of these two contrasting types are mated (assume that the snakes are homozygous for their character), then the F$_1$ snakes from this mating:

  a. will all prefer fish/frogs
  b. will prefer slugs
  c. will prefer neither fish/frogs nor slugs
  d. will show variation in their preferences, some liking slugs and some preferring fish/frogs
  e. none of the above, because the mating is not possible

Questions 5–14. Match each numbered statement with the best response from the _Key_.

  a. simple instinct   **c.** learned behavior
  b. fixed-action pattern   **d.** none of these

_____ **5.** black-headed gull reaction to emptied eggshells

_____ **6.** imprinting in goslings

_____ **7.** reaction of frogs to millipedes

_____ **8.** the behavior of greylag geese to egg removal following the initial rolling of the egg

_____ **9.** one-trial experiences

_____ **10.** habituation

_____ **11.** swallowing

_____ **12.** bill-pecking behavior in newly hatched herring gulls

_____ **13.** operant conditioning

_____ **14.** trial-and-error experiences

Key for questions 15–21, which refer to fixed-action patterns.

  a. True   **b.** False

_____ **15.** Specific sensory inputs serve as releasers.

_____ **16.** Sights and sounds are better releasers than tastes or odors.

_____ **17.** The pattern typically is either all or none.

_____ **18.** The pattern can be learned or unlearned by appropriate stimuli.

_____ **19.** The pattern proceeds in a definite sequence.

_____ **20.** The response typically shows variation within the species and among individuals of the same sex.

_____ **21.** Anatomical and physiological development may influence an animal's response to a releaser.

_____ **22.** The phenomenon of imprinting was discovered by:

  a. Laurens   **b.** Laurence   **c.** Lorents   **d.** Lorenz   **e.** Lawrents

_____ **23.** In early imprinting experiments it was shown that the major factor involved in imprinting was:

    a. a large honking object that moves away from the nest
    b. an object that looks like a goose
    c. any object with wings
    d. an object that is white
    e. an object with a goose shape that moves toward the nest

_____ **24.** Ticks show which of the following behaviors?

    a. phototaxis   **d.** two of these
    b. chemotaxis   **e.** all of these
    c. thermotaxis

Key for questions 25–29

    a. operant conditioning   **c.** insight learning
    b. classical conditioning   **d.** none of these

_____ **25.** A dog wraps its restraining rope around a tree and is trapped, demonstrating the absence of this.

_____ **26.** A chimpanzee stacks boxes to reach bananas.

_____ **27.** A primate uses sign language.

_____ **28.** Rats avoid any food associated with a particular odor.

_____ **29.** Bell-ringing causes an animal to salivate.

_____ **30.** Extensive studies on the migration of starlings show:

    a. Both orientation and navigation are learned responses.
    b. Neither orientation nor navigation is learned.
    c. Orientation is learned, navigation is inborn.
    d. Orientation and navigation are both conditioned responses.
    e. Orientation is inborn and navigation is partially learned.

_____ **31.** The term <u>circadian rhythm</u> is most closely associated with:

    a. internal clock   **c.** conditioned response   **e.** none of these
    b. learned response   **d.** instinct

_____ **32.** What oxide has been found in tissues near the brain in birds?

    a. iron   **b.** copper   **c.** lead   **d.** magnesium   **e.** calcium

_____ **33.** The orientation in space of a pigeon flying day and night from one place to another would indicate that the pigeon orients itself by:

    a. sun   **c.** magnetic fields   **e.** two of these
    b. stars   **d.** highways

_____ **34.** It has been demonstrated that in strong impalas males tend to establish:

    a. small, rich turfs
    b. large, rich turfs
    c. no turf, since it is better to roam
    d. any turf near a female
    e. any turf that does not have another male

35. Which best fits the "optimality" hypothesis?
   a. Obtain food quickly.
   b. Avoid predators.
   c. Obtain any food.
   d. Obtain the most food with the least effort and least danger.
   e. Expend the least effort in avoiding predators.

36. Indicate the chances of survival, in decreasing order, for the following numbered items:
   1. human babies; **2.** salmon eggs; **3.** bird eggs

   a. 1, 3, 2   c. 1, 2, 3   e. 3, 1, 2
   b. 3, 2, 1   d. 2, 3, 1

Key for questions 37–38

a. intersexual selection
b. intrasexual selection
c. both of these
d. neither of these

37. selection that typically is made by the female

38. the type of selection made by males among elephant seals, deer, antelope, buffalo

39. Firefly signals are used to locate:
   a. mates   c. offspring   e. all of these
   b. food   d. habitats

40. Pheromones are what kind of signals?
   a. chemical   b. light   c. sound   d. touch   e. electrical

41. Pheromones are:
   a. long-lasting
   b. species-specific
   c. easy to detect
   d. able to travel long distances
   e. all of these

42. In a beehive, if food is nearby what kind of dance does the forage bee display?
   a. round   b. square   c. single   d. double   e. waggle

43. The waggle dance of bees is described as what type of figure?
   a. eight   b. square   c. circle   d. spiral   e. round

44. In the "dim bulb" experiments with forager bees with their three simple eyes painted and their compound eyes untouched, the bees behaved as if:
   a. the sun were present   b. the hive were dark

45. In the "dim bulb" experiment, what did the other bees present do?
   a. They did nothing; they were confused.
   b. They interpreted the dance incorrectly.
   c. They interpreted the dance correctly.

Key Terms from the Text Chapter

Answer Section

Chapter 1

Thought Provoker

1. Two basic problems organisms face are the needs to take in energy to maintain the living state (overcome disorder) and to reproduce (overcome death). Being highly organized permits cells and organisms to carry out processes that extract energy from the environment; adaptations, metabolism, movement, and responsiveness all contribute to this process. Genes carry the information that governs virtually every aspect of the living state, including development. Reproduction ensures that this information is passed from generation to generation.

Self-Test

1. d   2. a   3. d   4. b   5. d   6. b   7. a   8. a
9. e   10. b

Chapter 2

Thought Provokers

1. pH measures the hydrogen ion concentration in a solution—essentially, its relative acidity. pH values range from 0 to 14; the lower end of the scale is more acid, while the upper end is more alkaline. pH is important to biological systems because enzymatic and other cellular functions occur in solution. If the pH is not appropriate, many enzymes cannot act. The optimal pH for most reactions is at or near the neutral value of 7.0.

2. Enzymes are proteins that act as catalysts for many essential cellular reactions. They make possible rapid biochemical reactions at temperatures common in living organisms. If all enzyme functioning stops, an organism quickly dies.

Self-Test

1. ab	2. b	3. b	4. b	5. e	6. d	7. ad	8. e
9. b	10. b	11. e	12. b,e	13. c	14. d	15. ab	16. b
17. e	18. a	19. bd	20. ad	21. b	22. b	23. b	24. c
25. e	26. c	27. a	28. abc	29. cde	30. d	31. c	32. a
33. c	34. a	35. b	36. d	37. b	38. e	39. c	40. a
41. b	42. d	43. c	44. a	45. ab			

Chapter 3

Thought Provokers

1. A basic cell would require: (1) a cell membrane to hold the cell contents, separate the cell from its environment, and regulate molecular and ionic traffic into and out of the cell; (2) a nucleus with DNA to store the information that guides cell activities and is transferred in reproduction; (3) RNA to transcribe and translate DNA; (4) ribosomes as sites of protein synthesis; and (5) enzymes to catalyze metabolic processes.

2. The internal membrane systems of a eukaryotic cell include the endoplasmic reticulum, the Golgi body, and organelles such as mitochondria and chloroplasts. Membranes increase the internal surface area on which various membrane-associated processes can take place, such as synthesis and storage of biochemicals.

3. Eukaryotic cells have a double-layered nuclear membrane perforated with pores that permit traffic with the cytoplasm. Prokaryotic cells lack a membrane-bound nucleus. Both cell types are enclosed within a plasma membrane, and contain DNA and RNA, enzymes, and ribosomes.

Self-Test

1. a	2. b	3. b	4. a	5. b	6. c	7. c	8. b
9. a	10. a	11. c	12. b	13. b	14. c	15. b	16. c
17. be	18. a	19. bc	20. e	21. ad	22. ab	23. ac	24. bc
25. ae	26. d	27. a	28. ab	29. bd	30. d	31. a	32. cd
33. b	34. cd	35. e	36. bd	37. d	38. e	39. b	40. d

Chapter 4

Thought Provokers

1. Materials can enter cells in a number of different ways. Large particulate materials and macromolecules can enter cells by means of phagocytosis and pinocytosis, respectively. These are essentially membrane-envelopment processes that require the expenditure of energy in the form of ATP. Water freely diffuses across the cell membrane and no energy expenditure is required. Some proteins carry materials into the cell. When no energy is expended this is termed *facilitated transport*; when energy is expended it is termed *active transport*.

2. The first law of thermodynamics states that energy may be neither created nor destroyed but may be changed from one form to another. Thus, cells do not create energy. Typically, plant cells convert light energy to chemical energy, and animal cells by their metabolism build up or break down biochemicals. Available energy in the form of ATP links and drives the metabolism of the cell. Therefore, cells only make use of the energy that is already available or extractable from energy sources. According to the second law of thermodynamics the entropy of natural systems tends to increase. Entropy is a measure of the disorder in a system; the more disorder the greater the entropy. Although cells tend naturally toward disorder, this disorder is overcome by an expenditure of energy.

3. Osmosis is the diffusion of water across a selectively permeable membrane. This diffusion requires no expenditure of energy by the cell. When the rate of water passing into a cell equals the rate of water exiting the cell the intra- and extracellular solutions are said to be isotonic. If the solution outside the cell contains more solute and less water, that solution is said to be hypertonic and there is a net loss of water from the inside of the cell to the outside. The solution inside the cell is said to be hypotonic when the concentration of solute is lower and the amount of water is greater than in the solution outside the cell.

4. Enzymes are protein catalysts that are vital to cellular life and activities. It is difficult to imagine that there would be any life without them. As a catalyst, an enzyme speeds up biochemical reactions. Each enzyme has an active site that reacts with a particular substrate or substrates. A brief enzyme-substrate complex forms and then falls apart as the reaction product is produced. The enzyme is then released to bind another substrate molecule. This process occurs repeatedly. The rate of biochemical reactions is influenced by the concentrations of enzyme and substrate, temperature, and pH.

Typically, an increase in the concentrations of substrate or enzyme increases the rate of the chemical reactions. If the product becomes too concentrated (that is, is not removed or used) the product may inhibit the rate of the reaction. For each $10°C$ rise in temperature the reaction rate may double.

Virtually all enzymes lower the activation energy that is necessary for biochemical reactions. Thus, many reactions can occur quickly at body temperature that otherwise might not occur or might occur far more slowly.

Self-Test

1. b	2. b	3. a	4. b	5. a	6. b	7. b	8. a
9. d	10. a	11. b	12. a	13. a	14. b	15. a	16. b
17. b	18. b	19. a	20. a	21. a	22. b	23. c	24. b
25. c	26. a	27. d	28. a	29. c	30. b	31. a	32. b
33. b							

Chapter 5

Thought Provokers

1. Organisms that rely solely on glycolysis for their energy needs are anaerobic. Unlike aerobes, they do not gain energy via oxidative metabolism and do not require oxygen. Thus, they can survive in environments lacking oxygen, where an aerobe would quickly die.

2. The Krebs cycle and electron transport chain, which require oxygen, generate large amounts of ATP to fuel cellular processes. Hence, oxidative metabolism in mitochondria extracts energy from nutrients much more efficiently than does glycolysis alone, and is one factor that permits life forms to be large and complex. Likewise, only very simple organisms with relatively simple energy needs can survive using glycolysis.

Self-Test

1. b	2. b	3. c	4. b	5. b	6. c	7. b	8. b
9. a	10. a	11. c	12. c	13. a	14. a	15. a	16. c
17. c	18. c	19. a	20. b	21. c	22. a	23. a	24. b
25. b	26. a	27. a	28. b	29. b	30. a		

Chapter 6

Thought Provokers

1. The baker would require a simpler and less complex response than would the biology student. Your responses might be as follows.

   To the baker: Crabgrass, like all grasses, needs light and warmth to grow. In very hot weather crabgrass actually can grow better than some other varieties because it has a way of trapping the gas it needs for growth without losing as much water. To get carbon dioxide the little pores in the leaves are opened, and both oxygen and water exit the leaf when carbon dioxide enters. In very hot weather the crabgrass can open and close its pores, take in and store the CO_2 it needs. In contrast, typical bluegrass or fescue has its pores open throughout the day and loses much moisture, wilting and drying as it takes up CO_2. The crabgrass flourishes because its leaf pores are not open at all times during the hot day and, consequently, crabgrass loses less water and grows better because of increased hydration.

   To the biology student: Some plants are C_3 plants and some are the C_4 type. Crabgrass is C_4 and can open and close stomata, or leaf pores, periodically to both trap CO_2 and permit oxygen and water to escape. To maintain a constant supply of CO_2, C_4 plants bind the excess CO_2 to phosphoenolpyruvate (PEP) via PEP carboxylase to form oxaloacetate. When CO_2 is needed they decarboxylate the oxaloacetate. Thus, the ability of C_4 plants to store CO_2 means they lose less water than do C_3 plants.

2. Photosynthesis is a specialized process that converts light energy into chemical energy. The overall formula is: $6CO_2 + 6H_2O \rightarrow 1$ glucose $+ 6O_2$. Photosynthesis can be considered a two-part process, with both a light-dependent phase and a light-independent "dark" phase. In the light phase, the green chlorophyll molecules capture the blue and the red wavelengths of light. This light energy is made to do chemical work by means of specialized molecules and enzymes that split water to release hydrogen nuclei (protons), electrons, and oxygen. Two electrons are energized by the light energy (photons). This boosts the electrons out of the reaction center to an acceptor molecule. The electrons transfer the captured light energy to other molecules in the chloroplast membrane, and various electron acceptor molecules work in conjunction with ATP synthetase to help generate ATP. This process occurs in the photosystem II (680) of the chloroplast. Photosystem I receives the two electrons and uses this energy to energize the same two electrons again. The energized electrons are passed onto $NADP^+$ and united with a proton to yield NADPH. In the light phase of photosynthesis, both ATP and NADPH are made. During the light-independent phase, ribulose biphosphate combines with CO_2 under the influence of RBP carboxylase to form an unstable six-carbon molecule that quickly breaks down into phosphoglyceric acid. Phosphoglyceric acid is reduced to phosphoglyceraldehyde by an enzyme with NADPH. At this point some PGAL is shunted to make glucose; most of the rest goes to make more RBP.

3. Two of the worst-case scenarios for the planet are the concepts of nuclear winter and the greenhouse effect. In both cases there is an excess of burning, or oxidation, with the production of large amounts of CO_2. In the greenhouse effect, an enlarged CO_2 layer traps heat and raises the temperature of the Earth significantly. Researchers believe that the result will be increased droughts and desertification, as well as melting of the polar ice caps that will cause flooding in coastal areas throughout the world. In the case of nuclear winter, the explosion of large numbers of atomic weapons is expected to create major fires, dust, and debris. The ensuing clouded atmosphere will prevent sunlight from reaching plants. The Earth's temperature will drop dramatically, and photosynthesis will slow or stop and huge numbers of plants and animals will die.

Self-Test

1. a	2. c	3. bd	4. b	5. ab	6. d	7. ce	8. ac
9. ad	10. e	11. a	12. d	13. d	14. a	15. d	16. d
17. d	18. c	19. e	20. bc	21. a	22. a	23. a	24. b
25. b	26. b	27. a	28. a	29. b	30. a	31. b	32. a

33. b   34. a   35. a   36. a   37. a   38. a   39. d   40. b
41. ab   42. b   43. ab

Chapter 7

Thought Provokers

1. Mitosis and meiosis are similar in some ways, yet they are distinctly different. Both processes regulate the amount of cellular DNA, via chromosome condensations, movement, and separation. Each has a prophase, a metaphase, an anaphase, and a telophase. In mitosis the chromosomes that have doubled to 4N (four times the haploid number) are halved to give 2N, the diploid (somatic) chromosome number. Both products of mitosis are, therefore, diploid. In meiosis, there are two sequential divisions, or two cycles of the four phases named for mitosis. In meiosis there are at least three important differences to be noted: (1) At prophase I of meiosis homologous chromosomes pair, frequently involving equal exchanges of chromosome parts. This is known as crossing over and is shown physically as chiasmata. (2) At metaphase I of meiosis the paternal and maternal homologous chromosomes (that is, those that are of the same type or kind and that control similar functions or features) have completed any chromosomal exchanges and will separate to opposite poles. Further, the distribution of the chromosomes is random, meaning that the movement of paternal and maternal chromosomes is independent of the behavior of other nonhomologous chromosomes. The chromosomes assort independently. (3) Four products result when meiosis is completed as each product of the first meiotic division goes from prophase II to telophase II.

2. Meiosis should be considered as a major process of importance to the evolution and development of organisms. Genes that control characteristics and functions of the organism are found on the chromosomes. Different types of genes can result from mutation, and these mutations can be passed on to the next generation. In meiosis different genes may be exchanged (between homologous, paternal and maternal chromosomes) and there is an independent assortment of chromosomes that leads to new combinations of chromosomes. This all means that after meiosis has occurred many different and varied types of gametes are produced. Different and varied gametes then combine to produce zygotes, or diploid products, that will develop into the varied types of individuals of a species. Those individuals, and their genes, that are best suited for survival in a particular environment or situation will grow and multiply. Hence, meiosis produces many experimental menus of chromosomes and their associated genes and from this the most fit and the best-adapted individuals will be selected. Mitosis does not provide variety of chromosomes and genes; meiosis does.

Self-Test

1. c	2. a	3. d	4. e	5. b	6. c	7. a	8. b
9. a	10. c	11. b	12. c	13. b	14. b	15. c	16. c
17. c	18. e	19. a	20. b	21. a	22. b	23. b	24. e
25. a	26. c	27. d	28. e	29. a	30. a,b,c	31. a,b,e	

Chapter 8

Thought Provokers

1. A chromosome consists of DNA, which in turn comprises genes, discrete units of chemically coded information. Each gene represents a specific type of information that is of value to the cell. Each gene occupies a specific locus, or site, on the DNA. Alleles are alternate or different forms of the same gene. Cells that are diploid contain pairs of chromosomes, with the two members of each pair having

similar kinds of genes. Haploid cells contain only one member of each diploid chromosome pair. The chromosome number of a particular cell depends on the species of organism and the type of cell involved. In general, most organisms have both haploid and diploid cell types. In diploid organisms genes that are always expressed when they are present are dominant genes, whereas recessive genes are expressed only when the corresponding dominant alleles are absent.

Genes that are on the same chromosome may show linkage—that is, they may be inherited together by offspring. Mutation is an inheritable change in a gene that usually results in a new or different allele of that gene.

The F_2 generation represents the offspring, or products, of an F_1 cross. To determine the probable traits of the F_2 generation one must know the genetic character, or genotypes, of the F_1 generation.

2. Mendel was able to show in pea plants that seven different contrasting characters, or traits, were inherited in a defined and precise manner. He demonstrated that both dominant traits and recessive traits in pure lines of peas always maintained their character. Crosses of these pure lines revealed that for each two contrasting traits (e.g., tall plants vs. short plants or round seeds vs. wrinkled seeds) one character only was seen in the F_2 generation. However, Mendel also proved that the unexpressed recessive character was not lost, but was only masked by the dominant character. The recessive character of the F_1 generation would reappear in some individuals when the F_1 progeny were mated. This cross usually resulted in an F_2 generation with a 3:1 ratio of dominant to recessive characteristics.

In spite of his ground-breaking discoveries Mendel did not know about some basic phenomena of genetics. For example, he did not know that: (1) some genes are linked to other genes on the same chromosome; (2) crossing over of genes can occur by the exchange of homologous chromosome segments; (3) genes can change through mutation; and (4) the hereditary material is DNA.

Self-Test

1. e	2. d	3. ac	4. c	5. ae	6. b	7. ab	8. bc
9. bd	10. ae	11. b	12. a	13. b	14. b	15. b	16. a
17. a	18. b	19. b	20. a	21. b	22. a	23. ab	24. ac
25. e	26. c	27. ab	28. d	29. ad	30. b	31. b	32. d
33. c	34. b	35. c	36. c	37. a	38. c	39. b	40. b

Chapter 9

Thought Provokers

1. A biologist would likely argue against proteins as master informational molecules on another planet. In part this is a biased choice based on what is already known about DNA and proteins. Neither structural nor enzymatic protein molecules are known to code for themselves on Earth, and it is neither logical nor probable that they would do so elsewhere. Another argument has to do with the structure of DNA: In spite of its fundamental simplicity, having only four nucleotide bases, these bases can be ordered in a vast number of combinations. As a result the molecule can store a prodigious amount of information—a necessary attribute for generating the huge numbers of distinct proteins in an organism. Replication is also a crucial requirement, and DNA wins out here, too. Instead of needing large numbers of different amino acids to create a new molecule, as would be required for a protein, the "recipe" for more DNA relies on the four nucleotide bases. Thus, DNA by its nature and structure would seem to be the best molecule for encoding large amounts of information and for replicating that information.

2. Researchers can trace the steps in a biochemical pathway by studying mutant microorganisms that lack the ability to synthesize substances required to complete the pathway. Such experiments involve trying to grow known mutants on a defined minimal growth medium—one on which normal microbes can flourish because they are able to synthesize necessary nutrients from the raw materials provided. The

mutants, however, will grow on the minimal medium only when a particular nutrient that they cannot synthesize is added. Thus, by doing a series of experiments, a researcher can see which substances are required in the pathway, and in what order.

Self-Test

1. b	2. b	3. d	4. c	5. b	6. a	7. b	8. a
9. a	10. b	11. b	12. b	13. a	14. a	15. b	16. a
17. a	18. a	19. b	20. a	21. e	22. c	23. b	24. a
25. b	26. a	27. d	28. c				

Chapter 10

Thought Provokers

1. A mutation is a change in the base sequence of an organism's DNA. Mutations may be caused by radiation (ultraviolet, gamma, X-rays) or chemicals, or they may occur spontaneously. Mutations are classed into the following types: (1) a deletion, in which a piece of the DNA is lost; (2) an insertion, in which a different, new base is inserted; (3) a substitution, in which one base pair replaces another; and (4) rearrangement, such as an inversion of base order.

The consequences of mutations are frequently significant, for the change in the DNA often means that there is a change in the products it encodes—RNA and proteins. Three types of coding problems are: (1) *Nonsense:* The base sequence contains a premature stop codon. In this case an incomplete protein results that usually is not functional. (2) *Frameshift:* An insertion or deletion of one or more base pairs that alters the RNA message and the subsequent protein. (3) *Missense*: A substitution of a different base pair that alters the RNA message and the protein.

Mutations usually are harmful. Cells and organisms with mutations often have shortened lives. Some mutations result in death shortly after the mutation occurs; in other cases the organism may live for a long time before negative effects appear.

---

2. Table: A comparison of information processing in prokaryotes and eukaryotes

Similarities:

1. DNA is double-stranded and codes for single-strand RNA.
2. Three types of RNA are made by DNA: mRNA (messenger RNA), rRNA (ribosomal RNA), and soluble or tRNA.
3. RNA binds to ribosomes. Translation into protein occurs at the ribosomal site. Twenty common, different amino acids are used to make the proteins.

Differences:

1. Eukaryotes have more genes than do prokaryotes.
2. Eukaryotes, therefore, produce more and different kinds of proteins than do prokaryotes.
3. In prokaryotes RNA transcribed from the DNA is in immediate and direct contact with the cytoplasm and the ribosomes; in eukaryotes the transcribed RNA must pass through the nuclear membrane to reach the cytoplasm and the ribosomes.
4. The proteins coded by DNA in eukaryotes and prokaryotes generally differ from one another, even though the same common amino acids are used. These variations are related to genetic differences between prokaryotes and eukaryotes.

Continues

---

2. **Table: A comparison of information processing in prokaryotes and eukaryotes (continued)**

5. Eukaryotic DNA contains many repetitive genes; prokaryotic genes are usually present as single copies.

6. Eukaryotic gene expression occurs in a spatial and temporal context (that is, influenced by the location of cells and the phase of an organism's life); prokaryotic gene expression occurs based on the condition of the internal and immediate external environment.

7. Eukaryotic DNA contains intervening sequences called introns that are transcribed into RNA. However, this intron RNA is cut out prior to translation; only exons are finally expressed. If the intron RNA is not removed, the RNA transcript will not leave the nucleus to be translated in the cytoplasm.

Self-Test

1. c	2. c	3. d	4. e	5. b	6. b,c,d	7. a,b,c,d	8. c
9. b	10. c	11. d, e	12. a	13. b	14. c	15. b,c,d	16. b
17. d	18. b	19. a	20. c	21. e	22. b	23. a	24. c
25. c	26. a,c	27. d	28. e	29. b	30. a	31. b	32. c
33. a	34. b	35. c	36. b	37. c	38. a	39. b	40. a
41. b	42. a	43. a	44. b	45. a	46. c	47. c	48. d
49. c	50. a						

Chapter 11

Thought Provokers

1. To obtain gene *Y* and produce product *Y* a researcher would use modern genetic engineering and gene cloning as follows:
   a. Isolate human DNA from human cells. For example, use DNA extracted from human leukocytes or from other human tissues or organs that are available.
   b. Use a restriction endonuclease to cut the DNA into pieces. These pieces should be of a size that keeps the gene intact.
   c. Take plasmids and with the same restriction endonuclease open up the plasmids.
   d. Mix the human DNA pieces with the plasmid DNA and join the pieces with ligating enzymes (ligases).
   e. Use the hybrid or chimeric DNA to transform appropriate bacterial cells.
   f. Select for the transformed cells that bear the plasmid marker. (All nontransformed cells will die, for example, if they lack an antibiotic-resistance gene that is on the plasmid; on the other hand, transformed cells with plasmids will be antibiotic-resistant).
   g. Check for the presence of the gene *Y* directly via specific *Y* gene probes, or look for the secretion of product Y into the medium around the bacterial colonies.
   h. Isolate any of the positive colonies and subculture. Check for purity and stability. Proceed to use the bacterial colonies to mass-produce product *Y*.

3. Genetic engineering is important because it enables researchers to: (1) Produce in prokaryotic cells large amounts of important substances made by eukaryotic cells. The prokaryotes (bacteria or yeast) can be grown quickly and in great numbers. (2) Make multiple copies of important genes and to use these genes to transform other cells; may lead to creation of new, useful types of microbes. (3) Determine the nucleotide sequence of genes and determine how genes differ from one another. (4) Determine what the RNA product of a gene will be. (5) Make gene probes useful for medical diagnoses and for other studies of organisms.

4. Problems associated with genetic engineering include: (1) the endonuclease may sever a desired gene; (2) the gene may not be spliced into the plasmid; (3) the desired gene may not transform the bacterial cell; (4) the chimera (hybrid-gene complex) may be broken down in the bacterial cell; (5) the gene may not be expressed in the bacterial cell; and (6) the gene product may be bound inside the cell and not released to the outside.

Self-Test

1. a	2. b	3. b	4. a	5. a	6. b	7. b	8. b
9. b	10. a	11. a	12. a	13. d	14. a	15. b	16. a
17. a	18. a	19. c	20. d				

Chapter 12

Thought Provoker

1. It is possible for harmful dominant or recessive genes to be maintained in the genome. First, we know that harmful genes do not disappear. If this were the case these harmful genes would not be around for us to study. If a gene were immediately harmful, as in the case of a dominant harmful gene, then the individual might die and never reproduce. However, some harmful dominant genes do not exert their effects at birth. In Huntington's disease an individual can lead a normal life up until 40 years of age or more. When the disease appears, the individual has probably already reproduced and passed the defective gene on to his or her offspring. Only if a person knows that they carry the defective gene can they decide, perhaps, not to have children and thus avoid passing the gene on. For harmful recessive genes the picture also is clear. An individual must have two copies of the gene in order to have the phenotype (the disease); that is, they must be homozygous recessive.

   A deleterious gene can be maintained in a population quite easily by one or more of the following mechanisms: (1) It does not cause early death and thus does not interfere with reproduction (male pattern baldness). (2) Even if lethal early in life (Tay-Sachs disease), there will always be heterozygous offspring that carry the gene but are protected by the normal allele. (3) Finally, due to medical intervention, even individuals who are homozygous recessive for a harmful trait may live and reproduce. As an example, hemophiliacs and people with cystic fibrosis can marry and pass their defective alleles to their children.

Self-Test

1. b	2. b	3. a	4. a	5. a	6. b	7. a	8. b
9. a	10. a	11. c	12. a	13. d	14. a	15. d	16. d
17. b	18. a	19. d	20. c	21. a	22. d	23. c	24. a
25. b	26. b	27. a	28. b	29. c	30. ac	31. d	32. ab
33. a	34. b	35. a	36. b	37. a	38. e	39. b	40. a

Chapter 13

Thought Provokers

1. Normal cell growth and development proceed in an ordered, regular, and controlled fashion. Normal cells grow and divide and assume special positions or locations in the organism. This process leads to specialized roles and functions; cells that have these characteristics are said to be differentiated. Growth factors lead cells to divide, and other factors, including chalones (stop-growth) factors, contribute to the overall order. In cancer, cell growth and division is uncontrolled. The cancer cells expand beyond their boundaries and crowd neighboring cells and tissues. Normal cells frequently become damaged and may die as crowding continues. Cancer cells may metastasize to other sites by traveling through the blood stream or lymphatic system. Cancer cells are malignant, transformed cells that are no longer subject to typical growth controls. It has been shown that some of these cancers have normal proto-oncogenes that have mutated or changed and now produce growth factors without restraint. Thus, cancer cells differ in significant ways from normal cells.

2. There are approximately eight key steps in development: fertilization, cleavage, gastrulation, neurulation, organogenesis, growth, gametogenesis, and fertilization.

   Fertilization: Normally, a sperm contacts an egg and penetrates into the egg. The egg or sperm may die prior to fertilization.

   Cleavage: The fertilized egg begins an ordered, definite, sequential series of divisions. If there is a genetic defect, the cleavage may be improper and the developing organism may die or be abnormal.

   Gastrulation: A three-layered embryo is produced with ectoderm, mesoderm, and endoderm. Each layer will give rise to a specialized type of tissue. Improper positioning or cell location may lead to abnormal tissues or death.

   Neurulation: The nerve tube is formed at this stage. Other cells and tissues will be influenced by the tube's position. Failure of the tube to close causes the condition spina bifida—an open, exposed nerve cord.

   Organogenesis: At this stage large masses of specific tissue become organized into brain, liver, lung, kidneys, intestines, and other structures. Faulty cell migration may cause a condition such as cleft lip or cleft palate. Or, if certain types of cells do not grow and differentiate, a region of tissue or organ, such as the stomach, may be absent.

   Growth: Differentiated tissues and organs now simply increase in size. Failure to grow appropriately may cause dwarfism, for example, when bones are unable to elongate.

   Gametogenesis: The animal matures and sex organs become active to produce egg or sperm. Problems with hormone secretion may result in sterility or infertility.

   Fertilization: After gametes form they are potentially able to unite in sexual union, to once again give rise to a complete organism. Immature or defective gametes will not function; gametes may die and, therefore, fertilization cannot occur.

Self-Test

1. a	2. b	3. b	4. b	5. b	6. b	7. b	8. a
9. a	10. b	11. a	12. b	13. a	14. a	15. b	16. b
17. b	18. b	19. b	20. b	21. c	22. c	23. a	24. b
25. a	26. c	27. c	28. b	29. b	30. a	31. a	32. b
33. b	34. a	35. b	36. a	37. a	38. a	39. b	40. b

Chapter 14

Thought Provokers

1. *Sperm:* Originate in testes (in the scrotum). Spermatogenic (gonial) cell develops into sperm, which travel from the epididymis, through the vas deferens, to the ejaculatory duct, and out through the urethra.

   Egg: Originates in ovary. Oocyte in follicle develops into an egg (ovum), which travels into the oviduct and thence to the uterus. If fertilized, the ovum develops into an embryo and lodges in the uterine wall; if not fertilized, it passes out through the cervix and vagina.

   The sex hormone regulatory systems in males and females are in some ways remarkably similar. In both, the hypothalamus releases a hormone that causes the pituitary to secrete FSH and LH, both of which hormones activate cells in the gonads. Since the target cells in males and females are different, however, the effects of the hormones are different: In males FSH stimulates the spermatogenic cells to produce sperm, while in females it stimulates the egg to mature into an ovum. In the testes LH stimulates the Leydig cells to secrete testosterone, while in females it stimulates the follicle cells to produce estrogen. Both testosterone and estrogens feed back and negatively inhibit releasing hormone of the hypothalamus. Decreased releasing hormone lowers the pituitary release of FSH and LH.

2. *Most effective* birth control methods: (1) abstinence—no intercourse; (2) male sterilization—vasectomy; (3) female sterilization—tubal ligation. *Less effective:* (4) condom plus spermicide; (5) birth control pill; (6) intrauterine device. *Least effective:* (7) rhythm method—intercourse only during infertile period for the woman; (8) withdrawal—coitus interruptus.

Self-Test

1. c	2. ab	3. e	4. d	5. ae, bd	6. e	7. a	8. b
9. a	10. ae	11. b	12. ae, bd	13. c	14. d	15. a	16. a
17. b	18. b	19. b	20. a	21. b	22. a	23. a	24. b
25. b	26. c	27. d	28. b	29. e	30. a	31. d	32. e
33. a	34. c	35. a	36. ab	37. e	38. a		

Chapter 15

Thought Provokers

1. **a.** Primitive Earth: gaseous planet, high heat, lightning conditions, probably struck by meteorites for millions of years

   b. Gases of NH_3, CO, HCN, CH_4, and H_2O interact under heat, pressure, lightning, and ultraviolet radiation to form simple amino acids, nitrogen bases, nucleotides, and simple sugars.

c. Eventually, polypeptides and simple nucleic acids of RNA and DNA form. RNA particularly is a possibility as the first self-replicating molecule.

d. Simple proteins and polypeptides interact with phospholipids to form proteinoid spheres with a typical membrane configuration and organization.

e. Inside some proteinoid spheres nucleic acids direct their own self-replication; other reactions occur in the external environment on clay surfaces, which act as catalysts.

f. Structures organized as proteinoid spheres begin to grow and replicate more efficiently than nonmembrane-bound structures. Due to enzyme activity and the presence of ATP, energy can be transferred or stored by these primitive cells.

g. No oxygen is available at this time in molecular evolution; therefore, energy is derived exclusively through anaerobic processes.

h. The earliest cells have DNA not bounded by a membrane. The cells are prokaryotic in character.

i. Some of the earliest cells are photosynthetic but do not generate oxygen. Later, oxygen-yielding photosynthesis occurs.

j. The presence of oxygen makes aerobic life possible.

2. Large organisms have great energy needs. All the cells in a large organism must be supplied with large amounts of ATP for growth, repair, and reproduction. Although the energy needs for organisms can be met by fermentation or anaerobic metabolism, the total amount of energy extractable from these processes is much less than the energy that may be obtained aerobically. Therefore, we would expect that large organisms, such as mammals, and plants would be aerobic, whereas smaller organisms, such as certain bacteria (*Clostridium*, for example), would function well with an anaerobic metabolism. As described earlier, some tissues of an aerobic organism, such as muscle, may function with an oxygen deficit. The brain, however, quickly dies when starved for oxygen.

Self-Test

1. b	2. d	3. b	4. e	5. d	6. b	7. a	8. a
9. e	10. a	11. c,d	12. a	13. e	14. a	15. e	16. d
17. a	18. e	19. a	20. c	21. d	22. a	23. b	24. d
25. b	26. e	27. d,e	28. c,d	29. e	30. c	31. d	32. a
33. d	34. b	35. d					

Chapter 16

Thought Provokers

1. The mastigophorans are flagellated, eukaryotic organisms and are heterotrophs. They are members of the Protista, and include several harmful types such as *Trypanosoma*, the flagellate parasite that carries African sleeping sickness, and *Giardia lamblia*, an organism that can cause severe gastrointestinal illness. A mastigophoran beneficial to the termite (but not to humans) is *Trichonympha*, which lives in the insect's gut. This flagellate produces enzymes that enable the termite to digest the wood it consumes.

Sporozoans typically are nonmotile, eukaryotic protists. They include the parasites that carry malaria; such organisms can grow and multiply inside red blood cells and cause serious disease and even death of the host.

Bacteria are prokaryotic organisms that contain both RNA and DNA. Some bacteria are harmful to humans, while others are beneficial. Harmful species include the bacteria that cause leprosy, botulism, and respiratory and urinary tract infections. Other bacteria are beneficial. Included in this group are microorganisms that carry out photosynthesis, fix nitrogen, and break down dead plant or animal materials and return their constituents to the soil.

Viruses make up a unique group of "organisms" that are exclusively parasitic. They include forms that cause diseases such as herpes, influenza, the common cold, and mumps and measles.

2. Bacteria comprise a diverse group, and not surprisingly their nutrition also is diverse and varied. Some are photosynthetic, using carbon dioxide as a sole source of carbon. The photosynthetic cyanobacteria also are able to fix nitrogen gas and convert it into organic compounds. Other autotrophic bacteria include the chemoautotrophic sulfur and methane bacteria that use carbon dioxide and hydrogen sulfide and hydrogen, respectively, to form the organic compounds they need. Finally, heterotrophic bacteria obtain carbon from sugars, alcohols, organic acids, and other forms of (already-fixed) organic carbon. These bacteria are saprobes (organisms that live on dead or nonliving organic carbon) or parasites (organisms that live on or inside another living organism). *Escherichia coli*, which inhabits the intestines of humans and other animals, is a typical saprobe. The bacterium responsible for leprosy is a true parasite.

Self-Test

1. d	2. e	3. b	4. a	5. a	6. a	7. b	8. a
9. c	10. a	11. d	12. b	13. d	14. c	15. a	16. b
17. b	18. a	19. a	20. d	21. e	22. a	23. b	24. a
25. d	26. b	27. a	28. a	29. b	30. c	31. c	32. b
33. b	34. b	35. a	36. a	37. c	38. a	39. a	40. b
41. d	42. a	43. c	44. d	45. b	46. a	47. c	48. b
49. c	50. c	51. a	52. a	53. d	54. a	55. b	56. c
57. b	58. d	59. c	60. a	61. b	62. b	63. c	64. c
65. b							

Chapter 17

Thought Provokers

1. Fungi and plants are similar in some ways and significantly different in other ways. Both are eukaryotic: They have membrane-bound nuclei and their cytoplasms contain structures such as mitochondria, endoplasmic reticulum, and Golgi bodies. Some fungi have walls with cellulose, and many (but not all) plants have walls with cellulose. Most of the organisms in each kingdom have haploid and diploid phases, with a distinct sexual phase characterized by meiosis and the formation of gametes or sex cells. Only the Fungi Imperfecti (Deuteromycetes) lack a regular, distinct sexual phase. Both groups include aquatic and terrestrial types.

    Differences: Fungi are basically heterotrophs, while plants are autotrophs. Fungi typically live as saprobes or parasites. Plants, because they contain chlorophyll, can photosynthesize and obtain energy from carbon dioxide fixation and the splitting of water. This is one of the most significant and important differences between the two kingdoms.

2. Mycorrhizae are symbiotic associations between certain types of fungi and plant roots. The fungi attach to the plant roots and take up from the soil nutrients needed by the plant. The fungus in turn has a home, and may receive other benefits.

    Lichen associations occur between algae and ascomycete fungi. Products of algal photosynthesis nourish the fungus; the fungus provides the alga with protection, a supply of water, and perhaps other benefits.

Self-Test

1. b	2. b	3. a	4. a	5. b	6. a	7. c	8. e
9. b	10. e	11. c	12. e	13. a	14. d	15. a	16. b
17. a	18. b	19. b	20. d	21. acde	22. b	23. b	24. a
25. a	26. b	27. b	28. d	29. e	30. d	31. b	32. d

33. d	34. c	35. a	36. c	37. a	38. c	39. b	40. a
41. a	42. b	43. b	44. a	45. a	46. b	47. b	48. b
49. b	50. a	51. a	52. d	53. a	54. a	55. d	56. e
57. d	58. d	59. a	60. a	61. a	62. b	63. b	64. a
65. b	66. e	67. a	68. d	69. b	70. a	71. a	72. b
73. a	74. b	75. a					

Chapter 18

Thought Provokers

1. The simplest invertebrates are the sponges (Porifera). Sponges are masses of amoeboid tissue with a primitive mouth and no anus. Their shape is maintained by spongin protein and spicules of calcium carbonate. They reproduce asexually by budding and sexually by means of eggs and sperm released into the water.

Cnidarians, such as sea anemones and jellyfish, are radial symmetrical. They are more advanced than sponges because they have three cell layers, a primitive gastrovascular cavity, and a rudimentary nervous system. Eggs and sperm are released into the water, where fertilization takes place.

Platyhelminthes, or flatworms (planaria, tapeworms), show bilateral symmetry and cephalization, the concentration of nerves toward the anterior of the animal. Three tissue layers are evident: ectoderm, mesoderm, and endoderm. True organs and organ systems appear for the first time in this phylum, whose members have well-developed digestive, excretory, and reproductive systems. In reproduction eggs and sperm are not freely shed into the water; instead worms pair up and exchange gametes via internal fertilization.

As in the platyhelminthes, roundworms (Nematoda) have bilateral symmetry and cephalization, plus the added feature of a digestive tract, or gut tube, with a mouth and an anus. A fluid-filled pseudocoelom surrounds the endoderm, and separates the endoderm from the mesoderm and ectoderm. This fluid space serves as a cushion and permits reproductive and digestive organs to grow to a larger size. Examples include common roundworms, hookworms, and whipworms.

Mollusks have a gill system for gas exchange and a heart and open circulatory system with sinus cavities. These are advances beyond more primitive phyla, where simple diffusion is the mechanism for the exchange of gases, nutrients, and wastes. Examples are gastropods (snails and slugs), bivalves (clams, oysters, mussels), and cepalopods (squid, octopus).

Segmented worms of the Annelida have a closed circulatory system that carries blood in vessels or tubes throughout major portions of the body. Contracting hearts are present. In the digestive tract, a crop temporarily stores food and a gizzard grinds it. The body segments permit partial separation of cells; excretory nephridia in each segment remove excess water and wastes from the body. Because of these specializations, segmented roundworms can grow larger than other worms. Example: common earthworms.

The Arthropoda encompass a tremendously varied and diverse assortment of animals that have the ability to move rapidly (specialized muscles) in directed, controlled ways (specialized nervous systems). They have protective exoskeletons of chitin and well-developed digestive systems. Specialized appendages of the mouth, head, and thorax enable these animals to effectively exploit a variety of ecological niches. Examples: spiders, shrimp, bees, ants, butterflies.

Echinoderms are the first animal group to be characterized as deuterostomes, with a radial pattern of early embryonic development in which the first indentation forms an anus. Furthermore, this is the first phylum to possess an internal skeleton (endoskeleton). Examples are sea urchins, sea stars, and sea lilies.

2. Protostomes and deuterostomes are terms that relate to two separate developmental pathways in animals. The protostomes include mollusks, annelids, and arthropods; the deuterostomes include the echinoderms and chordates. *Protostome* means "early or first mouth," and members of this group undergo spiral embryonic cleavage. The first indentation of a protostome embryo forms the animal's mouth. *Deuterostome* means "false mouth," and animals in this group undergo radial cleavage. The first embryonic indentation in deuterostome forms an anus.

   Open and closed circulatory systems: In an open circulatory system, fluid or blood escapes vessels or channels into open tissue spaces or sinuses. In contrast, a closed circulatory system has fluid-blood that typically is contained inside vessels and never escapes. The human circulatory system and that of earthworms are examples of closed circulation. The molluscs have open circulatory systems. The main purpose of a circulatory system is to carry nutrients and oxygen to tissues and to remove wastes.

   Cephalization: Cephalization is the concentration of nerves and sensory organs at the anterior or front end of the organism. In essence it represents the trend toward formation of a "brain," or major neuron cluster up front. Visual and olfactory responses are among the most important of the initial cephalization characteristics.

   Endoskeleton and exoskeleton: These each represent structural support for the animal body. The exoskeleton also serves as external protection; examples include mollusk shells of calcium carbonate and the chitin exoskeleton of insects. The first true endoskeleton appears in the Echinodermata. Human endoskeletons of bone (calcium phosphate) protect some internal organs (heart and lungs) and are points of attachments for tendons and muscles used in walking, running, and other activities.

Self-Test

1. e	2. d	3. b	4. e	5. b	6. d	7. b	8. e
9. ab	10. ad	11. a	12. ab	13. ad	14. d	15. ad	16. e
17. ae	18. ad	19. ac	20. a	21. b	22. b	23. a	24. b
25. b	26. a	27. b	28. b	29. a	30. b	31. a	32. a
33. b	34. a	35. a	36. b	37. a	38. b	39. b	40. a
41. a	42. a	43. a	44. a	45. a	46. e	47. b	48. b
49. b	50. a	51. b	52. a	53. a	54. a	55. a	56. a
57. b	58. b	59. b	60. a	61. a	62. a	63. a	64. a
65. b	66. a	67. b	68. b	69. a	70. b	71. a	72. b
73. c	74. a	75. ac	76. b	77. d	78. a	79. ad	80. c
81. ab	82. e						

Chapter 19

Thought Provokers

1. The primate family tree starts with the suborders Prosimii (lemurs, tarsiers, sifakas, among others) and the Anthropoidea (Old and New World Monkeys, chimpanzees, and humans). Most early primates were carnivores (insectivores) and were small tree-dwellers with opposable thumbs, a well-developed nervous system, and excellent stereoscopic vision. Later primates were similar in character but had more developed muscle systems; they began to assume a more upright position in trees and when moving about. Furthermore, their diets included increased amounts of vegetable materials and their back teeth (molars) became flattened and adapted for an omnivorous diet of animal and vegetable matter. Proconsul africanus, humanlike primates or hominoids, lived in Africa and spread throughout Africa, the Middle East, India, and Europe. *Dryopithecus*, *Ramapithecus*, and *Sivapithecus* represent hominoids from these regions. Fossil evidence of *Australopithecus afarensis* shows that these creatures of about 3.5 million years ago were small, upright walkers with teeth adapted to a vegetarian diet, an apelike skull, and brains similar in size to those of chimpanzees. *Homo habilis* is believed to have evolved from australopithecenes about 2 million years ago. These individuals were taller (1.5 m) and had larger brain capacity (700 cc) than their predecessors; they used stone and wood tools and ate meat. *Homo erectus* lived about 1.6 m.y.a. and showed some maturation of the human skeleton with a later puberty. Finally, about 1.5 m.y.a., *Homo sapiens* appeared. Early Neandertal and Cro-Magnon

types were characterized by brains of 1200–1400 cc. These individuals lived in communities, had diverse tools, wore cloths, and lived in specially built and varied shelters. Some hunted; others farmed.

2. Chordate evolution can be traced in the following sequence: (1) *Tunicates* (Urochordata)—notochords present in larvae but disappear in adults. (2) *Lancelets* (Cephalochordata)—notochords in larvae/ adults. (3) *Fishes*—the earliest vertebrates. Gill-filter feeders at first, followed by well-developed jaw-feeders. Cold-blooded. No lungs. Gill respiration. Simple heart. (4) *Amphibians*—cold-blooded animals with dual water/land habitat. Gills in water stage of development; lungs for land-adapted phase of life cycle. Require water for reproduction. In many species major respiration occurs through moist skin. Three-chambered heart permits some separation of oxygenated and deoxygenated blood. (5) *Reptiles*—cold-blooded animals with well-developed rib cage and lungs. Cleidoic egg permits reproduction on land. Heart structure permits a greater degree of separation of oxygenated and deoxygenated blood. (6) *Birds*—warm-blooded vertebrates. Lay eggs on land. Well-developed four-chambered heart; oxygenated and deoxygenated blood are completely separated. Efficient lungs with attendant air sacs. (7) *Mammals*—warm-blooded vertebrates. Four-chambered, well-developed heart. Produce milk and have hair or fur. Very diverse, varied and successful.

Self-Test

1. c	2. a	3. b	4. c	5. d	6. ab	7. e	8. b
9. d	10. b	11. ae	12. d	13. ac	14. b	15. a	16. d
17. ae	18. ab	19. b	20. a	21. d	22. ae	23. b	24. d
25. e	26. e	27. e	28. e	29. a	30. b	31. a	32. b
33. a	34. a	35. a	36. a	37. a	38. b	39. a	40. b
41. b	42. b	43. a	44. b	45. a	46. a	47. b	48. a
49. a	50. b	51. d	52. a				

Chapter 20

Thought Provokers

1. Negative and positive feedback systems are vital for the regulation and control of living systems. Both have the same three basic components: A receptor receives the stimulus; an integrator interprets the stimulus or signal; an effector renders a response, which may be voluntary or involuntary. Example: If a person's hand touches a hot burner the heat stimulus will send a message to the nerves, which automatically cause muscles to pull the hand away from the burner. This is a negative feedback loop, which acts to reduce or eliminate what caused the response in the first place. An example of a positive feedback is the oxytocin hormone response that stimulates uterine contractions; like all such loops, the response—uterine contractions—stimulates further change, in this case, more oxytocin release.

2. Homeostasis is a condition of physiological normalcy or equilibrium that provides optimum conditions for cell functioning. Ion concentrations and temperature are just two of the parameters that homeostatic mechanisms work to maintain. When the system strays too far from physiological equilibrium, cell functioning is endangered; in extreme cases the result may be death.

Self-Test

1. b	2. a	3. d	4. c,d	5. a	6. a	7. b	8. a
9. a	10. b	11. b	12. a	13. a	14. a	15. b	

Chapter 21

Thought Provokers

1. Circulation within the animal kingdom shows varied types of specialization. In the amoeba, circulation is based on passive diffusion or active transport across a selectively permeable membrane. However, as an animal becomes more complex, with more layers of tissue, simple diffusion will no longer suffice. In these cases some type of blood and channel system is necessary to penetrate tissues so as to supply nutrients and oxygen and remove wastes. Arthropods and mollusks have open circulatory systems with hemolymph but no developed channel system for delivery. The simplest closed circulatory system is characterized by separate vessels that transport materials toward and away from the heart.

   Fish have a two-chambered heart with an auricle that receives blood from the general circulation via veins and a ventricle that pumps blood out to the gills and then through the body via arteries. This is a single loop system.

   Amphibians and reptiles have a three-chambered heart with two atria and one ventricle. The ventricle pumps blood to the lungs and the general body circulation via arteries. Blood returns to the heart via veins from the lungs and the general body circulation. Lung blood delivered via veins empties into one atrium, while deoxygenated blood from the general body circulation returns via the other atrium. Both oxygenated and deoxygenated blood mix in the ventricle.

   The most complex circulatory system is found in mammals. The mammalian heart has four chambers, two atria and two ventricles. Each chamber is separated from the others by valves. The left ventricle pumps blood out through the aorta, the major artery for blood delivery to the general body circulation. Blood from the general circulation returns via the veins to the right atrium and then passes through a valve into the right ventricle. The right ventricle pumps blood to the lungs, where it is oxygenated. Blood returns via the pulmonary veins to the left atrium and then passes into the left ventricle, from where it is pumped to the rest of the body. This circulatory system is highly specialized and efficient. There is no mixing of oxygenated and deoxygenated blood.

2. Atherosclerosis is a disease caused by hardening of the arteries, which have become clogged and less flexible due to the accumulation of excess cholesterol-lipid complexes on the inner lining of the arterial walls. Narrowing of the walls causes blood pressure to increase. Actual blood flow may decrease, leading to diminished supply of oxygen and blood to tissues. If the heart muscle is deprived of oxygen and nourishment, the muscle will slowly die. If an artery becomes completely occluded, a heart attack may result. Death occurs if too much heart muscle is damaged. Even if the heart attack is not fatal, part of the heart muscle is damaged. Since heart disease is an important medical problem, the relationship of diet (what food is eaten), metabolism (how it is burned or used), and exercise have been investigated. Apparently, diets that are low in saturated fats and cholesterol are more healthful than diets high in animal fat and cholesterol.

   Although cholesterol is a normal component of all cell membranes, excess amounts are dangerous. In recent times, study of the relationship of low-density and high-density lipids (LDL and HDL) to cholesterol levels indicates that a high HDL:LDL ratio signifies that much of the cholesterol is handled effectively by the body. Individuals who have few LDL receptors for capturing and processing cholesterol, plus high levels of LDL, are more subject to atherosclerosis and heart disease.

   Diets that are rich in meat, milk, and eggs tend to promote heart disease in susceptible individuals. Lowering dietary intake of high-lipid and high-cholesterol foods and increasing consumption of vegetables, fish, and brans can maintain lower cholesterol levels in heart-disease–prone persons. Regular and properly managed exercise maintains cardiovascular fitness and good health.

Self-Test

1. d	2. c	3. b	4. d	5. b	6. e	7. a	8. c
9. a	10. b	11. b	12. b	13. a,b,e	14. b	15. a	16. a
17. ab	18. b	19. c	20. e	21. a	22. a	23. ab	24. d

25. c	26. b	27. e	28. a	29. ab	30. b	31. a	32. b
33. b	34. a	35. a	36. a	37. b	38. b	39. b	40. c
41. b	42. c	43. a	44. b	45. b	46. a	47. b	48. b
49. e	50. b	51. a	52. b	53. b	54. a	55. a	56. b
57. a	58. a	59. b	60. a	61. a	62. c		

Chapter 22

Thought Provoker

1. An intact immune system can detect foreign materials or antigens and determine whether they are harmful. At the same time, the immune system normally does not react against its own tissues. This phenomenon is called the recognition of "self" versus "nonself." The immune system is composed of monocytes (macrophages) and T- and B-lymphocytes. B-cells make antibodies. These proteins are produced by specific B-cells that react with specific foreign antigens. Almost 100 million antigen combinations are possible, and an approximately equal number of antibodies can be made that can react with these antigens. An animal's body contains "self" antigens, but B-cells and their clones that are specific for "self" are eliminated or die out. B-cells specific for foreign antigens survive. T-cells either suppress or help the survivor B-cells in their antibody-producing activities. When a foreign antigen enters the body, monocytes attack the antigen and process it. Next, they present these foreign antigens on their surfaces to B- and T-cells, which respond to the antigens. B-cells make antibodies and helper-T cells make other substances, such as B-cell growth factors and differentiation factors, interleukin-2 to stimulate cytotoxic T-cells, interleukin-3 to stimulate differentiation of leukocytes in the bone marrow, and interferon.

Self-Test

1. a	2. b	3. b	4. b	5. e	6. b	7. d	8. d
9. c	10. b	11. a	12. d	13. b	14. a,c	15. c	16. c
17. d	18. e	19. d	20. a	21. a	22. b	23. d	24. b
25. a	26. b	27. a	28. b	29. e	30. a	31. c	32. b
33. b	34. e	35. b,c	36. a	37. c	38. b	39. d	40. b

Chapter 23

Thought Provokers

1. If the world were totally anaerobic, it would be very different from the oxygen-dependent world we see in higher plants and animals. In animals, no respiratory tracts would be needed to deliver oxygen to tissue sites. Tissues would function completely normally without oxygen, and tissues at an animal's surface would function as well as those deep in the animal. However, a means of ridding the body of accumulated wastes and delivering essential nutrients would still be necessary. A circulatory system without oxygen carriers such as hemoglobin or myoglobin would probably be typical.

2. Table: Types of animal respiratory systems

Animal	Characteristics of respiratory system
Amoeba	Simple membrane with passive diffusion of gases into and out of cell.
Flatworms	Simple diffusion of gases across membranes and into tissue spaces. Passive diffusion from high-concentration areas to low-concentration areas.
Insects	Spiracles (pores) with tracheae leading into body cavity and connecting with capillaries. Hemolymph carrier of oxygen.
Fish	Gills with countercurrent circulation mechanism to permit optimal exchanges of gases. Blood as an oxygen carrier.
Amphibians	Primitive lungs with tidal flow and gas exchange mechanism. Blood oxygen carrier.
Birds	Air sacs and lungs that maximize gas exchange with constant flow mechanism and no tidal volume. Blood as an oxygen carrier.
Mammals	Classic lungs with in-and-out ventilation, i.e., tidal volume. Gases move by diffusion from regions of highest concentration to regions of lowest concentration.

Self-Test

1. a	2. a	3. b	4. b	5. a	6. a	7. b	8. a
9. b	10. a	11. a	12. b	13. c	14. d	15. b	16. d
17. a	18. b	19. c	20. a	21. c	22. a	23. a	24. c
25. b	26. a	27. b	28. a	29. e	30. b	31. a	32. b
33. a	34. b	35. a	36. a	37. a	38. a	39. b	40. b
41. b	42. a						

Chapter 24

Thought Provokers

1. The ability of an organism to use various foods or nutrients depends on its biochemistry—or, more specifically, on its enzymes. In turn, the enzymes of an organism are determined by its genes. For example, plants can make complex nucleic acids, proteins, lipids, and carbohydrates from simple inorganic nutrients such as carbon dioxide, water, and minerals. They can fix carbon dioxide into organic molecules and also convert ammonia and nitrates/nitrites into amino acids, proteins, and nucleic acids. All these conversions and biochemical transformations are dependent on enzymes present in a plant. In contrast, humans cannot convert carbon dioxide or ammonia and nitrates into organic compounds. Humans require preformed organic carbon molecules, such as sugars (glucose, sucrose) and starches, for basic energy needs. They must also consume in the diet essential amino acids—those that the body cannot synthesize. Hence, humans lack the enzymes necessary to effect the synthesis of all the compounds critical for life. Another obvious contrast: Plants are autotrophic in their nutrition, humans heterotrophic. The presence or absence of certain genes determines the capabilities of each organism's metabolism. Although the maxim "You are what you eat" is essentially correct, a more appropriate maxim might be "You are what you metabolize."

2. The nutrition/digestion of humans and amoebae are similar in the following ways: (1) Each organism is a heterotroph; (2) both ingest food in large, whole pieces; and (3) both use enzymes to break down the food into smaller pieces.

   Differences: (1) The amoeba has no mouth and ingests food by way of pseudopodia. Food is egested in vacuoles; there is no digestive tract with a mouth and anus. Humans have a mouth for taking in food, and a complete digestive tract with an anus through which wastes are expelled. (2) Digestion in the amoeba occurs in vacuoles only. Digestion in humans begins in the mouth, where amylase enzymes are released from the salivary glands. In the stomach, HCl and pepsin start the breakdown of protein. Digestion continues in the small intestine, where many enzymes break down carbohydrates, proteins, lipids, and nucleic acids. Organs such as the liver and pancreas produce enzymes and molecules essential for digestive processes. Because humans are complex multicellular organisms, the circulatory system transports digested material throughout the body to all body cells. In an amoeba, simple diffusion suffices to deliver materials from the food vacuole to the interior regions of the single-celled creature. Another significant digestive difference is that in humans a number of digestive processes are regulated by hormones.

Self-Test

1. b	2. b	3. c	4. a	5. b	6. b	7. b	8. c
9. a	10. c	11. a	12. d	13. a	14. d	15. c	16. c
17. c	18. a	19. c	20. a	21. c	22. c	23. d	24. c
25. c	26. a	27. a	28. b	29. a	30. a	31. c	32. d
33. ac	34. a	35. b	36. bc	37. d	38. e	39. ab	40. a
41. e	42. d	43. a	44. a	45. a	46. b	47. c	48. d
49. b	50. e	51. d	52. e	53. c	54. e	55. e	56. a
57. b	58. d	59. b	60. a	61. b	62. a	63. a	64. c
65. b	66. a	67. b	68. ab	69. b	70. a	71. b	72. b
73. c	74. a	75. a	76. c	77. a	78. a	79. e	80. ab
81. ac	82. ad	83. a	84. c	85. e			

Chapter 25

Thought Provokers

1. No human can live without kidneys or a substitute such as medical dialysis therapy. When a person's kidneys fail, it is impossible for the skin alone to rid the body of all urea and other fluid metabolic wastes that have accumulated in the blood. These wastes must be removed, or death results. In dialysis therapy the patient's venous blood is directed into a dialysis chamber, where filters remove wastes. The blood is then returned to the body via an artery. Dialysis must be performed several times a week. A kidney transplant is the only alternative to dialysis.

2. The prime components of a human kidney are the approximately 1 million nephrons. Each nephron includes a Bowman's capsule; the proximal convoluted tubule; the descending limb; the loop of Henle; the ascending limb; the distal convoluted tubule; and collecting ducts. Veins and arteries that carry blood are an intimate part of the whole kidney structure. The capillary blood supply (glomerulus) is enveloped by podocytes from Bowman's capsule. Due to capillary pressure, fluid is expressed from the blood into the capsule, which is a small collecting sac for the initial urine. Next, in the convoluted proximal tubule, with its long, twisting structure, Na^+, Cl^-, sugars, and amino acids are actively transported back into the blood. Urine next flows to the descending limb, which is permeable to water. Because the region surrounding the limb is hypertonic, water leaves the descending limb. The ascending limb actively pumps out Cl^-, and Na^+ passively follows. The ascending limb is not freely permeable to water; hence there is little water loss at this site. The ascending limb then connects with

the collecting ducts, which are permeable to water. The urine is concentrated (carrying urea and some salts) as it passes into the renal pelvis and the ureters, which connect to the bladder.

3. The internal environment of a freshwater fish is hyperosmotic relative to the water in which the fish swims; hence, there is a net gain of water. Such fish produce urine to rid themselves of wastes and excess water, and in the process lose some salt. Salt uptake occurs by active transport in the gills. Saltwater fish are hypoosmotic relative to the water in which they swim; hence, there is a net loss of water from the body. The fish drink salt water to compensate, and as a result their bodies tend to accumulate salt. This excess salt is excreted through the gills. In humans, the amount of urine is regulated by either increased or decreased water uptake in the distal tubules. ADH, made by the hypothalamus and stored in the pituitary, precisely regulates this process. When there is a need to conserve water, ADH is released and the distal tubules take up more water. When there is excess water in the body, ADH is not released, water uptake slows, and consequently a greater volume of water passes out of the body. In addition, aldosterone can increase the uptake of sodium ions and corresponding water uptake while increasing the secretion of K^+ in the urine.

Self-Test

1. a	2. a	3. b	4. b	5. b	6. d	7. c	8. b
9. d	10. c	11. a	12. d	13. b	14. c	15. e	16. c
17. b	18. a,c	19. a	20. b	21. b	22. e	23. ac	24. b
25. d	26. b	27. ad	28. ab	29. ac	30. ad	31. ae	32. d
33. a	34. b	35. a	36. b	37. b	38. a	39. b	40. b
41. a	42. e	43. a	44. a	45. b	46. a	47. a	48. a
49. c	50. b	51. b	52. a	53. a			

Chapter 26

Thought Provokers

1. Common human diseases related to hormonal deficiencies include diabetes, goiter, and cretinism. Diabetes is a condition of excess sugar in the blood due to inadequate amounts of insulin. The beta cells of the pancreas do not make enough insulin and hence sugar cannot move from the blood and tissue spaces into cells. Symptoms include excessive urination, thirst, and itching of the skin; the disease can be life-threatening if not treated with injected insulin or insulin implants.

Goiter and cretinism are diseases related to thyroid hypofunction. In goiter, there is deficiency of iodine, which is needed for the production of thyroxin; when iodine is supplied the disease is effectively cured. In cretinism the thyroid does not produce enough thyroxin. This results in sluggishness, low body temperature, and poor metabolism of proteins and carbohydrates. The disease can be treated via regular injections of thyroxin.

2. Human hormones compared to those of lower animals: Chemically, the hormones of humans and lower animals show some biochemical relatedness; in both groups they include polypeptides, steroids or steroidlike hormones, and hormones with fatty acid components. However, hormones in humans and, say, insects, function in different ways: They act differently on target cells, and effect different responses. In terms of numbers and types of hormones and major hormone-producing organs, humans possess large numbers of varied hormones produced by a range of organs; in lower animals, the numbers, types, and sources of hormones are much more limited.

3. Epinephrine is released from the adrenal glands under the influence of the pituitary gland, which secretes ACTH. The epinephrine travels via the bloodstream to specific target cells, which have receptors for the hormone. The epinephrine then attaches to target sites on these cells. With attachment, shape changes occur in the receptor, a nearby transducer (G-protein), and, finally, in an amplifier

enzyme, adenyl cyclase. Internally, a second messenger activates one or more enzymes in the cell. Thus, a hormone can have multiple, cascading effects on a variety of other cellular substances.

Self-Test

1. a	2. a	3. b	4. a	5. b	6. b	7. b	8. a
9. a	10. a	11. c	12. b	13. a	14. d	15. a	16. a
17. c	18. a	19. b	20. d	21. c	22. d	23. d	24. c
25. e	26. e	27. c	28. e	29. e	30. b	31. a	32. ab
33. b	34. a	35. a	36. e	37. d	38. ae	39. a	40. ac
41. e	42. ae	43. e	44. c	45. ac	46. b	47. a	48. b
49. d	50. c	51. e	52. d	53. e	54. b	55. b	

Chapter 27

Thought Provokers

1. Nerves fire according to the principle of "all or none," which means that the nerve will either fire or not fire, and that once activated the entire nerve cell will fire. A typical resting nerve cell has a resting potential of approximately -70 mV. This potential is the result of the charge distribution inside and outside the nerve cell. There is an overall net positive charge outside the cell and a net negative charge inside. Sodium channels do not permit sodium to leak out of the neuron, whereas potassium channels do permit some leakage of potassium. The sodium-potassium pump pushes "lost" ions back into the cell. When a nerve cell is activated, some sodium channels open and the potential of the nerve cell in that region is changed, becoming less negatively charged. The cell is depolarized when the charge distribution reverses (the outside of the neuron becomes negative and the inside becomes positive). The response continues along the nerve, in sequence, and the action potential is generated. Tetrodotoxin is a sodium-ion channel blocker that blocks the nerve-firing response and can kill a person, if taken in high enough dose. In myelinated nerves, ions can flow only across the gap region known as the *nodes of Ranvier*. In these myelinated nerves, impulses can rapidly leap from one gap to another.

---

2. Comparison of rapid-relay synapses and slow-relay synapses:

	Rapid-relay Synapses	Slow-relay Synapses
Advantages	1. Very quick response	1. Moderated and modified responses possible
	2. Life-saving or injury-saving response possible	2. Can be adjusted to circumstance, and modified
Disadvantage	Fixed, not modifiable	Slow
Transmission Type	Electrical synapse	Chemical synapses and neurotransmitters

---

Self-Test

1. e	2. a	3. a	4. b	5. a	6. a	7. b	8. a
9. b	10. b	11. a	12. a	13. b	14. b	15. b	16. a

17. b   18. a   19. c   20. b   21. d   22. b   23. b   24. b
25. a   26. a   27. a   28. b   29. b   30. a

Chapter 28

Thought Provokers

1. The human nervous system is extremely complex and well-integrated. The brain and spinal cord form the central nervous system (CNS), which processes incoming signals and sends out its own signals to the peripheral nervous system. Through the CNS the major sensory systems of vision, hearing, olfaction, taste, and skin sensation must be processed and interpreted. Sensory neurons pass information through the dorsal ganglia of the spinal cord, where interneuronal synapses occur. Some impulses travel to the brain for interpretation, whereas other impulses pass through the ventral spinal root to signal various muscles. The ventral root motor neurons stimulate the somatic nervous system muscles that are under voluntary control, and also the autonomic nervous system muscles that are not under voluntary control. Two groups of autonomic neurons function in the body—the sympathetic (norepinephrine) system and the parasympathetic (acetylcholine) system. Norepinephrine (noradrenalin) speeds up organ activities, whereas acetylcholine tends to slow down these activities. The parasympathetic system maintains blood pressure, intestinal activity, and heart and lung functions at normal levels. In times of stress or danger the sympathetic system causes decreased intestinal activity and more rapid heart beat and respiration. These mechanisms all enhance an organism's chances for survival.

2. In recent years researchers have made a number of interesting discoveries about the brain. One is that the brain is asymmetrical: Different functional activities reside in different brain regions. Similarly, biologists now know that there is essentially a left and a right brain, each controlling the opposite side of the body. Damage to selected areas of the brain can produce strange effects, including the failure to recognize faces, while the ability to recognize voices remains. Right-side parietal lobe injury may result in failure to recognize the left side of the body as one's own. Damage to the hippocampus results in failure to establish memory of recent events, whereas memory prior to the injury remains intact. Damage to language centers (such as after a stroke) may result in the inability to speak even though understanding of written and spoken communication of others remains unaffected.

Self-Test

1. a	2. e	3. a	4. b	5. e	6. b	7. a	8. a
9. b	10. a	11. e	12. d	13. a	14. c	15. b	16. a
17. a	18. a	19. a	20. a	21. b	22. e	23. c	24. d
25. b	26. ac	27. a	28. ab	29. abcde	30. c	31. ab	32. a
33. b	34. a	35. b	36. a	37. b	38. b	39. a	40. b

Chapter 29

Thought Provokers

---

1. Features of muscle

Type of Muscle	Where Found	Morphology	Function
Skeletal	All over the body	Striated sarcomere not connected in network	Voluntary movement
Smooth	Digestive tract, blood vessels, bladder		Involuntary movement
Cardiac	Heart	Striated sarcomere connected in network	Pumping of blood

---

2. Bending your little finger is a voluntary action. Overall, it takes place when the nerve-to-muscle signal generates an action potential that reaches the synaptic junction and causes acetylcholine release at the nerve ending. The sequence of events is: nerve $\rightarrow$ action potential $\rightarrow$ acetylcholine released $\rightarrow$ muscle $\rightarrow$ action potential $\rightarrow$ from surface to tubules into $\rightarrow$ sarcoplasmic reticulum $\rightarrow$ Ca^{++} released $\rightarrow$ troponin and tropomyosin released from actin fibrils $\rightarrow$ myosin head regions bind to actin + ATP $\rightarrow$ actin pulled past myosin, and muscle contracts $\rightarrow$ ATP pump restores Ca^{++} to sarcoplasmic reticulum, and troponin and tropomyosin bind again to actin.

3. Any muscular contraction requires a great deal of energy; continued muscle contraction requires even more. This energy is supplied in a series of responses: (a) *Initial response*—free, available ATP is used for contraction. (b) *Second response*—creatine phosphate transfers PO^4 to ADP $\rightarrow$ ATP. (c) *Tertiary response*—within minutes the cell supplies more ATP, via glycolysis, for a short time. (d) *Quaternary response*—the Krebs cycle and electron transport generate large amounts of ATP.

4. Slow-twitch and fast-twitch fibers compare as follows: *Slow-twitch fibers* are deep red, with many mitochondria, and are rich in myoglobin. They are characteristic of highly oxygenated muscles, have high Krebs activity, and function in extended contractions. *Fast-twitch fibers* are white and rich in Actin-myosin. They are involved in quick and strong responses, and get energy from glycolysis.

5. Nervous and endocrine systems regulate physical activity. Exercise stimulates heart rate. Increased turnover of nutrients, including sugars, starches, fats, and proteins. Muscles enlarge and thicken. With regular, consistent, and proper exercise, heart stroke volume increases and resting heart rate decreases. There is increased efficiency of oxygen storage by myoglobin. Mitochondria become branched and more efficient at extracting energy from food substrates. Endorphins released during exercise reduce pain and provide an increased sense of well-being. During vigorous exercise the hypothalamus signals the body, via the sympathetic nervous system, to raise blood glucose and fatty acids; increase breathing, heart rate, and blood pressure; and divert blood from involuntary to voluntary muscles. All of these events contribute to a healthier and more responsive body.

Self-Test

1. a	2. a	3. a	4. a	5. b	6. a	7. b	8. a
9. b	10. a	11. a	12. a	13. a	14. d	15. b	16. b
17. d	18. b	19. e	20. a	21. a	22. b	23. a	24. b
25. a	26. b	27. e	28. d	29. e	30. c		

Chapter 30

Thought Provokers

1. Leaves, stem, and roots are integrated parts of a plant that each contribute to the plant's survival. The leaves are the main photosynthetic organs. They are also essential gas exchange structures that permit CO_2 to enter and oxygen to escape during photosynthesis, and the reverse to occur during respiration. Leaves receive water and minerals absorbed by the root hairs and roots and transported by xylem elements throughout the stem. The stem holds the plant upright and contains meristematic regions that permit plant growth. The stem supports leaves and may have branches from which other leaves are formed; it also supports flowers and fruits. The stem has xylem and phloem elements that are continuous with the leaves and also the roots. This channel system enables water and minerals to be transported upward and food such as sugars and amino acids to be transported to regions of lower concentration in the stem and roots.

2. (a) The *Casparian strip* is found in the endodermis of roots; because of its waxy nature it prohibits the movement of water from one endodermal cell to the next. As a result, water moves across the epidermis of root hairs to the cortex, thence to the endodermis, and finally into the vascular elements. (b) *Stomata* are openings in leaves, usually on the underside, formed by two guard cells that open and close to regulate the passage of gases and water vapor. (c) *Meristem tissue* is a region of active cell division at the tips of stems and roots. It is responsible for the elongation of the stem and roots. (d) *Cambium* is an active region of cell division in stems and roots that is responsible for growth in the girth of both structures. (e) A perfect *flower* is a structure with sepals, petals, and both male and female parts. The latter include stigma, style, ovary, and (male) stamens (anthers and filaments). Example: pea flower.

Self-Test

1. a	2. b	3. e	4. a	5. c	6. b	7. b	8. b
9. c	10. c	11. b	12. c	13. a	14. c	15. a	16. b
17. b	18. a	19. b	20. a	21. b	22. a	23. b	24. b
25. a	26. a	27. b	28. a	29. c	30. a	31. b	32. a
33. b	34. a	35. b	36. a	37. a	38. b	39. a	40. d
41. a	42. b	43. a	44. a	45. b	46. d	47. b	48. a
49. e	50. c	51. e	52. a	53. a	54. b	55. d	56. d
57. c	58. a	59. d	60. e				

Chapter 31

Thought Provokers

1. Plant and Animal Hormones Compared and Contrasted

	Plants	Animals
Functions affected	Growth, cell division	Same
	Abscission	Reproduction
	Flowering	Development
	Metabolism/physiology	Same
Mode of action	Generally related to growth responses	Varied

Continues

1. Plant and Animal Hormones Compared and Contrasted (continued)

	Plants	Animals
Differences	Slow acting	Rapid, quick responses
Target sites	General and broad regions of tissue	Specific tissues
Examples	Auxin, gibberellins, ethylene	ACTH, cortisol, insulin, thyroxin

2. *Phototropism* is the tendency of a plant or plant parts to grow or move toward light. These responses are mediated by auxins, which trigger extensive elongation and growth in regions where the auxins are most abundant. *Flowering* is a physiological-biochemical response to phytochrome and to environmental signals. As your text describes, phytochrome acts as a "timer" that measures day-length, a crucial factor in many species for regulating the maturation of certain tissues into reproductive structures (flowers). *Bud maturation* depends on auxins. Apical buds produce auxin that inhibits the development/maturation of lateral buds in a plant. The distribution of auxins in trees is responsible for their ultimate shape. In conical trees such as firs the apical bud is strongly dominant and inhibits lateral bud development. Deciduous trees have a more bushy and expanded appearance that is related, again, to auxin distribution. The apical bud is less dominant, and cytokinins moving upward from the root counteract the effects of auxin inhibition. *Seed germination* is controlled by inhibitors present in the seed that prevent growth hormones from functioning until environmental conditions are appropriate. Cold periods or light-dark cycles as well as specific moisture conditions must be present to destroy or remove these inhibitors. When this happens a seed will germinate to form the new plant.

Self-Test

1. c	2. b	3. a	4. b	5. e	6. a	7. c	8. a
9. b	10. e	11. d	12. a	13. d	14. a	15. a	16. a
17. a	18. e	19. b	20. e	21. a	22. b	23. a	24. b
25. a							

Chapter 32

Thought Provokers

1. The circulatory systems of plants and animals are similar in some ways (mainly function) and distinctly different in other ways.

	Plants	Animals
Similarities:	Food (nutrients) and water are distributed to tissues throughout organism. Distribution takes place via channels and specialized cells.	
Differences:		
Circulatory "motor"	No pump; osmotic differences essential for circulation	Heart muscle pump
Circulation rate	Slow	Relatively rapid
Channel system	Phloem and xylem	Veins, arteries, capillaries
Special carriers	None	Hemoglobin for O_2

2. Classical methods of plant breeding have been and will continue to be highly useful for developing improved varieties. They are well understood and reliable and require no elaborate laboratory machinery or techniques. Nevertheless, these methods have limitations: They are slower than some of the new genetic engineering and recombinant DNA approaches to generating new strains, and only certain kinds of crosses, generally between closely related plants, are possible. On the other hand, with the new technologies it is possible to excise desirable genes from one organism and insert them into the genomes of recipient plants. For example, a gene for salt tolerance can be transferred from a plant adapted to saline soil conditions to another, unrelated plant—say, tomato. Once the salt-tolerance gene is isolated, the next step is to insert it into bacterial plasmids, which in turn serve as vectors for carrying the gene into the DNA of the recipient species. This and other new methods greatly expand the range of genetic alterations on which researchers can call as they try to develop improved plant varieties.

3. Water is pulled upwards from a tree's roots by means of a transpiration-pull mechanism. Water molecules present in the tree's xylem channels tend to adhere to each other and to the walls of the channels in chainlike fashion. As water at the "top" of the chain evaporates by transpiration, the remaining molecules in the chain move upward. New water molecules enter the chain at the root.

Self-Test

1. b	2. b	3. b	4. a	5. b	6. a	7. b	8. a
9. b	10. b	11. b	12. b	13. a	14. a	15. b	16. d
17. bc	18. ae	19. a	20. e	21. ab	22. ac	23. ad	24. c
25. c							

Chapter 33

Thought Provokers

1. An organism's genotype is its genetic library. The genes in this library determine the organism's biochemical and physiological characters. From a biological perspective, then, what an organism can and cannot do is prescribed by its genes and the proteins that can be made by those genes. "Survivability" is related to factors in the environment such as temperature ranges and the availability of food/nutrients. If an organism is capable of exploiting or using a particular environment as habitat, it will survive and prosper. If the environment becomes harmful (too many predators, not enough of the right nutrients, presence of toxic substances), organisms may soon die and whole species may become extinct. Alternatively, a species' genome may include variant alleles that permit some individuals to survive in an altered environment.

2. The frequency of genes/alleles in populations can be changed in a number of significant ways, including: (1) Mutation, which creates new alleles in a species' genome. These mutant genes may become predominant or significant in the population, especially if there are special advantages to the organisms that possess the new genes. (2) Emigration of individuals out of the population, which may remove a gene or genes from the genome. (3) Immigration into the population of new individuals, which may introduce novel genes. (4) The loss of genes due to selection against a certain genotype; for example, a light-colored variety of a plant, rather than a dark-pigmented variety, may be eaten preferentially by insects. (5) In a small population, any dramatic change such as large-scale death, emigration, or immigration can cause major fluctuations in the gene pool.

Self-Test

1. b	2. a	3. a	4. e	5. b	6. a	7. d	8. b
9. e	10. a	11. a	12. b	13. a	14. b	15. a	16. a

17. b	18. b	19. c	20. a	21. b	22. a	23. b	24. a
25. b	26. a	27. b	28. a	29. d	30. d	31. a	32. a
33. b	34. c	35. a	36. c	37. a	38. e	39. d	40. e
41. b	42. a	43. c	44. d	45. e			

Chapter 34

Thought Provokers

1. Limits on the global distribution of any group of organisms include physical and geographical factors, such as availability of food, water, and living space, and geographical barriers, such as mountain ranges and rivers, as well as limits imposed by the presence or absence of other species, such as predators.

2. Some 2,000 years ago the Hohokam Indians lived in the Arizona desert in successful agrarian communities that eventually included almost a million people. The Hohokams used "high technology"—irrigation techniques—to provide water for crops that supported their growing population. However, possibly due to ecological changes such as drought and the accumulation of alkali salts in the soil, Hohokam crops eventually began to fail. The Hohokam may also have exhausted other resources of their desert home, such as firewood. As a result the population probably suffered starvation and associated disease that led to its subsequent crash. Like all populations of organisms, the Hohokam eventually had to confront the limits imposed by finite resources.

Self-Test

1. b	2. e	3. c	4. b	5. c	6. a	7. a	8. a
9. a	10. a	11. b	12. c	13. c	14. b	15. c	16. b
17. b	18. a	19. a	20. a	21. b	22. e	23. b	24. d
25. c	26. a	27. a	28. a	29. b	30. b	31. d	

Chapter 35

Thought Provokers

1. Resource partitioning is a division of natural resources (such as food or physical space) by one or more species, in different ways, times, or areas. Sometimes two or more species compete for the same resource at the same time, a situation of direct competition. When the resource is partitioned, competition falls off, enhancing the survival prospects for each species. Example: One insect eats the leaves of a plant; another feeds on nectar from the plant's flowers. Both feed on the same plant, but in different regions.

2. Assume two insect species that happen to have genes that cause them to resemble each other—more or less—in appearance. However, one species has poison glands that produce toxins deadly to any predator that consumes it, while the other species has no poison glands. As predators catch and eat both types of insect, the predator learns to recognize and avoid the toxic insects. Likewise, predators tend to avoid members of the nontoxic species that most resemble the poisonous species. Over time, as predators consume proportionately more of those members of the benign species that do not bear a close resemblance to the toxic species, the frequency of alleles shifts in the nontoxic group. Eventually all or most nontoxic individuals have the genotype that makes them mimics of the poisonous species.

Self-Test

1. a	2. b	3. a	4. b	5. b	6. b	7. b	8. a
9. a	10. a	11. c	12. e	13. c	14. d	15. a	16. a
17. a	18. a	19. a	20. a	21. e	22. a	23. e	24. a
25. b	26. c	27. d	28. b	29. a	30. c	31. c	32. b
33. a	34. a	35. e	36. a	37. a	38. a	39. a	40. a

Chapter 36

Thought Provokers

1. Autotrophs are self-feeders that obtain carbon from carbon dioxide and energy from light or from chemical sources. In contrast, heterotrophs obtain carbon and energy from carbohydrates formed by autotrophs such as algae and green plants. Heterotrophs include primary consumers that eat grass or phytoplankton and secondary consumers that ingest herbivores. Tertiary consumers are heterotrophs that ingest secondary consumers. A simple example: Cats are carnivores that eat mice, which in turn are herbivores that have ingested grain and seeds (autotrophs) as their main food. Detritivores, such as bacteria and fungi, break down dead animal and plant matter and derive energy therefrom.

2. The statement "Life is not possible without plants" is only partially correct. Life as we know it now would certainly not be possible without green plants, which are the primary energy source for all other life forms and produce oxygen for aerobic organisms. Some simple life forms, such as anaerobic bacteria, *could* exist without green plants; indeed, in a world without oxygen there would only be anaerobic organisms. Thus, life without green plants is possible, but it would be a drastically different kind of life and world than the one we know—and we would not be in it!

3. Concentration and biological magnification in living systems occur with various toxins and poisons. The effects are cumulative, with increasing concentration occurring as one moves "upward" through the food chain. Initially, photosynthesizers accumulate toxins such as metals (mercury, lead) or DDT. Next, as herbivores feed on the photosynthesizers, the toxins accumulate and are magnified about tenfold. The process repeats in carnivores that consume the herbivores. Thus, at each trophic level concentration and magnification occur, with serious consequences. In birds, for example, the shells of eggs produced by DDT-laden females become thin and crack, and the offspring die. Mercury that accumulates in fish may poison people who ingest the fish, causing severe neurological damage. Biological magnification of toxins is a major consequence of environmental pollution.

Self-Test

1. a	2. b	3. d	4. a	5. b	6. a	7. c	8. b
9. a	10. b	11. a	12. a	13. a	14. d	15. e	16. e
17. b	18. a	19. c	20. e	21. a	22. a	23. c	24. b
25. a	26. d	27. b	28. c	29. a	30. e		

Chapter 37

Thought Provokers

1. Normally, the Galapagos and surrounding areas are bathed in cool waters as air and water currents move northward and westward from the South Pole. About every five years, the trade winds reverse, and the waters move eastward and warm these same regions. This El Niño increases rainfall; the warming and wetting trend decreases phytoplankton in the waters around the Galapagos because ocean nu-

trients in the ocean's depths do not upwell. As a result, organisms throughout the food chain starve, including major losses among the fish and seal populations.

2. (a) *Biomes:* major communities of organisms on land. (b) *Coriolis effect:* the six different major air currents or coils that are generated by warm air rising from the equator and spun by the rotating Earth into swirls and spirals. (c) *Chaparral:* temperate scrubland with hot, dry summers and cool, wet winters. Plants in this biome are short, with hairy/leathery leaves, and are green all year. (d) *Thermocline:* boundary region between dense, cool, bottom waters and lighter, warmer top waters.

Self-Test

1. e	2. b	3. a	4. a	5. b	6. a	7. a	8. a
9. a	10. b	11. b	12. a	13. a	14. ae	15. c	16. a
17. b	18. b	19. b	20. a	21. ad	22. a	23. e	24. ae
25. d	26. ad	27. a	28. ad	29. a	30. d	31. a	32. c
33. b	34. c	35. d	36. c	37. b	38. c	39. c	40. d
41. c	42. a	43. ab	44. ac	45. b	46. b	47. b	48. d
49. a	50. c	51. b	52. e	53. d	54. e	55. d	56. a
57. d	58. b	59. c	60. d				

Chapter 38

Thought Provokers

1. The proximate cause of behavior is the specific event, such as color, shape, or other visual cue; sound; or odor that evokes behavior. The ultimate cause of a behavior is that selective advantage that accrues to the animal as a result of the behavior.

2. The effects of certain genes on behavior are obvious in some cases. Examples include bees removing diseased and dead larvae from the hive, and the food preferences of snakes. In these situations it can also be shown that certain behaviors are dominant and others recessive. By performing appropriate crosses and analyzing the offspring, a scientist can uncover information about the presence or absence of obvious genetic controls. It seems clear that all behavior is ultimately rooted in genes, although in some cases many genes may contribute to a single behavior.

3. *Instinct:* an inborn, unlearned characteristic that is basically unchangeable. *Imprinting:* recognition and attachment (bonding) responses of a young animal to its parent or an object or other animal. *Trial-and-error learning:* operant conditioning in which an animal associates a response (operant) with a reinforcer (reward or punishment). *Insight learning:* reasoning; occurs only among the highest animals, the primates. Insight learning means that life situations are solved by use of cognitive and memory abilities and that a suitable or acceptable solution is attained in the mind (brain) before the solution is actually used or tried.

Self-Test

1. d	2. b	3. c	4. a	5. a	6. c	7. c	8. b
9. c	10. c	11. b	12. b	13. c	14. c	15. a	16. b
17. a	18. b	19. a	20. b	21. a	22. d	23. a	24. e
25. c	26. c	27. c	28. b	29. b	30. e	31. a	32. a
33. e	34. b	35. d	36. a	37. a	38. b	39. a	40. a
41. e	42. a	43. a	44. b	45. b